Total Maximum Daily Load Development and Implementation

Other Titles of Interest

Concentrate Management in Desalination: Case Studies, 2nd Edition, edited by Berrin Tansel, Conrad G. Keyes Jr., Luzma F. Nava, and April J. Lander (ASCE/EWRI 2021). This report reviews the state-of-the-practice for managing the chemical concentrates resulting from the desalination process. (ISBN 978-0-7844-1569-6)

Computational Fluid Dynamics: Applications in Water, Wastewater, and Stormwater Treatment, edited by Xiaofeng Liu, Ph.D., P.E., and Jie Zhang, Ph.D (ASCE/EWRI 2019). This book provides an introduction, overview, and specific examples of computational fluid dynamics and their applications in the water, wastewater, and stormwater industry. (ISBN 978-0-7844-1531-3)

Statistical Analysis of Hydrologic Variables: Methods and Applications, edited by Ramesh S. V. Teegavarapu, Jose D. Salas, and Jery R. Stedinger (ASCE/EWRI 2019). This book provides a compilation of statistical analysis methods used to analyze and assess critical variables in the hydrological cycle. (ISBN 978-0-7844-1517-7)

Adventures in Managing Water: Real-World Engineering Experiences, edited by Pete Loucks and Laurel Sato (ASCE/EWRI 2019). This book provides valuable insight for students and professionals into real-world experiences of water engineers and other water management professionals. (ISBN 978-0-7844-1533-7)

Sustainable Water Resources Management, edited by Chandra S. P. Ojha, Rao Y. Surampalli, András Bárdossy, Tian C. Zhang, and Chih-Ming Kao (ASCE/EWRI 2017). This book presents the most current thinking on the environmental, social, and political dimensions of sustainably managing water supply at the local, regional, or basin levels. (ISBN 978-0-7844-1476-7)

ASCE Manuals and Reports on Engineering Practice No. 150

Total Maximum Daily Load Development and Implementation

Models, Methods, and Resources

Prepared by the
Total Maximum Daily Load Analysis and Modeling Task Committee

Sponsored by the
Watershed Management Technical Committee of the
Watershed Council of the
Environmental and Water Resources Institute
of the American Society of Civil Engineers

Edited by
Harry X. Zhang, Ph.D., P.E.
Nigel W.T. Quinn, Ph.D., P.E., D.WRE
Deva K. Borah, Ph.D., P.E.
G. Padmanabhan, Ph.D., P.E.

ENVIRONMENTAL &
WATER RESOURCES
INSTITUTE

Published by the American Society of Civil Engineers

Library of Congress Cataloging-in-Publication Data

Names: Zhang, Harry X., editor. | Environmental and Water Resources Institute (U.S.). Total Maximum Daily Load Analysis and Modeling Task Committee, author. | Environmental and Water Resources Institute (U.S.). Watershed Management Technical Committee, sponsoring body.
Title: Total maximum daily load development and implementation : models, methods, and resources / edited by Harry X. Zhang, Ph.D., P.E., Nigel W.T. Quinn, Ph.D., P.E., D.WRE, Deva K. Borah, Ph.D., P.E., G. Padmanabhan, Ph.D., P.E. ; prepared by the Total Maximum Daily Load Analysis and Modeling Task Committee ; sponsored by the Watershed Management Technical Committee of the Watershed Council of the Environmental and Water Resources Institute of the American Society of Civil Engineers.
Description: Reston, Virginia : American Society of Civil Engineers, [2022] | Series: ASCE manuals and reports on engineering practice ; no. 150 | Includes bibliographical references and index. | Summary: "MOP 150 provides detailed descriptions of several watershed and receiving water quality models used in total maximum daily load (TMDL) analysis and modeling, highlighting recent advancements in TMDL development and implementation"-- Provided by publisher.
Identifiers: LCCN 2021043349 | ISBN 9780784415948 (print) | ISBN 9780784483824 (PDF)
Subjects: LCSH: Water--Pollution--Total maximum daily load--Simulation methods. | Water--Pollution--Total maximum daily load--Measurement.
Classification: LCC TD423 .T67 2022 | DDC 628.1/68--dc23/eng/20211028
LC record available at https://lccn.loc.gov/2021043349

Published by American Society of Civil Engineers
1801 Alexander Bell Drive
Reston, Virginia 20191-4382
www.asce.org/bookstore | ascelibrary.org

MANUALS AND REPORTS ON ENGINEERING PRACTICE

(As developed by the ASCE Technical Procedures Committee, July 1930, and revised March 1935, February 1962, and April 1982)

A manual or report in this series consists of an orderly presentation of facts on a particular subject, supplemented by an analysis of limitations and applications of these facts. It contains information useful to the average engineer in his or her everyday work, rather than findings that may be useful only occasionally or rarely. It is not in any sense a "standard," however, nor is it so elementary or so conclusive as to provide a "rule of thumb" for non-engineers.

Furthermore, material in this series, in distinction from a paper (which expresses only one person's observations or opinions), is the work of a committee or group selected to assemble and express information on a specific topic. As often as practicable, the committee is under the direction of one or more of the Technical Divisions and Councils, and the product evolved has been subjected to review by the Executive Committee of the Division or Council. As a step in the process of this review, proposed manuscripts are often brought before the members of the Technical Divisions and Councils for comment, which may serve as the basis for improvement. When published, each manual shows the names of the committees by which it was compiled and indicates clearly the several processes through which it has passed in review, so that its merit may be definitely understood.

In February 1962 (and revised in April 1982), the Board of Direction voted to establish a series titled "Manuals and Reports on Engineering Practice" to include the manuals published and authorized to date, future Manuals of Professional Practice, and Reports on Engineering Practice. All such manual or report material of the Society would have been refereed in a manner approved by the Board Committee on Publications and would be bound, with applicable discussion, in books similar to past manuals. Numbering would be consecutive and would be a continuation of present manual numbers. In some cases of joint committee reports, bypassing of journal publications may be authorized.

A list of available Manuals of Practice can be found at https://www.asce.org/bookstore.

CONTENTS

FOREWORD

The total maximum daily load or TMDL is a regulatory term associated with the United States Clean Water Act describing a plan for restoring the quality of impaired waters. The TMDL analysis establishes the maximum amount of a pollutant a waterbody can receive and still meet the applicable water quality standards. The term *TMDL program* is used to describe how the US government working with states, territories, and approved tribes (jurisdictions) manages the point and nonpoint sources of pollution to restore impaired waters. Implementing TMDLs is important to protect the environment and to reverse the adverse impacts of urbanization and agriculture on the waters of the United States.

Developing TMDLs is often supported by the applications of watershed and receiving water quality models that can provide rigor and clarity to the process. Concerns related to developing TMDLs include the following: the overwhelming numbers of models and analytical methods, potential for inappropriate selection of models, lack of uncertainty estimates, extensive data requirements, and infrequency of postimplementation assessments of performance. These concerns often lead to difficulties in the development, implementation, and sustainability of the TMDLs.

The ASCE EWRI Watershed Management Technical Committee (WMTC) formed the Task Committee on TMDL Analysis and Modeling in 2011 in response to the aforementioned concerns related to the use of models in TMDL development and implementation. The task committee consists of a diverse group of individuals representing important organizations that have a stake in the success of TMDL modeling. Committee members include practicing professionals, academics, and federal, state, and county experts in the TMDL process. The task committee recommended that an ASCE manual of practice be developed to assist practitioners carry out the steps of TMDL model selection, model input data collection and synthesis, model calibration, and independent testing of the model against known data or other observations to define uncertainty. Along the way, in generating this manual, the task committee published an ASCE EWRI report (book) in 2017 and, in 2019, published a collection of papers in the Journal of Hydrologic Engineering. In addition, the committee has held numerous planning and organizational meetings, both in-person and by conference and video calls. With the encouragement and guidance from the parent WMTC, task committee members have led TMDL workshops and technical sessions and have given presentations at ASCE EWRI and other conferences. This manual is the culmination of the combined efforts of the task committee.

The manual provides detailed descriptions, together with their relative strengths and limitations, of a large number of watershed models, receiving water quality models, and analytical methods/tools, some of which are widely used and others that have great potential for use in TMDL development and implementation. The manual highlights recent advances in TMDL analysis and modeling representing the state-of-the-art. However, the main purpose of the manual is to describe the state-of-the-practice as it relates to TMDL development and implementation, which includes the use of remote sensing and geographic information systems (GIS), standardized procedures for model calibration, validation, and testing; techniques for uncertainty analysis and protocols for defining the TMDL margin of safety. The manual provides example applications and sources (links) to previous TMDL study reports from around the United States. An online search tool is introduced that has the capability of performing detailed queries of the US Environmental Protection Agency (USEPA) ATTAINS database with respect to impairments, modeling techniques of interest, and constituents of concern.

The process leading to the development of this manual must have been both challenging and rewarding. I trust this manual will become a valuable reference and resource for those engaged in the practice of TMDL analysis and modeling, in that it provides a logical progression of steps for the development and implementation of TMDLs. Engineers, water quality professionals, regulators, and other water resource and watershed managers charged with the development and implementation of TMDLs should find this manual beneficial.

On a personal note, it has been a pleasure watching this group at work for the last several years. I want to commend the group—collectively and individually—for their dedication and hard work.

Donald K. Frevert, Ph.D., P.E., F.ASCE, Past-Chair
Watershed Council
Environmental and Water Resources Institute

PREFACE

The Total Maximum Daily Load or TMDL is a scientific and a regulatory term. Scientifically, it refers to the maximum amount of a pollutant a waterbody can receive and still meet the applicable water quality standards. In a regulatory context, TMDL is used in the United States to describe a document or plan of action to manage both point and nonpoint-source pollution of waterbodies. In this sense, a TMDL is a set of actions to restore clean water by examining water quality problems, identifying sources of pollutants, and specifying actions that create solutions. It is a written, quantitative plan and analysis for attaining and maintaining water quality standards in all seasons for a specific waterbody and pollutant. TMDLs are intended to be a part of a comprehensive watershed strategy to restore ambient water quality to meet its designated use (DU) and should involve collaboration with a wide variety of stakeholders.

As is the case with most natural systems, there are no experimental or direct methods to derive TMDL estimates. Developing a TMDL requires an analysis linking sources with loadings to an impairment for one or more pollutants, for which watershed and receiving-water quality modeling is vital. As found in the USEPA Assessment and Total Maximum Daily Load Tracking and Implementation System (ATTAINS), 76,127 TMDLs have been developed throughout the United States from 1975 through 2017 using various analytical or empirical methods or simple models, watershed models, and receiving water quality models. Models or methods are typically chosen by the individual TMDL developers as there exists no clear guidance or requirement regarding the analysis procedures or models to be used.

The TMDL Analysis and Modeling Task Committee of the ASCE EWRI was formed in October 2011 at the direction of the ASCE EWRI Watershed Management Technical Committee, which is under the ASCE EWRI Watershed Council, to address current concerns and advance the practices of analysis and modeling in TMDL development and implementation in terms of analysis technique and model selection, determining data requirements and processing, model calibration and validation, and uncertainty analysis and reporting. Members of the task committee are among the best available experts on TMDL analysis and modeling in the nation drawn from academia; federal, state, and local governments; and consulting firms. Membership has been stable over the period since the formation of the task committee with the exception of some leaving because of personal reasons and new members joining. The task committee met monthly via teleconferences and face-to-face at the annual ASCE EWRI World Environmental and Water Resources Congress during its existence and its members presented their work at the Congresses through workshops and technical sessions.

The task committee first reviewed the current practices of analysis and modeling in TMDLs and documented its findings in an ASCE EWRI book, *Total Maximum Daily Load Analysis and Modeling: Assessment of the Practice* in 2017. The members and subject expert authors involved in this publication were recognized. In addition, members of the committee completed a special collection of articles that were published under the title "Total Maximum Daily Load Analysis and Modeling: Assessment and Advancement" in the *Journal of Hydrologic Engineering* during the period 2018 to 2021. These articles provide state-of-the-art and state-of-the-practice overviews of sixteen relevant topics on TMDL analysis and modeling.

The ASCE-EWRI Task Committee on TMDL Analysis and Modeling then directed its attention to developing the current ASCE Manual of Practice titled, *Total Maximum Daily Load Development and Implementation: Models, Methods, and Resources* that reviews and evaluates current practices and potential future approaches to TMDL analysis and modeling in TMDL development and implementation. The primary goal of this manual was to support a more comprehensive and effective TMDL development and implementation that will prove to be beneficial to the public through eliminating current and future impairments to waterbodies and improving water quality for designated uses with confidence and certainty. The members of the task committee are responsible for authorship of this manual. Chapter authors are listed below under Contributing Authors and under the title of each chapter. All members of the task committee are also listed below with their affiliations, each contributed to this endeavor either by writing one or more chapters and/or participating in the review, and tasks of editing, revising, or providing constructive comments on various chapters. The book was organized and compiled by four editors listed on the cover page who are also long-serving and distinguished members of the task committee.

Thus, this manual on TMDL analysis and modeling for TMDL development and implementation resulted from research and deliberations of the task committee written in its 12 chapters by its members reflecting their collective expertise and experience. The 12 chapters consist of an introduction and a comprehensive coverage of eleven subtopics on TMDL modeling, methods, and resources needed to develop a TMDL and its implementation plan.

Deva K. Borah, Ph.D., P.E., F.ASCE, Life M.ASCE, Chair
TMDL Analysis and Modeling Task Committee
Environmental and Water Resources Institute

TMDL ANALYSIS AND MODELING
TASK COMMITTEE

Deva K. Borah, Ph.D., P.E., F.ASCE, Life M.ASCE, *Chair*
City of Chesapeake Department of Public Works

Saurav Kumar, Ph.D., P.E., M.ASCE, *Vice Chair*
Texas A&M AgriLife Research

Rosanna J. La Plante, P.E., F.ASCE, *Secretary*
Washington Suburban Sanitary Commission

G. Padmanabhan, Ph.D., P.E., F.ASCE, Life M. ASCE, *Past Chair*
North Dakota State University, Retired

William H. Frost, P.E., D.WRE, F.ASCE, *Past Secretary*
KCI Technologies, Inc.

Ebrahim Ahmadisharaf, Ph.D., M.ASCE
FAMU-FSU College of Engineering

Rene A. Camacho-Rincon, Ph.D., M.ASCE
Tetra Tech, Inc.

Xiaobo Chao, Ph.D., M.ASCE
University of Mississippi

Xing Fang, Ph.D., P.E., D.WRE, F.ASCE
Auburn University

Mohamed M. Hantush, Ph.D., M.ASCE
US Environmental Protection Agency

Sanaz Imen, Ph.D., P.E., M.ASCE
Stantec Engineering Services Company

Seshadri S. Iyer, Ph.D., P.E., F.ASCE
GKY & Associates, Inc.

Liping Jiang, Ph.D., A.M.ASCE
Montana Tech

Navaratnam Leelaruban, Ph.D., P.E., M.ASCE
HNTB Corporation

R. Craig Lott
Virginia Department of Environmental Quality

Steven C. McCutcheon, Ph.D., P.E., D.WRE (Ret.), F.ASCE
University of Georgia

Yusuf M. Mohamoud, Ph.D., P.E., M.ASCE
(Former member with coauthorships to chapters)
Natural Resources, Environment, and Technology Institute

Andrew Parker, M.ASCE
Tetra Tech, Inc.

Nigel W.T. Quinn, Ph.D., P.E., D.WRE, F.ASCE, Life M. ASCE
Lawrence Berkeley National Laboratory

Vamsi K. Sridharan, Ph.D., M.ASCE
University of California, Santa Cruz

Harry X. Zhang, Ph.D., P.E., M.ASCE
The Water Research Foundation

Zhonglong Zhang, Ph.D., P.E., M.ASCE
Portland State University

BLUE-RIBBON PANEL REVIEWERS

Latif Kalin, Ph.D.
Professor of Hydrology, Auburn University

Leslie Shoemaker, Ph.D.
President, Tetra Tech, Inc.

M. Todd Walter, Ph.D., M.ASCE
Professor of Biological and Environmental Engineering, Cornell University

CONTRIBUTING AUTHORS

Chapter 1: Introduction
Nigel W.T. Quinn, Steven C. McCutcheon, Vamsi K. Sridharan, Rosanna J. La Plante, Harry X. Zhang, Deva K. Borah, G. Padmanabhan

Chapter 2: Watershed Models
Deva K. Borah, Ebrahim Ahmadisharaf, G. Padmanabhan, Sanaz Imen, Harry X. Zhang, Yusuf M. Mohamoud, Zhonglong Zhang

Chapter 3: Receiving Water Quality Models
Rene A. Camacho-Rincon, Zhonglong Zhang, Xiaobo Chao

Chapter 4: Integrated Modeling Systems and Linked Models
Harry X. Zhang, Yusuf M. Mohamoud, Seshadri S. Iyer

Chapter 5: Simple Models and Methods
Harry X. Zhang, Nigel W.T. Quinn

Chapter 6: Critical Condition Determination for Total Maximum Daily Load Modeling
Harry X. Zhang, G. Padmanabhan

Chapter 7: Model Data, Geographical Information Systems, and Remote Sensing
Nigel W. T. Quinn, Saurav Kumar, Sanaz Imen, Vamsi K. Sridharan

Chapter 8: Model Calibration and Validation
Ebrahim Ahmadisharaf, Rene A. Camacho-Rincon, Harry X. Zhang, Mohamed M. Hantush, Yusuf M. Mohamoud

Chapter 9: Model Uncertainty Analysis and the Margin of Safety
Mohamed M. Hantush, Harry X. Zhang, Rene A. Camacho-Rincon, Ebrahim Ahmadisharaf, Yusuf M. Mohamoud

ACKNOWLEDGMENTS

This Manual of Practice on engineering practices of TMDL analysis and modeling in developing and implementing TMDLs was prepared by the ASCE/EWRI Task Committee on TMDL Analysis and Modeling under the Watershed Management Technical Committee of the Watershed Council, ASCE/EWRI, over a period of ten years (2011 to 2021) of focused and progressive efforts. Dr. G. Padmanabhan founded the task committee in 2011 as its chair, with Dr. Ashok Pandit as the vice chair and Mr. William Frost as secretary. Under their leadership, the task committee first published an ASCE EWRI book in 2017 titled *Total Maximum Daily Load Analysis and Modeling: Assessment of the Practice*. In 2017, the leadership of the task committee transitioned to Dr. Deva Borah as chair, Dr. Saurav Kumar as vice chair, and Ms. Rosanna La Plante as secretary. Under their leadership, the task committee published a special collection of articles on "TMDL Analysis and Modeling: Assessment and Advancement" in the *Journal of Hydrologic Engineering* during 2018 to 2021 (Guest editors: Dr. Deva Borah, Dr. G. Padmanabhan, and Dr. Saurav Kumar) and now this ASCE manual, edited by Dr. Harry Zhang, Dr. Nigel Quinn, Dr. Deva Borah, and Dr. G. Padmanabhan.

The editors thank all the members of the task committee for their contributions and/or serving as internal reviewers of the manual, in addition to their roles in achieving the task committee goals. The thoroughness of the reviews, editorial suggestions, and comments by Dr. Steven C. McCutcheon and Dr. Vamsi K. Sridharan are appreciated. The editors also thank the Blue-Ribbon Panel for reviewing the draft manual and providing helpful comments. The combined leadership, continued support and guidance of both the ASCE/EWRI Watershed Management Technical Committee and the Watershed Council were essential in helping the task committee achieve its stated goals.

In conclusion, we wish to express gratitude to the parent organizations of task committee members for providing staff time and committing other resources that helped to streamline the task committee endeavor to produce this manual.

EXECUTIVE SUMMARY

BACKGROUND AND RATIONALE

A total maximum daily load (TMDL) is the maximum allowable loading limit of a particular water quality constituent such as nutrients, sediment, temperature, salinity, pathogen counts, and others that can enter an impaired water system (receiving waterbody) identified under Section 303(d) of the Clean Water Act (CWA) of 1972, so that the applicable water quality standards can be met. In a regulatory context, the TMDL facilitates a plan of action to manage both point source (PS) and non-point-source (NPS) pollution. The minimum elements in a TMDL required by the USEPA's *Guidelines for Reviewing TMDLs under Existing Regulations* issued in 1992 are the following:

1. Identification of waterbody, drainage area, pollutant(s) of concern, pollutant sources, and a reasonable load reduction possibility scenario;
2. Development of applicable Water Quality Standards (WQS) or numeric water quality targets;
3. Assessment of pollutant assimilative Load Capacity (LC) for the receiving water of concern;
4. Computation of pollutant load allocations (LAs), waste load allocations (WLAs), and a margin of safety (MOS);
5. Consideration of seasonal variations and critical conditions;
6. Analysis of uncertainty and development of reasonable assurance guidance that pollutant PS/NPS load reductions are achievable;
7. Development of an implementation plan with involvement of stakeholders;
8. Formulation of an appropriate, cost-effective monitoring plan to track TMDL effectiveness; and
9. Management of project outreach and public participation.

As is the case with most natural systems, there are no experimental or direct methods to derive a TMDL. Developing a TMDL is a systematic process that quantifies the extent of pollutant loading to a waterbody and develops a plan to address the water quality impairment for which the use of watershed and receiving water quality models is key. As documented in the USEPA Assessment and TMDL Tracking and Implementation System (ATTAINS), 76,127 TMDLs were developed across the United States during the period 1975 through 2017 employing a wide variety of analytical or empirical procedures/methods, simple models, watershed models, and receiving water quality models. The tools were chosen by the individual TMDL developers without the benefit of clear guidance or standardized protocols that might have guided the analysis procedures and led to better choice of model.

Although guidance manuals have been developed by USEPA for the purpose of pollutant load allocations, neither USEPA nor any state agency has developed specific guidance on TMDL analysis and modeling. The EWRI Watershed Management Technical Committee of the ASCE first chartered the Total Maximum Daily Load Analysis and Modeling Task Committee (TMDL-TC) in 2011 to explore the development of an ASCE Manual of Practice (MOP) on TMDL analysis and modeling for the development and implementation of TMDLs. After a careful review of current and past practices, the TMDL-TC confirmed the inadequacy of existing guidance for TMDL analysis and modeling. As stated in an ASCE book authored by the TMDL-TC in 2017, an ASCE MOP was both timely and critical to achieve the water quality objectives established by the CWA. In 2019, as an interim step, the TMDL-TC members published a special collection of papers in the ASCE Journal of Hydrologic Engineering that sought to define the scientific basis more clearly for TMDL modeling and describe the state-of-the-art. . The MOP that followed the 2017 ASCE book and the special collection of associated technical papers relates the state-of-the-practice to the state of the art in TMDL analysis and modeling. It was not always possible to draw a clear distinction between these designations, given the rapid innovation in the embrace of technologies such as GIS and remote sensing and the realization that certain current practices may become obsolete in the not-too-distant future. The MOP addresses this and other relevant topics/subjects in each of the MOP chapters.

SUMMARY OF CHAPTERS

The 12 chapters contained in the MOP are on TMDL analysis and modeling and other related topics needed in the development and implementation of TMDL arranged in an order corresponding to a typical

TMDL development workflow to guide the readers. The chapters describe the various watershed and receiving water models; discuss the integration or linking of these models for complex waterbody systems; simple analytical and empirical procedures/methods and models; critical condition determinations; data types and sources; calibration, validation, and performance quantifications of the models; model uncertainty analysis and margin of safety quantification for TMDL developments; a database of USEPA-approved TMDL reports and a computer search tool to search those reports; a model selection protocol for TMDLs, the principal steps involved in modeling for TMDL development and implementation planning along with an implementation planning case study; and current analysis and modeling practices for TMDL implementation planning.

Brief summaries of the individual chapters are given below:

Chapter 1 Introduction: The chapter provides a brief history of the TMDL program and the overall TMDL process. It expands on the TMDL definition and rationale and purpose of the MOP that is summarized in the section above.

Chapter 2 Watershed Models: The chapter presents watershed models that are primarily needed and used in TMDL development and implementation. Fourteen prevalent watershed models, listed subsequently, were selected based on their documentation including user manuals, successful applications on various watersheds, evaluations, and acceptances found in the literature. In Chapter 2, these 14 watershed models are further evaluated to determine their capabilities suitable for TMDL development and implementation.

1. Agricultural Nonpoint Source (AGNPS) and Annualized AGNPS (AnnAGNPS),
2. Areal Nonpoint Source Watershed Environment Response Simulation (ANSWERS),
3. Dynamic Watershed Simulation Model (DWSM),
4. Gridded Surface and Subsurface Hydrologic Analysis (GSSHA),
5. Generalized Watershed Loading Function (GWLF),
6. Hydrologic Engineering Center–Hydrologic Modeling System (HEC–HMS),
7. Hydrological Simulation Program–Fortran (HSPF),
8. Kinematic Runoff and Erosion (KINEROS),
9. Loading Simulation Program in C++ (LSPC)–HSPF based,
10. Mike Systém Hydrologique Européen (MIKE SHE),
11. Soil and Water Assessment Tool (SWAT),
12. Storm Water Management Model (SWMM),
13. Watershed Assessment Model (WAM), and
14. Watershed Analysis Risk Management Framework (WARMF).

Brief descriptions of these watershed models, including sources, capabilities, and applicability, are presented in Chapter 2. General information such as intended watershed (agriculture, urban or mixed), simulation type (event, continuous or both), simulated variables, uncertainty analysis, graphical user interface, and availability of the 14 models is presented in a comprehensive tabular form to compare the attributes of the models. The theoretical basis for the various hydrologic and water quality processes (phases or components) for each of the 14 models are tabulated for easy comparison of the models. Looking at the theoretical basis of models is important as it suggests expected performance and accuracy and dictate model features such as structure, input data, and model parameters. Among these, the water routing procedures derived from approximations of the St. Venant shallow water equations are the primary drivers of the models, based on which the models are compared and ranked on pictorial graphs based on the level of physical basis or accuracy against complexity. For example, the GSSHA and MIKE SHE models rank high on the simulation of overland flows and the SWMM ranks high in channel or pipe flow routings using the most accurate physical process–based equations—also being the most numerically complex. The GWLF model ranks at the bottom with respect to both flow simulation methodologies. The remainder of the models falls in between the two end members, although the DWSM model is the most computationally efficient among the kinematic wave models. Notable strengths and limitations of the watershed models for TMDL development and implementation are tabulated. This valuable compilation of information on the subject models is unique and should aid comparisons of relative model reliability and help guide selections for TMDL and other environmental applications.

Of the 14 watershed models presented in Chapter 2, applications of 12 (HSPF, LSPC, GWLF, SWAT, SWMM, WARMF, AGNPS, ANSWERS, HEC–HMS, KINEROS, WAM, and MIKE SHE) can be found in TMDL studies. However, caution should be exercised to their appropriateness for all applications - misuses of models are sometimes found in past TMDL study reports. Although the DWSM and GSSHA models have not been used in TMDL applications, these two models have been evaluated and used in other watershed management and best management practices (BMP) evaluation studies and, therefore, would be suitable for future TMDL development and implementation studies.

Chapter 2 outlines future research on watershed modeling. This research should include further comparisons of models performance based on other key aspects such as simulation capabilities of processes, uncertainty analyses, required resources, and ability to characterize pollutant loading from complex watersheds. Robust physically based algorithms, uncertainty analysis capabilities, and improvements in the facility of use of remotely sensed and high-resolution data for model development are recommended to be part of the future advancement in modeling technology, application, and solution rigor.

Chapter 3 Receiving Water Quality Models: The chapter describes the following 11 receiving water quality models that were previously used in TMDL development and implementation planning:

1. CE-QUAL-ICM Three-Dimensional Eutrophication Model,
2. Water Analysis Simulation Program (WASP),
3. Environmental Fluid Dynamics Code (EFDC),
4. CE-QUAL-W2 Two-Dimensional Longitudinal–Vertical Hydrodynamic and Water Quality Model,
5. Hydrologic Engineering Center River Analysis System (HEC–RAS),
6. Center for Computational Hydroscience and Engineering Model (CCHE-1D/2D/3D),
7. Georgia Environmental Protection Division River Model (EPD-RIV1),
8. QUAL2K River and Stream Water Quality Model,
9. MINTEQA2/Visual MINTEQ Geochemical Equilibrium Specification for Dilute Aqueous Systems,
10. One-dimensional Transport with Equilibrium Chemistry Model (OTEQ), and
11. MIKE11-ECOLAB River Hydraulics and Sediment Transport with Water Quality Simulations Model.

The sources, simulation capabilities, and applications of each of the 11 receiving water quality models are presented and briefly described in Chapter 3. Availability of these models in the public domain and specific capabilities of each of the models, such as 1D, 2D, or 3D hydrodynamic routings; types of modeling systems (rivers, lakes, reservoirs, or estuaries); and simulating pollutants (temperature, salinity, dissolved oxygen, carbon, nitrogen, phosphorous, algae, sediment, pathogen, toxics, and metals) are summarized in a table/matrix facilitating comparisons and the best selections of the models for applications in various TMDL studies (analysis). Like watershed modeling, receiving water quality modeling has also been researched and developed for over half a century. Thus, in this instance, the state-of-the-practice has caught up with the state-of-the-art. Chapter 3 serves as a valuable resource to understand the capabilities of the 11 models and match those with the conditions of the impairments and the impaired waterbodies for selecting the best model(s) for TMDL development and implementation.

Chapter 4 Integrated Modeling Systems and Linked Models: In this chapter, integrated modeling systems and linked models are described with examples. Linking of different models is needed to represent complex natural systems such as watersheds and their estuaries when such systems cannot be represented by a single model. Linkages can be static or dynamic. A static linkage takes output from one model and uses it as input to a second model. A dynamic linkage can be bidirectional, where information from each time step transfers back and forth between the models and affects simulations of all. Integrated modeling systems and linked models can satisfy multiple model application criteria because they include the capabilities of multiple models, provide various software tools, and include data and analysis support. Chapter 4 presents two widely used integrated modeling systems, briefly summarized in the following two paragraphs, along with a listing or brief descriptions of example applications in TMDL studies. Also, as summarized subsequently, three example applications of linked models are presented in Chapter 4 along with an important discussion on the performance evaluations of integrated modeling systems and linked models in TMDL applications.

1. BASINS: The Better Assessment Science Integrating point and Nonpoint Sources (BASINS) System developed by USEPA, initially in 1996 and continually updated with the latest BASINS 4.5 release in 2019, is an integrated modeling system using various components and utilities and currently supporting seven models, AQUATOX, GWLF-E, HSPF, PLOAD, SWAT, SWMM, and WASP, for TMDL development and implementation. The origin and history of BASINS, its various components and utilities, and brief descriptions and one TMDL application example of each of the supporting models are presented and/or listed in Chapter 4.
2. WMS: The Watershed Modeling System (WMS) of the US Army Corps of Engineers is a comprehensive graphical modeling environment for all phases of watershed hydrology and hydraulics, which has also been used to support TMDL development. The WMS supports hydrologic modeling with the HEC-1/HEC–HMS, TR-20, TR-55, Rational Method, National Flood Frequency Program (NFF), HSPF, and GSSHA. It also supports hydraulic models such as the HEC–RAS and CE-QUAL-W2. A few example applications of the WMS are briefly described in Chapter 4.

In addition to citing a few applications of linked models, Chapter 4 describes the following three example applications of linked models in TMDL development and implementation:

1. Chesapeake Bay TMDL in the Mid-Atlantic United States: Chesapeake Bay TMDL was developed linking the HSPF, modeling its 64,000-sq mi watershed, with CMAQ, a Community Multi-Scale Air Quality model, simulating atmospheric deposition of nutrients, and with the Water Quality and Sediment Transport Model (WQSTM) for estuaries, simulating hydrodynamics, sediment and nutrient

transport, and eutrophication processes inside the Bay for allocating total nitrogen, total phosphorus, and sediment loads from the sources to reduce the size of the oxygen-depleted zones in the Bay and for restoring its living resources.

2. The Saugahatchee Creek Watershed in Alabama: The Alabama Department of Environmental Management (ADEM) identified two segments within the Saugahatchee Creek watershed of the Lower Tallapoosa River basin as being impaired for nutrients and organic enrichment/dissolved oxygen. The LSPC, EFDC, and WASP models were linked to simulate, respectively, runoff- and flow-generated sediment and phosphorus loadings from nonpoint sources, hydrodynamics, and water quality in the impaired waterbodies in an effort to determine load allocations from the sources and meet the water quality standards of the impaired waterbodies for the designated uses.

3. The Lynnhaven River in the Atlantic coast of Virginia: The HSPF from the BASINS was linked with the UnTRIM and CE-QUAL-ICM to simulate, respectively, runoff-generated flow and pollutant loadings from the Lynnhaven River watershed, hydrodynamics in this tidal estuary, and water quality in this estuarine river in an effort to determine load allocations from the sources and meet the water quality standards of the Lynnhaven River that was impaired with fecal coliform, nitrogen, phosphorus, and sediment.

Chapter 5 Simple Models and Methods: The chapter presents simple models and methods that are used to support assessment of the relative significance of different pollutant sources and to guide decisions for management plans. These models and methods are typically derived from empirical relationships between the physiographic characteristics of the watershed and pollutant exports and are often used when data limitations and budget and time constraints preclude using more detailed approaches. These approaches fit the needs of stakeholders tasked with implementing TMDLs where the focus is developing an understanding of the sources and quantification of pollutants causing impairments in a waterbody and determining how best to reduce the loads from prioritized pollutant sources that had been identified in the TMDL from previous monitoring, modeling, and analysis. The following is a list of 13 simple models and methods available to simulate watersheds (10 models/methods) and receiving waterbodies (three models/methods) that are discussed in Chapter 5:

A. Simple Watershed Models and Methods

1. Simple mass balance,
2. Simple method to estimate urban stormwater loads,
3. Watershed Treatment Model (WTM),

 4. Spreadsheet Tool for Estimating Pollutant Loads (STEPL),
 5. Revised Universal Soil Loss Equation 2 (RUSLE2),
 6. Load Estimator (LOADEST),
 7. Spatially Referenced Regressions on Watershed Attributes (SPARROW),
 8. Long-Term Hydrologic Impact Analysis (L-THIA),
 9. Simple Transient Mass Balance Models,
    a. Wetland Management Simulator (WETMANSIM)
    b. San Joaquin River Input–Output Model (SJRIO)
 10. Geographical Information System (GIS) Workflow Models.

 B. Simple Receiving Water Models and Methods

 1. BATHTUB,
 2. Stream Segment Temperature Model (SSTEMP), and
 3. Load Duration Curve (LDC).

The aforementioned procedures and models are limited in many ways and, therefore, a knowledge of these limitations is critical in the successful application of the procedures and the models. One major advantage is that these tools can provide a rapid means of identifying critical loading areas with minimal effort and data requirements. A major disadvantage is that only gross estimates of nutrient loads can be provided and are of limited value for determining loads on a seasonal or finer timescale. Another disadvantage is that these techniques may be too generalized and of limited use for evaluating the effectiveness of various BMPs. However, a strategy that starts with simple models in the initial phases and then progresses to more complex frameworks as additional data are collected, and as appropriate remedial measures are assessed, can be successful and cost-effective. Thus, simple models and methods can play an important role in TMDL development and evaluation as model selection invariably involves trade-offs involving model complexity, required reliability, cost, and time.

Chapter 6 Critical Condition Determination for Total Maximum Daily Load Modeling: In this chapter, critical condition determination in developing a TMDL and the appropriate model or methodologies are discussed. According to the Clean Water Act, the USEPA TMDL program requires a consideration of the critical conditions for streamflow, loading, and water quality parameters for the development of TMDLs. The intent is to ensure that the water quality of an impaired waterbody is protected during times when it is most vulnerable, such as during low- or high-flow periods. The following four methods have been used in critical condition modeling and analysis in TMDL development and implementation (examples are provided in this chapter):

 1. Steady-state models for analyzing impairment under constant flows,
 2. Dynamic continuous simulation models for analyzing impairment under variable flows,

3. Statistical-based Load-Duration Curves (LDC) for all possible flow conditions, and

4. Event-based critical flow storm (CFS) with risk-based approach to combined conditions.

Low-flow analyses are performed using steady-state models. For TMDLs related to impaired waterbodies affected by pollutants from both point and nonpoint sources, a dynamic continuous model is commonly used along with the selection of a representative period to account for the varying climatic and hydrologic conditions in a watershed (e.g., to cover dry, wet, and average years of precipitation). The load-duration curve method is a simple screening tool for problem characterization as part of TMDL development. The event-based critical flow-storm method is essentially a risk-based approach that explicitly addresses critical condition as a combination of streamflow, the magnitude of a storm event, and initial watershed conditions. Decision-making authorities could substantially benefit from information on risk and the associated probabilities of various combinations of rainfall, river flow conditions, and the pollutant loads generated under these combinations.

Chapter 7 Model Data, Geographic Information Systems, and Remote Sensing: The chapter outlines the data requirements in modeling for TMDL development and describes the geographic information system (GIS) and remote sensing (RS) technologies available for the acquisition of high-resolution spatial and temporal data needed to set up, initialize, and run detailed watershed models. Data requirements for a TMDL model setup are tabulated; also tabulated are data requirements for running the TMDL models. An overview of the GIS and an up-to-date evolution of the RS are presented. Also discussed are the specific data needs for certain TMDL applications and how the RS platforms can be matched to these specific data requirements. RS has added another dimension to measuring and retrieving hydrologic and atmospheric data for water quality and hydrologic modeling. Along with the advancements in RS technology, acquisition, and processing of large amounts of information are being managed using robust and easy-to-use GIS software both in the commercial and in the public domain. ArcGIS and other GISs are ubiquitous and have evolved to a point where these tools are extensively used in watershed and impaired waterbody modeling. Chapter 7 provides an overview of the more common GIS and RS technologies used in hydrologic, water quality, and TMDL modeling applications.

Chapter 8 Model Calibration and Validation: The chapter presents and discusses state-of-the-art approaches in model calibration and validation as found in the literature as a guide for the calibration and validation of models applied in TMDL development and implementation. The chapter focuses on watershed models, although the same are applicable to receiving water models as well. Model data requirements and sources of the model data presented in Chapter 7 are further expanded and refined in this chapter by tabulating various types of data and sources and providing website links of the well-maintained data sources. Discussions on data management and guidance on pre-calibration; calibration, including manual calibration and auto-calibration; and validation are presented. The principal parameters requiring calibration in the 14 watershed models presented in Chapter 2 (a few exceptions) are tabulated separately for hydrologic and water quality simulations, which are valuable resources to modelers. Measuring model performance or calibration success is discussed, including a tabulation of various formulas found in the literature for the goodness-of-fit measures of watershed and receiving water quality model predictions. Acceptance criteria of some of the measuring formulas or methods are also tabulated.

Chapter 9 Model Uncertainty Analysis and Margin of Safety: The chapter presents and discusses uncertainties in modeling, and accounting these in a Clean Water Act mandated margin of safety (MOS) in TMDL development and implementation, along with several estimation methods, including explicit, implicit, and risk-based MOS methods. In addition, a survey of sampled 17 TMDL reports is presented in a table compiling the TMDL case study, the state in which they are located, impairment (pollutants), the TMDL model or method used, and the MOS estimation method used. A comprehensive review of uncertainty analysis methods, including MOS estimations, are presented and discussed, and practitioners may find them helpful in TMDL development and implementation. Uncertainty analysis methods applied in 19 water quality modeling studies are tabulated listing the methods and the models used, the impairments (pollutants), and study references, a valuable resource for modelers or practitioners. Detailed descriptions and some of the equations of some of those methods are presented. The methods are (1) first-order variance analysis, (2) Monte Carlo method, (3) Bayesian Monte Carlo analysis, (4) the generalized likelihood uncertainty estimation (GLUE) method, (5) the Markov Chain Monte Carlo method, and (6) Kalman Filtering.

Chapter 10 USEPA Total Maximum Daily Load Report Archive and Report Search Tool: The chapter briefly describes the USEPA TMDL report archive database and online system, called ATTAINS (Assessment and Total Maximum Daily Load Tracking and Implementation System), and presents a new online tool developed for searching TMDL reports for certain search categories such as specific pollutants (impairments), models, or others. Previously published TMDL reports may serve as helpful guides in developing new TMDLs. A web-based software (tool) called the "TMDL Report Selection" (TRS) tool was developed as part of the TMDL Analysis and Modeling Task Committee's efforts to search and analyze published TMDL reports found in ATTAINS. The TRS tool is a state-of-the-art search tool that promotes greater use of information found in reports of USEPA-approved TMDL projects in the USEPA archive ATTAINS.

In Chapter 10, the TRS tool and its application examples provide statistics from TMDL reports published during the period 1975 to 2017. These statistics include (1) the number of reports published in each of the 55 states; (2) number of reports published during each of the years 1975 to 2017; (3) number of reports using each of the selected methods or models including watershed models, receiving water quality models, and simple models; (4) number of reports addressing each of the impairments; and (5) number of reports using each of the selected methods or models that address each of the selected impairments. Guidance on using the TRS tool is also provided.

Chapter 11 Model Selection and Applications for Total Maximum Daily Load Development: In this chapter, a TMDL model selection protocol is presented with descriptions of its basis and various considerations (technical, management, and stakeholder and expert engagements) in the development process and summarizing these in an easy-to-read flowchart. The chapter also describes the process of applying models in the development and implementation of TMDLs and briefly describes a case study for evaluating TMDL load reduction scenarios in the form of an appendix in this chapter. It first lists the types of models used to develop TMDLs and then presents a holistic approach and a protocol to select a practical and dependable model for TMDL development and implementation. In this protocol, rigorous hypothesis testing of the selected model is emphasized, particularly if the model has not already been rigorously peer reviewed. The holistic protocol covers all aspects of the model application, from conceptualization and stakeholder collaboration to implementation planning and outreach. These considerations are translated into technical and management selection criteria and synoptic data requirements. Model performance evaluation, calibration, validation, and uncertainty estimation are all model application steps that influence selection of the model as described in Chapter 11. It also includes the modeling procedures necessary to support TMDL determination, allocation, and implementation planning. Looking into these steps ensures that the selected TMDL model is appropriate and likely to be successful and approved by the USEPA, which also issues National Pollution Discharge Elimination System (NPDES) permits. Other federal, state, and local agencies and stakeholders have roles in applying best management practices and other controls and overseeing the collection of synoptic data for calibration, validation, and determining model reliability. Finally, a discussion on the current state of the TMDL modeling practices and potential future innovations (developments) is presented.

Chapter 12 Modeling for Total Maximum Daily Load Implementation: The chapter discusses state-of-the-practice on the uses of models in TMDL implementation planning. Ideally, the same model used in TMDL development can also be used for TMDL implementation and related assessment; however, this is not always the case. Communities, organizations, agencies, and other stakeholders implementing a TMDL typically seek the most reliable and importantly the most cost-effective methods to achieve the load reductions required. They invariably intend to compare different scenarios that provide trade-offs among measures such as higher load reduction, lower cost, lower maintenance, available land, or easier implementation. In making these comparisons, the use of an easily understood and reliable model to estimate the load reduction from different planning scenarios is an important element of decision-making for TMDL implementation.

Chapter 12 discusses the uses of the following few watershed-specific models:

1. Chesapeake Assessment Scenario Tool (CAST) for TMDL implementation with the Chesapeake Bay watershed;
2. ArcView Generalized Watershed Loading Function (AVGWLF) based on the GWLF model (Chapter 2) and MapShed for Pennsylvania watersheds;
3. Source Loading and Management for Windows (WinSLAMM) for Wisconsin watersheds; and
4. P-8 Urban Catchment Model for Wisconsin watersheds.

Chapter 12 also discusses two spreadsheet analysis packages:

5. Watershed Treatment Model (WTM) (Chapter 5), and
6. Spreadsheet Tool for Estimating Pollutant Load (STEPL) (Chapter 5).

Critical comparative information (structure, capabilities, and treatment practices) of the aforementioned six models are tabulated for comparisons. Finally, a brief description of custom modeling using GIS geodatabases is presented with the example of the integrated modeling tool for scenario development for the District of Columbia. From an overall implementation perspective, Chapter 12 summarizes a number of ways by which TMDL implementation can be carried out with a better probability of success, including an adaptive management approach for complex TMDLs.

CONCLUDING REMARKS

This manual describes the state-of-the-practice and provides guidance to practitioners in selecting analytical tools and models in the development of a TMDL and its implementation plan. It includes detailed descriptions of a variety of watershed and receiving water quality models that can be used, highlighting recent advances in TMDL analysis and modeling.

This manual comprising 12 chapters is expected to serve as a useful resource to engineers, practitioners, regulators, and other water resource and watershed managers charged with developing and implementing TMDLs. The manual will also serve as a useful resource to planners, environmental scientists, students, educators, the concerned citizens, watershed stakeholders, and the public.

All chapters are based on state-of-the-art reviews of the respective topics, except Chapters 10 and 11, which introduce a state-of-the-art TMDL report search tool in the ATTAINS database and a state-of-the-art TMDL model selection protocol. All chapters serve as useful resources or tools in developing and implementing reliable and successful TMDLs.

As more TMDL studies result in implementation, the use of models for management planning and alternate analysis is increasing; for example, explicit incorporation of BMPs and low-impact development (LID) in the watershed and water quality models has advanced in recent years. The advent of machine learning techniques and other statistical data science technologies can assist communities and watershed stakeholders in achieving TMDL pollutant load reduction goals in a more sustainable and cost-efficient manner. Thus, this Manual of Practice expects to become a living document and needs to be updated in the future to account for potential advances in the practice of TMDL analysis and modeling for the development and implementation of TMDLs.

CHAPTER 1
INTRODUCTION

Nigel W.T. Quinn, Steven C. McCutcheon, Vamsi K. Sridharan, Rosanna J. La Plante, Harry X. Zhang, Deva K. Borah, G. Padmanabhan

1.1 DEFINITIONS AND HISTORY OF THE TOTAL MAXIMUM DAILY LOAD APPROACH

1.1.1 Total Maximum Daily Load Definition and Approach

The 1972 United States Clean Water Act (CWA) as amended in 1977, 1987, and 2000 (Public Law 92-500) requires that all states, territories, and approved tribes (i.e., jurisdictions) biennially list all waterbodies or specific segments of waterbodies that fail to meet jurisdictional water quality standards. After listing all impaired waters, each jurisdiction must prioritize the impaired waters, typically in a water quality management plan for the jurisdiction, which should include deadlines for cleaning up the impairments. The CWA requires that each state or other jurisdiction identify each pollutant that impairs a waterbody (i.e., a stream, lake, or coastal water of the United States) and make a determination of the total mass of the pollutant that can be safely assimilated by the environment. This quantity is referred to as the total maximum daily load (TMDL) for that pollutant. The steps that led to the determination of the TMDL must be documented and the TMDL document must be reviewed and approved by the USEPA. If an agency disapproves a submitted TMDL or a state fails to determine a scheduled TMDL, USEPA is required to take responsibility for the determination of the TMDL. For some complex TMDLs, USEPA and the jurisdiction that is responsible cooperate in determining, allocating, and planning implementation of the TMDL. USEPA recommends that these actions be part of a comprehensive watershed strategy that involves close stakeholder collaboration to restore ambient water quality to meet the required designated uses. This collaboration may involve volunteer groups, contractors, local governments, or other state and federal agencies (e.g., USGS or US Forest Service). Other organizations may determine and implement a TMDL, but the TMDL document must be submitted by the state, territory, or an approved tribe with jurisdictional responsibility (USEPA 2008a).

Thus, in a regulatory context, the approved TMDL document is a plan of action to manage both point sources (PS) and diffuse nonpoint sources (NPS) of pollution of waterbodies. Hence, an approved TMDL document is a set of actions designed to restore water to as close to its pristine quality as required to meet the prevailing water quality standards by examining water quality problems, identifying sources of pollutants, and specifying actions that solve the problem. It is a written plan with a quantitative analysis for attaining and maintaining water quality standards during all seasons.

Quantitatively, a TMDL is the estimated maximum amount of a specific pollutant that can be permitted to enter an impaired waterbody such that the water quality standards for that pollutant can still be attained and continue to be met. This maximum allowable pollutant load is (USEPA 1999b, 2018a)

$$TMDL = LC = \sum WLA + \sum LA + MOS \qquad (1\text{-}1)$$

where LC is the receiving waterbody load capacity or the waste assimilative capacity, and $\sum WLA$ is the sum of all waste load allocations for the National Pollutant Discharge Elimination System (NPDES) permitted PS discharges of treated municipal and industrial wastewaters, municipal and industrial stormwater discharges, combined sewer overflows, and livestock feeding operation discharges. The WLA may include a reserve capacity component for any anticipated NPDES permitting and other sources that are treated as PS discharges (Pidot 2020) into an impaired or threatened waterbody. $\sum LA$ is the sum of all load allocations for the manageable nonpoint sources, background loads, and reserve loads for future nonpoint sources entering the waterbody. The MOS is a margin of safety. The MOS required by the CWA [Public Law 92-500; United States Code Section 303(d)(1)(C)] and the USEPA regulations [40 Code of Federal Regulations (CFR) Section 130.7(c)(1)] account for inadequate knowledge and other uncertainties in the relationship between PS and NPS loads and impaired water quality (USEPA 1999b, 2002a).

USEPA (40 CFR Section 130.2) defines a TMDL as follows:

The sum of the individual WLAs for PSs and LAs for nonpoint sources and natural background. If a receiving water has only one PS discharger, the TMDL is the sum of that PS WLA plus the LAs for any nonpoint sources of pollution and natural background sources, tributaries, or adjacent segments. TMDLs can be expressed in terms of either mass per time, toxicity, or other appropriate measure. If best management practices (BMPs) or other nonpoint source pollution controls make more stringent load allocations practicable, then waste load allocations can be made less stringent. Thus, the TMDL process provides for nonpoint source control tradeoffs.

In addition to the TMDL determined for a single impaired waterbody segment contaminated by a single pollutant [represented in Equation (1-1)], USEPA (2008a) recommends that multiple TMDLs be determined simultaneously to better use available expertise, funding, and time. This applies in instances when (1) multiple TMDLs are to be developed for different pollutants contributing to the same waterbody impairment, (2) phased TMDLs that will require more than 1 year to complete, and (3) watershed-scale TMDLs will be developed for hydrodynamically linked waterbodies with more than one impaired water segment contaminated by more than one pollutant. The determination of multiple TMDLs for a single impaired water segment or multiple such segments is cost-effective because most receiving water quality and any necessary auxiliary watershed models simulate several pollutants simultaneously. Where several water quality standards are violated in an impaired waterbody, the load reduction necessary to address the most severe violation typically addresses the impairment caused by the other pollutants.

South Carolina was an early adopter of the watershed-scale TMDL approach (SCDHEC 1998). The state selected five river basins or groups of similar watersheds for TMDL determinations once every 5 years when NPDES permits were typically due for renewal. Multijurisdictional TMDL determinations can encompass the entire drainage of a major regional waterbody, for example, Chesapeake Bay, Ohio River, or Klamath River. Whether led by USEPA, an individual state, or an interstate regional organization of jurisdictions, these TMDL determinations involve close coordination of effort from multiple states, territories, and approved tribes and sometimes multiple USEPA regional offices, in addition to all voluntary groups and agencies. Multijurisdictional watershed TMDL determinations are often of a larger geographic scope than typical watershed TMDL determinations.

Watershed TMDLs that involve interstate (or interjurisdictional) and multiple jurisdictional determinations typically require complex, integrated models (USEPA 2008a) (Chapter 4). States using the watershed approach for water quality management found that watershed-scale TMDL determinations minimized costs and maximized the number of specific TMDLs developed biennially.

Despite the implication that determining watershed-scale TMDLs requires the application of a watershed model, this may not be necessary where the PS and NPS loads can be distinguished having separate tributary boundary conditions for a receiving water quality model. In addition, overland transport from any NPS must not change the load that flows into the waterbody substantially. By contrast, a single river reach (segment) TMDL defined in Equation (1-1) addresses only a single impaired waterbody, whether the impairments are owing to single or multiple violations of the water quality standards. USEPA (2008a) noted the obvious synergistic opportunities for integrating the determination of watershed-scale TMDLs and other watershed management programs, such as watershed planning, permitting, and water quality trading.

1.1.2 History of the Total Maximum Daily Load Approach to Water Quality–Based Management

The United States Congress first enacted legislation to control water pollution with the Rivers and Harbors Appropriation Act of 1899 to prevent dumping of refuse and other wastes into the navigable waters of the nation by foreign and domestic ships, including into the tributaries, thus initially defining the waters of the United States. The Congress enacted the Water Pollution Control Act of 1948 to "enhance the quality and value of our water resources and to establish a national policy for the prevention, control, and abatement of water pollution" primarily by the use of water quality standards and a water quality–based approach.

The 1948 Act was amended by the Federal Water Pollution Control Act of 1956 and the Water Quality Act of 1965 to better establish surface water quality standards enforceable by state and federal authorities. These amendments improved reporting and enforcement and added an antidegradation clause that eventually led to the water quality (standards)–based approach. However, this approach initially failed to prevent the "burning rivers and dead lakes" of the 1960s.

The Federal Water Pollution Control Act Amendments of 1972 radically changed US water quality management by requiring a technology-based approach; all dischargers were equally required to apply a minimum level of treatment such as secondary biological treatment for municipal sewage (33 United States Code Section 1251 et seq. 1972). These seminal 1972 amendments that may be cited as the "Federal Water Pollution Control Act" (33 United States Code § 1251, note § 519) were further amended by Congress with the 1977 Clean Water Act, 1987 Water Quality Act, and 2000 BEACH Act. Congress and USEPA refer to the 1972 amendments of the Federal Water Pollution Control Act combined with the amendments of 1977, 1981, 1987, and 2000 as the CWA.

Since the passage of the CWA in 1972 that defines and requires TMDL determinations, the following amendments to the CWA were passed, a number of USEPA regulations and rules were issued (Copeland 2014) as required by the Act, and several United States Supreme Court and federal court rulings defined how the Act was to be interpreted:

1972: United States Congress enacted and the president signed the CWA, later amended in 1977, 1981, 1987, and 2000 (Public Law 92-500) that (USEPA 2020a) with the following results:

- Established the basic approach for regulating pollutant discharges into the waters of the United States by making discharge of any pollutant from a point source into navigable waters unlawful unless a permit was obtained.
- Gave USEPA the authority to implement pollution control programs such as setting wastewater standards for industry and authority to maintain the integrity of wetlands.
- Maintained existing requirements to set water quality standards for all contaminants in surface waters.
- Funded the construction of sewage treatment plants under the construction grants program.
- Recognized the need for planning to address the critical problems posed by NPS pollution.

1975: USEPA issued a rule for watershed or basin-wide water quality planning that included the key requirement of allocating the TMDL for a pollutant for the various sources of the pollutant. The initial *Water Quality Inventory Report* was submitted to the Congress.

1977: This amendment, titled by the Congress as the Clean Water Act of 1977, addressed long-term funding for wastewater treatment facilities, sludge management, toxic pollutants, wetland protection, and nonpoint source management (United States Code 1251 et seq. dated 11/27/2002).

1978: Under court order [Environmental Defense Fund, Inc. v. Costle, 657 F.2d 275, 295 (D.C. Circuit 1981)], USEPA issued a ruling stating that all pollutants are technically amenable to a TMDL determination and clarified water quality management and planning recommendations.

1981: Revised regulations streamlined the municipal construction grants process, thus improving the capabilities of treatment plants (USEPA 2020a).

1983: Chesapeake Bay Agreement among USEPA, the state of Maryland, the commonwealths of Pennsylvania and Virginia, and the District of Columbia (and later West Virginia, New York, and Delaware) to fully address the extent, complexity, and sources of pollutants entering the Chesapeake Bay (Chesapeake Bay Program 1999).

1985: The USEPA rule "Water Quality Management and Planning" elaborated on the earlier regulations of 1975 and 1978 focused on the continuous planning process, monitoring, waste load allocation for point sources, load allocation for nonpoint sources, and TMDL allocations at a contributing watershed scale. The biennial *Water Quality Inventory* defined loading capacity, waste load allocation, and load allocation, as defined in Equation (1-1). The agency rule also recommended allocation of reserve capacity if future impairments were anticipated. The USEPA published the guidelines for deriving numerical national water quality criteria for the protection of aquatic organisms (Stephen et al. 1985) to consistently measure aquatic acute and chronic toxicity, on which several TMDL determinations have been based.

1987: Amendments of the CWA, the Water Quality Act of 1987, clarified the administration of various lists of impaired waters and established stormwater permitting, new water quality assessments, NPS pollution control, the Great Lakes and Chesapeake Bay protection programs, toxics control, and strengthened many water quality management programs. USEPA asked states, territories, and approved tribes to combine Water Quality Assessment Act evaluations and CWA Section 305(b) listings of impaired waters and prepare clean water strategies to prioritize and address impairments. The construction grants program was replaced with the State Water Pollution Control Revolving Fund, commonly known as the Clean Water State Revolving Fund (USEPA 2020a).

1980s to 1990s: Numerous federal lawsuits filed by environmental groups against USEPA and select states (Conway 1997, Malone 2002) charged that states were not developing 303(d) lists quickly enough and that the agency was not developing lists and TMDLs when a state failed to do so. Many consent decrees required that the USEPA work with states in determining thousands of TMDLs under strict deadlines. Some states may have used oversimplified, unreliable methods to determine, allocate, and plan implementation of a TMDL.

1991: USEPA (1991) published *Guidance for Water Quality–Based Decisions: The TMDL Process* that recommended the integration of TMDL determinations for state watershed management. The selection and application of models was implicitly left to the states and other jurisdictions, with final approval of the TMDL document by USEPA.

1992: Revised TMDL regulations required states to update CWA 303(d) lists biennially, recommended watershed TMDL determinations, presented guidance for load and waste load allocations, clarified requirements for the margin of safety, required prioritization of TMDL determinations for impaired waters, published criteria to guide USEPA regional reviews of all TMDL documents [40 CFR Part 130; CWA Section 303(d)], published a compendium of watershed-scale models for TMDL determination (USEPA 1992) that identified the most widely used watershed models to assist in model selection.

1994: The USEPA Office of Water established the Watershed Academy to provide training and education on the basics of watershed TMDL determinations.

1995: USEPA (1995a, b, c) published the *Technical Guidance Manual for Developing Total Maximum Daily Loads* and the initial TMDL guidance for concentrated animal feeding operations and established a Watershed Protection Approach.

1996: USEPA updated the 1991 *Guidance for Water Quality–Based Decisions* with the draft *TMDL Program Implementation Strategy*, which recognized the importance of the watershed approach in TMDL allocations, extended the frequency of reporting, combined report categories, and established many agency resources for assistance in TMDL determination (Malone 2002). USEPA developed the Better Assessment Science Integrating Point and Nonpoint Sources (BASINS) modeling framework (Lahlou et al. 1996) to support more effective model selection and data management at a time when some states and USEPA were subject to federal court decrees to accelerate the completion of backlogged TMDLs.

1997: USEPA issued interpretive guidance for the states, territories, and approved tribes to develop long-term schedules for determining TMDLs on a watershed basis. In addition, USEPA published the *Compendium of Tools for Watershed Assessment and TMDL Development* (Shoemaker et al. 1997).

1998: More than 41,800 impairments affecting approximately 20,000 waterbodies were reported by states.

1999: USEPA (1999a, b, c) clarified and strengthened the TMDL program and revised the NPDES regulations. USEPA released the *Protocol for Developing Sediment TMDLs* (USEPA, 1999b) and the *Protocol for Developing Nutrient TMDLs* (USEPA, 1999c). The United States Department of Agriculture and USEPA released the final Unified National Strategy for Animal Feeding Operations in March 1999.

2000: Congress (Department of Veteran Affairs, Housing and Urban Development, and Independent Agencies Act, Public Law 106-377, 114 Statute 1441, 1441A-3, 2000) required that the National Research Council review the new regulations and that the USEPA TMDL program determine (1) information necessary to identify the sources of pollution, the degree to which each source impairs water quality and how pollutant load reductions should be allocated among sources, (2) if that information can be reliably obtained by the states, and (3) what methodology should be used to obtain the information. USEPA promulgated revisions to the Water Quality Planning and Management Regulation and to the NPDES program (65 Federal Register 43,586, 588, 590, and 591 July 13, 2000) that included (1) NPS be explicitly included within the TMDL, as shown in Equation (1-1); (2) 17 states had to schedule the determinations of TMDLs by 2010; (3) all impaired waterbodies were to be placed on a four-part list and prioritized; and (4) 19 States were further required to provide an implementation plan and "reasonable assurance" that TMDL waste loads and load allocations would be met. The CWA was amended to support updated water quality standards for monitoring of pathogen indicators in recreational waters (USEPA 2020b). USEPA published the Unified Federal Policy for a Watershed Approach to Federal Land and Resource Management (65 Federal Register 62,566 October 18, 2000).

2001: The National Research Council (NRC 2001) review of the TMDL program found that there was sufficient scientific information available to determine TMDLs, but the MOS in Equation (1-1) must explicitly include estimates of scientific uncertainty. USEPA postponed the release of the proposed Water Quality Planning and Management Regulation until 2003 to accommodate the National Research Council (NRC 2001) findings and other comments (Malone 2002). USEPA (2001a, b) estimated that national costs to industry to implement the TMDL program could range from less than $1 billion to $4.3 billion annually. USEPA provided the states the opportunity to combine the biennial reports for 303(d) listing of impaired waters and the 305(b) inventory of state water quality into a single integrated report to reduce reporting requirements. In addition, USEPA published the *Protocol for Developing Pathogen TMDLs* (USEPA, 2001c).

2002: USEPA (2002a, b) developed guidance for regional agency reviews of TMDL documents and improved definition of the steps in the development of TMDLs, including for stormwater sources.

2003: USEPA withdrew the 2000 proposed Water Quality Planning and Management Regulation as unworkable. The program requirements under the 1992 regulations and court sanction of schedules for TMDL determinations remained in effect. USEPA issued the Final Water Quality Trading Policy and published the final rule for regulation of concentrated animal feeding operations (68 Federal Register 7,175 to 7,274; February 12, 2003).

2004: USEPA issued guidance for the development of watershed implementation plans.

2005: USEPA released the extensive "TMDL model evaluation and research needs" (Shoemaker et al. 2005) that evaluated more than 65 models for TMDL determinations.

2007: USEPA (2007a, b) issued guidance on NPDES permitting and water quality trading.

2008: USEPA (2008b) issued a draft handbook for watershed-scale TMDL determinations that simultaneously addressed all violations of water quality standards in multiple, hydrologically connected impaired waterbodies.

2009: The president signed an executive order recognizing the Chesapeake Bay as a national treasure and called on the federal government to lead a renewed effort to restore and protect the largest American estuary and contributing watershed (USEPA 2020c).

2011: USEPA [40 CFR 130.7(c)(1)] required that the states and other jurisdictions "take into account the critical conditions for stream flow, loading, and water quality parameters." The landmark Chesapeake Bay TMDLs were approved (USEPA 2020c). USEPA (2011) provided guidance on genetic fingerprinting of fecal indicator bacteria to identify sources, allocate load reductions, and plan implementation.

2015: American Farm Bureau Federation v. USEPA, 792 F.3d 281, 288 (Third Circuit 2015) clarified and expanded Agency authority to regulate NPS pollution.

2016: Waters of the United States Rule was promulgated to protect critical streams and wetlands by ensuring that waters protected under the Clean Water Act were more precisely defined (USEPA 2020c). See revised rule in 2020.

2017: USEPA revised the 1985 guidelines for deriving numerical national water quality criteria for the protection of aquatic organisms (Elias et al. 2017).

2020: The United States Supreme Court ruled in the County of Maui v. Hawaii Wildlife Fund case that some nonpoint sources are the "functional equivalent of a direct discharge" to navigable waters, such as the subsurface injection of wastewater that flows quickly to the waters of the United States. The court instructed USEPA to define such functional equivalents, most likely based on the distance the pollutants traveled, time to reach navigable waters, and any subsurface physical or chemical attenuation of the pollutants in the vicinity of the injection wells, which controls pollutant loading into the waters of the United States (Pidot 2020).

The contributing watershed or basin of many impaired waterbodies crosses the boundaries of states and other jurisdictions. In such cases, USEPA encourages states and other jurisdictions to put in place legal agreements to coordinate the determinations, allocations, and implementation planning for all TMDLs for multijurisdictional impaired waterbodies.

The Chesapeake Bay Program is an outstanding example of multijurisdictional coordination. The 92 watersheds draining into Chesapeake Bay, the largest estuary in the United States, cover an area of 166,000 km^2 (64,000 mi^2). The Chesapeake Bay Program is a remarkable regional partnership that champions the restoration of the Bay. The Chesapeake Bay TMDLs for nutrients and sediment are being implemented using the most comprehensive hydrodynamic, water quality, and watershed models available as of 2020. In 2000, the Chesapeake Bay Program partners signed Chesapeake 2000, a detailed agreement that established a basin-wide strategy to guide watershed and aquatic restoration through 2010. This collaboration eventually came to include seven additional jurisdictions besides the USEPA Region 3 Chesapeake Bay Program Office: Delaware, District of Columbia, Maryland, New York, Pennsylvania, Virginia, and West Virginia (USEPA 2010). In 2010, these eight jurisdictions finalized landmark Chesapeake Bay watershed-scale TMDLs. The Chesapeake Bay TMDL allocations set limits on nutrient and sediment loads that enter the bay and the major tributaries while meeting all water quality standards of the seven jurisdictions. Each of the seven bay jurisdictions created a watershed implementation plan that defined the detailed, specific steps that each jurisdiction is taking to achieve the necessary load reductions by 2025 (Chesapeake Bay Program 2019).

1.2 PROCESS OF DETERMINING TOTAL MAXIMUM LOADS

Figure 1-1 outlines the process necessary to determine, allocate, and implement a single TMDL (USEPA 1999b), phased TMDLs, watershed-scale TMDLs (USEPA 2008b), or multijurisdictional TMDLs (USEPA 2008b). Given that the water quality management policies and priorities differ for each state, territory, and approved tribe, Figure 1-1 does not go beyond implementation planning. State and other jurisdictional laws, regulations, and other policies usually guide the implementation of approved TMDLs. However, state and other jurisdictional policies on TMDL implementation are not expected to substantially affect model selection and application for use in TMDL implementation planning.

To understand why model (or method) selection and application can be critical, the following two subsections present the steps in developing a TMDL (USEPA 1999b). These steps provide guidance on the importance of

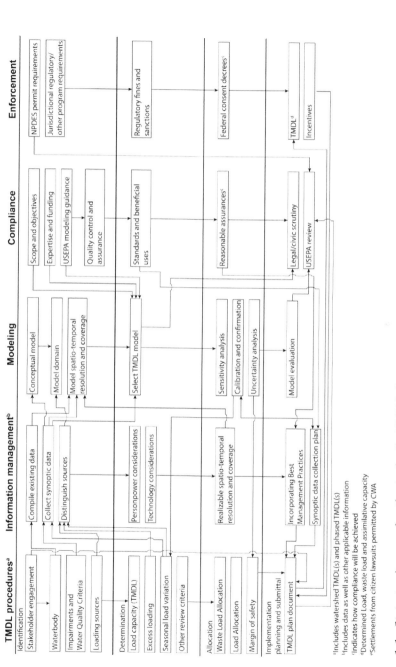

Figure 1-1. State, territory, and authorized tribe TMDL determination, allocation, and implementation.

Note: Each column is categorized by rows that represent (a) identification of the impaired waters and loading; (b) determination of TMDL after compilation and collection of information and model selection; (c) allocation of specific load reductions; (d) implementation planning, submission, and deployment. The arrows define the flow of information between the various actions.

Notes: BMP = best management practice, NPDES = National Pollutant Discharge Elimination System, TMDL = total maximum daily load, USEPA = federal Environmental Protection Agency.

collecting synoptic data to calibrate and test the reliability of models (or methods) used to develop TMDLs, allocate load reductions, and implement plans. The vital synoptic data for calibration and validation of these models (or methods) should be viewed separately from existing monitoring data, which is rarely complete enough to reliably calibrate or test models or methods used to develop the TMDL.

1.2.1 Procedure for Total Maximum Daily Load Determination, Allocation, and Implementation Planning

The TMDL document or report submitted for USEPA review and approval should include the following information [40 Code Federal Regulations 130.33(b)] (USEPA 1999b, 2002a). These requirements are also documented in the 1992 USEPA review guidelines for submissions of TMDL documents (USEPA 2002a) that outline the procedure to develop a TMDL, formulate load allocations, and implement the TMDL plan.

1.2.1.1 Identification

1. Impaired waterbody: Regulation 40 CFR 130.27(c) requires the name and geographic location of the impaired or threatened waterbody for which each pollutant the TMDL addresses, along with the names and geographic locations of the upstream waterbodies that contribute significant pollutant loads.
2. Pollutants: Identification of the pollutant for each TMDL determination is necessary. In cases where there are multiple pollutants, priority ranking the impairments will promote optimal management for water quality.
3. Water quality standards: This includes a description of the violated water quality standards consisting of known beneficial uses of the receiving water and a numeric water quality target. In place of numeric water quality targets (USEPA 2002a), water quality experts typically rely on numeric water quality criterion. Not all water quality standards include a numeric criterion. Some standards are limited to a beneficial use or narrative criterion, such as standards for oily wastes (McCutcheon 1988). For complex multijurisdictional watersheds, TMDL determinations are especially difficult to quantify because of absent or conflicting numeric criteria among the jurisdictions. The Chesapeake Bay TMDLs were difficult to determine because of absent or conflicting numeric criteria for the impairment of aquatic habitat owing to eutrophication, anoxia, and water clarity that caused a reduction in the abundance of seagrasses as measured by chlorophyll-a, dissolved oxygen, and the light extinction coefficient, respectively. These impairments were ultimately ascribed to excess nitrogen, phosphorus, and sediment loads (Wainger 2012).

4. Pollutant sources and loads: The regulations 40 CFR 130.2(f) and 40 CFR 130.2(g) require an identification of the pollutant source category, source subcategory, or individual source descriptions for the pollutant for which waste load allocations and load allocations are necessary.

1.2.1.2 Determination

5. TMDL: This is the determination of the amount or degree by which the current pollutant loads discharged to the waterbody deviate from the pollutant loading permissible to attain and maintain water quality standards.
6. Consideration of seasonal variation of loads: Requires that water quality standards for the allocated pollutant will be attained and pollutant assimilative capacity not exceeded during all seasons of the year.

1.2.1.3 Allocation

7. Waste load allocations: Section 402 of the CWA requires waste load allocation for all NPDES permitted sources of the pollutant for which the TMDL is being established, including (1) each industrial and municipal point source, and (2) discharges of stormwater, combined sewer overflows, leachate from abandoned mines, drainage from combined animal feeding operations, or any other discharges subject to a general NPDES permit. The reductions to PS loads may be allocated to categories of sources, subcategories of sources, or individual sources. PS loads that do not need to be reduced to attain or maintain water quality standards may be included within a category of sources, subcategory of sources, or natural background loads. The TMDL document submitted to USEPA must include supporting technical analyses demonstrating that the documented waste load allocation, when implemented, will attain and sustain attainment of water quality standards.
8. Load allocations: This is the required pollutant load allocations of NPSs, ranging from accurate assessments to gross allotments and must also include atmospheric deposition and natural background sources. If possible, a separate load reduction should be allocated to each source of natural background loading and to atmospheric deposition. Load allocations should be allocated to manageable categories of sources, subcategories of sources, or individual sources. Pollutant loads that do not need to be reduced may be included within a category of sources, subcategory of sources, or as part of background loading. The load allocation must be supported by technical analyses demonstrating that these allocations, when satisfied, will attain and maintain water quality standards in the receiving waterbody.

9. Margin of safety: This ensures attainment of water quality standards for the pollutants and must be explicitly expressed as unallocated assimilative capacity or implicitly based on the (1) use of conservative cause-and-effect expressions used in determining the TMDL, (2) conservative derivation of numeric criteria, and (3) conservative forecasts of the effectiveness of the best management practices to be implemented.

10. Reserve capacity: An allowance for future growth that accounts for reasonably foreseeable increases in pollutant loads.

11. Reasonable assurances: This is to ensure that when a TMDL is determined based on both PS and NPS loads, the NPS control measures will ensure that sufficient load reductions will occur.

1.2.1.4 Implementation planning and compliance

12. Implementation plan: An implementation plan, while not explicitly required by the CWA, is nonetheless recommended to be submitted so that watershed management, monitoring, logistics, and operations can be documented. Such plans also involve enumerating partners and establishing priorities (USEPA 2018b). The implementation plan can typically also include details on public participation and a submittal letter and outline the processes for administrative record retention.

Although not explicitly stated in the TMDL procedure (USEPA 1999b) or the review criteria (USEPA 2002a), matching the pollution loads with the impairments to calculate a TMDL typically requires a model or at least a reliable method. These models or methods are selected from a range of techniques, from simple mass balance calculations to complex water quality modeling as elaborated in Chapters 2 to 5. The selection of the model or method is based on a variety of factors, including the waterbody type, complexity of flow, and pollutants causing the impairment, among others described in Chapter 11. Table 1-1 provides a ranking of the impaired constituents (water quality variables) in the US waterbodies along with modeling objectives outlined for TMDL determination, allocation, and implementation planning for each of the impaired constituents in various studies listed in the table with references.

1.2.2 Synoptic and Monitoring Data Requirements

Two types of data collection are necessary to apply the legally mandated TMDL approach to water quality management: (1) synoptic data to support reliable TMDL analysis and modeling, and (2) the less complex ambient monitoring to list impaired waters and to delist waters that consistently meet the water quality standards.

Table 1-1. Water Quality Variables and Modeling Objectives for TMDL Determination, Allocation, and Implementation Planning.

Water quality variables	Some modeling objectives for TMDL determination, allocation, and implementation planning under critical conditions	References
Pathogen indicators	Distinguish human and livestock sources from wildlife sources for all NPS and PS	Benham et al. (2006, 2008), Mishra et al. (2018, 2019)
	Determine cause and effect among all important sources for suspended fecal indicators, fecal particles, and deposited and resuspended indicators for the full extent of impairment	
	Simulate efficiency of landscape and instream best management practices and wastewater treatment process upgrades to best allocate load reductions	
Sediments	Simulate event loading or long-term geomorphologic changes in sediment deposition, erosion, and flushing rates usually for three classes: sand, silt, and clays to distinguish landscape erosion from bank erosion	Borah and Bera (2003, 2004), Borah et al. (2006), Benham et al. (2008), Gillett et al. (2016), Wallace et al. (2018)
	Simulate manageable and distinguishable classes of landscape and bank erosion to guide application	
	Assess nutrient enrichment of sediments and waterbodies owing to sediment loading	
	Determine the effects of sediment loads on aquatic ecosystems	
	Simulate sorption to and release from suspended, bedload, and deposited sediments	

(Continued)

Table 1-1. (*Continued*)

Water quality variables	Some modeling objectives for TMDL determination, allocation, and implementation planning under critical conditions	References
Nutrients (nitrogen and phosphorus in various forms), plankton, aquatic plants, and eutrophication	Evaluate the water quality impairment owing to pollutant loading Simulate the effects of best management practices on agricultural, urban, and other land uses, including septic systems and nonagricultural fertilized areas (lawns, golf course, parks) for implementation planning Determine nutrient limitations to manage eutrophication, toxic algae, anoxia, hypoxia, fish kills, and other ecosystem impairments Simulate the nutrient sources, including benthic storage that cause algal and cyanobacterial blooms that are toxic, deplete oxygen, kill fish, and shade plants	Borah et al. (2006), Benham et al. (2008), Hoornbeek et al. (2008), Keisman and Shenk (2013)
Dissolved oxygen	Evaluate the effects of organic loading (measured as biochemical oxygen demand (BOD) and chemical oxygen demand (COD) loads on benthos and aquatic ecosystem function Assess anoxia, hypoxia, fish kills, and other ecosystem impairments	Thomann and Mueller (1987), USEPA (1995a), Martin and McCutcheon (1999), Vellidis et al. (2006), Benham et al. (2008), Hoornbeek et al. (2008)

BOD, COD, and organic matter or carbon	Evaluate organic matter loading and decomposition rates of different types of organic carbon on dissolved oxygen and sorption of toxic compounds	Thomann and Mueller (1987), USEPA (1995a), Martin and McCutcheon (1999), Gillett et al. (2016)
	Investigate impacts of different allocations of source reductions from agricultural wastes that are plant versus animal based	
Water temperature	Evaluate the riparian shading effects on diurnal heating and cooling	McCutcheon (1989), Chen et al. (1998), Martin and McCutcheon (1999), Ritchie and Cooper (2001), Benham et al. (2008), Daniels et al. (2018)
	Simulate cooling water discharge near field mixing and far field heat transport and surface and bottom exchange	
	Evaluate effects of reservoir and lake management on downstream temperature	
	Correct all biological and chemical rate constants, and viscosity and density for variation in temperature	
Metals including trace metals and metalloids	Calculate equilibrium speciation of toxic metals and metalloids in the receiving water and in each source to relate toxic species to PS and NPS	Hoornbeek et al. (2008)
	Simulate watershed impacts of all feasible best management practices to allocate source reductions for the toxic species that violate standards	

(Continued)

Table 1-1. (*Continued*)

Water quality variables	Some modeling objectives for TMDL determination, allocation, and implementation planning under critical conditions	References
Solid wastes	Evaluate disruption to water supply, re-creation, and aquatic habitat	ADEQ (2017)
Salinity or total dissolved solids	Calibrate estuarine dilution by seawater Evaluate the dilution of runoff from irrigated agriculture	Ketchum (1951a, b), Pritchard (1969), Mills et al. (1985), McCutcheon (1989), Chapra (1997), Martin and McCutcheon (1999, pp. 599–612), MacWilliams et al. (2015)
Pesticides, other toxic chemicals, and oils	Simulate fate and transport of concentrations or changes in toxicity among all sources and impaired waters Simulate soil and sediment sorption and release of toxic chemicals and oil	Mills et al. (1985), Muñoz-Carpena et al. (2006), Benham et al. (2008), Hoornbeek et al. (2008), Moriasi et al. (2012, 2015)

Source: https://iaspub.epa.gov/waters10/attains_nation_cy.control#causes

Note: Ranked by impairment frequency in United States rivers and streams.

1. Synoptic observations are used to define reliable cause-and-effect relationships between loading and impairment. The general categories of synoptic data include pollutant sources, ambient water quality, hydrodynamics, and meteorology. Any auxiliary application of watershed modeling must characterize topography, soil characteristics, and land use/land cover. These data must have sufficient coherent spatial and temporal resolution and coverage to reliably define all impairments and prevailing water quality gradients during critical conditions (McCutcheon 1985).
2. Well-designed water quality (ambient) monitoring is used to list impaired waterbodies reliably and delist unimpaired waters. Most existing monitoring data are inadequate to calibrate water quality models (Martin et al. 1991). The design of monitoring programs is almost always heuristic, rarely coherent, and may require data collection for conflicting purposes not all related to water quality management. Nevertheless, of the more than 5,500 approved TMDLs within the last 5 years, nearly 35% were based on ambient monitoring (Sridharan et al. 2021), but the reliability of this determination was not always established by hypothesis testing.

The National Water Portal (NWQMC 2020) is the major repository of water quality and flow data for receiving waters in the United States. This federal data repository was developed by the USGS and USEPA from the USEPA STORET Warehouse and the USGS National Water Information System. A third major contributor is the Agricultural Research Service of USDA. The portal serves as a repository for data collected by more than 400 federal, state, tribal, and local agencies. USEPA also compiles information from watershed groups, other volunteer groups, and universities [40 CFR 130.7(b)(5)(iii)]. The National Water Portal provides links to other major repositories for groundwater and coastal and ocean monitoring as well as the California Water Quality Monitoring Council web portal: My Water Quality.

1.3 MODELING REQUIRED TO DETERMINE A TOTAL MAXIMUM DAILY LOAD

The determination of TMDLs requires the use of a process model or an analogous simplified method to define the cause-and-effect relationship reliably between pollutant sources and water quality impairments. Due diligence in the use of these estimation techniques requires a sequential procedure that starts with defining the scope of the TMDL determination, load allocation, and implementation.

In defining the scope of TMDL determinations, the pollutant causing the waterbody impairment must be identified. The water quality modeling team and water quality managers must use professional judgment to select among the following three alternatives: (1) a single TMDL determination for a specific violation of a water quality standard in a waterbody or segment, (2) a phased approach to determine TMDLs, or (3) to simultaneously determine multiple TMDLs on a watershed basis. The phased approach is used to determine a single TMDL or multiple watershed-scale TMDLs. Phased TMDL determinations are straightforward in model selection and synoptic data collection but require more than a year to schedule the series of tasks involved.

The determination of TMDLs requires the selection of a reliable model or an equivalent method of analysis that ranges from simple mass balance calculations to complex, process-based, mechanistic water quality models (Chapters 2 to 5 and 11) (McCutcheon 1989, Martin and McCutcheon 1999, Sridharan et al. 2021). From the last 5 years of approved TMDL documents, less than 10% were determined using simplified analytical methods, whereas nearly 50% were determined using receiving water quality models.

Simple methods, by definition, rely on more approximation, typically from the algorithmic lumping of important water quality processes. Such simplification paradoxically requires greater expertise in applying and interpreting these simulations or estimates and more data collection to develop these methods (Martin and McCutcheon 1999). Too many applications of oversimplified or overly complex methods fail to consider the expertise necessary to understand and interpret these simulations (McCutcheon 1983) and fail to consider reliability during model selection. In many determinations, comprehensive, reliable, process-based models are unavailable or insufficiently developed (Martin and McCutcheon 1999, pp. 44 to 46 and Figure 18). Insufficiently developed (defined as over- or underparameterized) numerical water quality and auxiliary watershed models often cannot be calibrated uniquely and, as a consequence, are not well-adapted for practical TMDL analysis and simulation modeling (Martin and McCutcheon 1999).

One or more contributing watersheds must be simulated if the substantial pollutant loads contributing to the impairment cannot be distinguished if a separate boundary condition cannot be established or if it suspected that substantial changes may occur between the source area and the discharge point to the waterbody. In addition, if the impaired waters are stream reaches, a few watershed models (Chapter 2) are capable of simulating both the receiving water quality and the contributing watershed nonpoint sources. The watershed models (Chapter 2) and receiving water models (Chapter 3) should be calibrated and tested simultaneously if the implementation plan requires an assessment of the placement and performance of best management practices to achieve the necessary load reductions. The most extensive and complex watershed-scale TMDL determinations, load allocations, and implementation plans, especially when applied across multiple jurisdictions (e.g., Chesapeake Bay and contributing watersheds), will often require a phased development and implementation of TMDLs primarily because of financial resource limitations and the complexity of the tasks involved.

1.4 BENEFITS OF THE TOTAL MAXIMUM DAILY LOAD APPROACH

In addition to achieving the beneficial uses and any numerical criteria to avoid fines and other enforcement actions, the determination and implementation of a TMDL result in secondary socioeconomic and environmental benefits not typically quantified or accounted for in attaining the water quality standards. These incidental benefits accrue when communities are willing to invest additional resources in environmental restoration and protection. The determination and implementation of TMDLs leave a legacy of water quality data and calibrated simulation models that are useful in subsequent water resource and land-use planning. Well-organized and engaged stakeholders active in the TMDL implementations often help lobby governors, legislatures, and local governments for funding needed to fund water quality management. For example, the watershed-scale TMDLs determined for the Chesapeake Bay, one of the most complex and valuable waterbodies nationally, and western Long Island Sound are managed across seven and two jurisdictions, respectively. In western Long Island Sound, located between Connecticut and New York, a phased TMDL determination was made after 303(d) listing by both states to reduce nitrogen loading into the estuary that was impaired by eutrophication and hypoxia (USEPA 2017). The primary outcomes of the determinations of the Chesapeake Bay TMDLs (Wainger 2012) will be a continued reduction in nitrogen and phosphorous loads and an overall improvement in Bay water quality. These improvements will invigorate the invaluable seagrass habitat and world-renowned crab and other fisheries, including shellfish that can rapidly filter large volumes of poor-quality water. These ongoing improvements have already increased waterfront real-estate values as well as increased commercial and recreational fishing, swimming, and boating activities (Cropper and Isaac 2011).

The Chesapeake Bay marketplace for trading water quality credits and the provision of state tax incentives to dischargers who improve treatment performance (Wainger 2012) have already resulted in substantial economic savings in the upgrade of wastewater treatment plants and implementation of best management practices. The Bay marketplace for nutrient reduction credits helps polluters who release smaller loads of nutrients, such as municipalities with very expensive costs for wastewater treatment plant expansions, to offset some of the pollutant loads generated by farmers who tend to produce large nutrient loads that can be partly reduced by less-expensive and effective best management practices (Chesapeake Bay Foundation 2020). The trading of credits for nitrogen loading reductions into western Long Island Sound are projected to save $200 to $400 million in wastewater treatment upgrades in Connecticut and $600 million in New York (USEPA 2017).

Other ancillary benefits from water quality–based management involve financial, environmental, and social improvements that impact public policy. One of the secondary benefits of the Florida TMDL program was the construction of low-impact, appealing, green infrastructure to reduce nonpoint source pollution from new and existing urban development (USEPA 2008a). In the Central Valley of California, the TMDLs necessary to realize the aquatic life beneficial use in the San Joaquin River basin have resulted in state- and stakeholder-sponsored ecological restoration (CDWR 2019) that complement and enhance best management practices used for TMDL implementation. These few examples indicate a shift toward a more sustainable water quality management that is not specifically required by the CWA.

1.5 PURPOSE OF THIS MANUAL OF PRACTICE

The primary objective of this Manual of Practice is to guide watershed and receiving water model selection, synoptic data collection and compilation, calibration, and independent testing to define uncertainty for the users of the largely ad hoc models for determining TMDLs to manage point and nonpoint source pollution in the United States. Unlike the waste load allocation process for control of PS pollution, the United States has not holistically planned and developed all the specialized models or the technical guidance necessary for professionals to reliably develop TMDLs for all impaired waters. As a result, the development of TMDL modeling has been somewhat ad hoc and erratic, and in the last 15 years, much of the ad hoc developments were decentralized to the USEPA regions and state agencies. The exceptional development and support of a few models do not cover the full needs of TMDL modeling or correct the incomplete development of a comprehensive modeling and analysis framework. The sporadic development of simplified, unsupported TMDL models in response to unrealistic federal court decrees is especially problematic. Furthermore, many TMDL determinations use models developed by other agencies for different purposes, such as soil and water conservation or floodplain analysis. Thus, the models available to TMDL analysts are a patchwork covering some modeling requirements but leaving some determinations to rely on models developed for very different purposes, particularly those models developed for research or not developed into well-documented, practical models.

This manual of practice is necessary because too many TMDL determinations fail to select and use the most appropriate models of cause and effect for PS and NPS control of pollutants and water quality impairments. Monitoring and statistical analyses and other simple methods are selected too frequently despite the fact that many of these empirical, heuristic methods have not been established to predict reliably that load reduction strategies will correct and prevent future water quality impairments. The lack of clear guidance on parsimonious, reliable model selection and the lack of well-defined data requirements for determining cause and effect seem to be the reasons for some states and other jurisdictions resorting to unsuitable models and the expense of trial-and-error approaches under the banner of adaptive management. More important, hypothesis testing of calibration and confirmation (validation) has not been applied to establish that simulations or estimates of TMDLs are reliable.

1.6 INTENDED AUDIENCE FOR THIS MANUAL

ASCE publishes manuals and reports on engineering practice to serve as guidance for practicing and supervising engineers. This Manual of Practice is primarily intended for engineers and other technologists with state water pollution control agencies, USEPA and other federal water and natural resource agencies, and the contracting experts who are called on to support these state and federal water quality analysts. The state and federal water quality and watershed managers entrusted with the responsibility of determining TMDLs and conducting implementation planning are an important audience, as are engineers, applied scientists, and managers with the businesses and industries that discharge pollutants into the waters of the United States. This Manual of Practice is also useful to attorneys, urban and watershed planners, environmental and ecological restoration engineers and scientists, graduate students, educators, and concerned citizens with some technical experience.

1.7 ORGANIZATION OF THIS MANUAL

This manual has 12 chapters. Chapter 1 defines critical concepts in TMDL determination and implementation planning and provides the history of federal, legal, and regulatory requirements and guidance that defines the rationale to guide model (or method of analysis) selection and application. Chapters 2, 3, 4, and 5, respectively, present watershed models; receiving water quality models; integrated modeling systems and linked models; and lastly, simple models and methods. These derive from the published literature and contain applications of TMDL development and implementation as well as complementary studies that can support TMDL development and implementation. Chapter 6 presents guidance on critical condition modeling and analysis; Chapter 7 presents summaries of available geographic information system and remote sensing tools that are increasingly being used to support TMDL development; Chapter 8 emphasizes the importance of model calibration and validation to ensure success in the TMDL enterprise; and Chapter 9 introduces model uncertainty analysis and explains the concept of MOS. The goal of Chapters 2 to 9 is to define the state of the practice in the use of analytical procedures, numerical models, critical conditions, model calibration and confirmation testing, and model uncertainty analysis and aid in the calculation of the MOS for a specific TMDL. Chapter 10 introduces the USEPA Total Maximum Daily Load Tracking and Implementation System that archives the TMDL documents submitted to and approved by the USEPA and presents a new online tool developed for searching the TMDL reports there for certain search categories. Chapter 11 presents a rational model selection process (protocol) to support TMDL determination, load allocation, and implementation planning. Current modeling practices for planning and implementing TMDLs are presented in Chapter 12. Please see Executive Summary for comprehensive summaries of all the chapters.

Chapters 2 through 10 and 12 are based on and aligned with the ASCE (2017) TMDL Analysis and Modeling Task Committee 2017 report and state-of-the-art papers published in the *Journal of Hydrologic Engineering* special collection on "Total Maximum Daily Load Analysis and Modeling: Assessment and Advancement." The announcement of the special collection with a brief background and citations of all the papers can be found in Borah et al. (2019). Chapter 11 is based on Sridharan et al. (2021).

REFERENCES

ADEQ (Alaska Department of Environmental Quality). 2017. "Total maximum daily load (TMDL) for residue adjacent to the waters of the Matanuska River in Palmer, Alaska." Accessed October 24, 2020. https://dec.alaska.gov/water/water-quality/impaired-waters/#impaired-water-tabs.

ASCE. 2017. *Total maximum daily load analysis and modeling: Assessment of the practice.* Prepared by TMDL Analysis and Modeling Task Committee of the Environmental and Water Resources Institute of ASCE. Reston, VA: ASCE.

Benham, B. L., C. Baffaut, R. W. Zeckoski, K. R. Mankin, Y. A. Pachepsky, A. M. Sadeghi, et al. 2006. "Modeling bacteria fate and transport in watersheds to support TMDLs." *Trans. ASABE* 49 (4): 987–1002.

Benham, B., R. Zeckoski, and G. Yagow. 2008. "Lessons learned from TMDL implementation case studies." *Water Pract.*, 2 (1): 1–13.

Borah, D. K., and M. Bera. 2003. "Watershed-scale hydrologic and nonpoint-source pollution models: Review of mathematical bases." *Trans. ASAE* 46 (6): 1553–1566.

Borah, D. K., and M. Bera. 2004. "Watershed-scale hydrologic and nonpoint-source pollution models: Review of applications." *Trans. ASAE* 47 (3): 789–803.

Borah, D. K., G. Padmanabhan, and S. Kumar. 2019. "Total maximum daily load analysis and modeling: Assessment and advancement." *J. Hydrol. Eng.* 24 (11): 02019001.

Borah, D. K., G. Yagow, A. Saleh, P. L. Barnes, W. Rosenthal, E. C. Krug, et al. 2006. "Sediment and nutrient modeling for TMDL development and implementation." *Trans. ASABE* 49 (4): 967–986.

CDWR (California Department of Water Resources). 2019. "California EcoRestore program." Accessed December 2, 2020. http://files.resources.ca.gov/ecorestore/.

Chapra, S. C. 1997. *Surface water-quality modeling.* New York: McGraw Hill.

Chen C.W., J. Herr, R.A. Goldstein. 2008. Model Calculations of Total Maximum Daily Loads of Mercury for Drainage Lakes, 08 October 2008, *Journal of the American Water Resources Association* 44(5):1295–1307, DOI: 10.1111/j.1752-1688.2008.00224.x

Chesapeake Bay Foundation. 2020. "Water quality trading." Accessed October 27, 2020. https://www.cbf.org/issues/water-quality-trading/.

Chesapeake Bay Program. 1999. "1983 Chesapeake Bay agreement." Accessed December 7, 2020. https://www.chesapeakebay.net/content/publications/cbp_12512.pdf.

Chesapeake Bay Program. 2019. "Bay program history." Accessed July 18, 2020. https://www.chesapeakebay.net/who/bay_program_history.

Conway, D. K. 1997. "TMDL litigation: So now what?" *Va. Environ. Law J.* 17: 83–93.

Copeland, C. 2014. *Clean Water Act and pollutant total maximum daily loads (TMDLs).* Report for Congress No. R42752. Washington, DC: Congressional Research Service.

Cropper, M. L., and W. Isaac. 2011. *The benefits of achieving Chesapeake Bay TMDLs (total maximum daily loads): A scoping study.* Washington, DC: Resources for the Future.

Daniels, M. E., V. K. Sridharan, E. M. Danner, and S. N. John. 2018. *Calibration and validation of linked water temperature models for the Shasta Reservoir and the Sacramento River from 2000 to 2015.* United States National Oceanic and Atmospheric Administration Technical Memorandum NOAA-TM-NMFS-SWFSC-597. Santa Cruz, CA: National Marine Fisheries Service.

Elias, M., G. Ankley, M. Barron, C. Bergeron, R. Burgess, S. Cormier, et al. 2017. *Update on US EPA's revision to the 1985 guidelines for deriving aquatic life criteria.* Abstract. Minneapolis, MN: Society of Environmental Toxicology and Chemistry.

Gillett, N. D., Y. Pan, J. E. Asarian, and J. Kann. 2016. "Spatial and temporal variability of river periphyton below a hypereutrophic lake and a series of dams." *Sci. Total Environ.* 541: 1382–1392.

Hoornbeek, J., E. Hansen, E. Ringquist, and R. Carlson. 2008. *Implementing total maximum daily loads: Understanding and fostering successful results.* Kent, OH: Center for Public Administration and Public Policy, Kent State University.

Keisman, J., and G. Shenk. 2013. "Total maximum daily load criteria assessment using monitoring and modeling data." *J. Am. Water Resour. Assoc.* 49 (5): 1134–1149.

Ketchum, R. H. 1951a. "The flushing of tidal estuaries." *Sewage Ind. Wastes* 23 (2), 198–209.

Ketchum, R. H. 1951b. "The exchanges of fresh and salt waters in tidal estuaries." *J. Mar. Res.* 10: 18–38.

Lahlou, M., L. Shoemaker, M. Paquette, J. Bo, S. Choudhury, R. Elmer, and F. Xie. 1996. *Better assessment science integrating point and nonpoint sources–BASINS. Version 1.0 user's manual.* Rep. No. EPA 823-R-96-001. Washington, DC: Exposure Assessment Branch, Standards and Applied Sciences Division, Office of Science and Technology, United States Environmental Protection Agency.

MacWilliams, M. L., A. J. Bever, E. S. Gross, G. S. Ketefian, and W. J. Kimmerer. 2015. "Three-dimensional modeling of hydrodynamics and salinity in the San Francisco estuary: An evaluation of model accuracy, X2, and the low–salinity zone." *San Francisco Estuary Watershed Sci.* 13 (1): 37.

Malone, L. A. 2002. "The myths and truths that ended the 2000 TMDL program." *Pace Environ. Law Rev.* 20: 63–87. Also see Faculty publications 223. College of William and Mary Law School, Williamsburg, VA. Accessed September 29, 2020. https://scholarship.law.wm.edu/facpubs/223.

Martin, J. L., and McCutcheon, S. C. 1999. *Hydrodynamics and transport for water quality modeling.* Boca Raton, FL: CRC Press.

Martin, J. L., W. L. Richardson, and S. C. McCutcheon. 1991. "Modeling studies for planning: The Green Bay project." *Water Resourc. Bull.* 27 (3): 429–436.

McCutcheon, S. C. 1983. *The evaluation of selected one-dimensional stream water-quality models with field data.* Waterways Experiment Station Report E-11. Vicksburg, MS: United States Army Corps of Engineers.

McCutcheon, S. C. 1985. *Water quality data for the West Fork Trinity River in Fort Worth, Texas.* Water Resource Investigation Rep. 84-4330, NSTL. Pearl, MS: USGS.

McCutcheon, S. C. 1988. *Investigation of the fate of oily wastes in streams as a tool for hazardous waste screening: A preliminary identification of research approach and model development.* United States Environmental Protection Agency Internal Rep. Athens, GA: Environmental Research Laboratory, 530-R-88-113, Washington, DC: Office of Solid Waste.

McCutcheon, S. C. 1989. *Water quality modeling: Vol. I, river transport and surface exchange.* Boca Raton, FL: CRC Press.

Mills, W. B., D. B. Porcella, M. J. Ungs, S. A. Gherini, K. V. Summers, M. Lingfung, et al. 1985. *Water quality assessment: A screening procedure for toxic and conventional pollutants.* EPA/600/6-85/002a. Athens, GA: United States Environmental Protection Agency.

Mishra, A., E. Ahmadisharaf, B. L. Benham, D. L. Gallagher, K. H. Reckhow, and E. P. Smith 2019. "Two-phase Monte Carlo simulation for partitioning the effects of epistemic and aleatory uncertainty in TMDL modeling." *J. Hydrol. Eng.* 24 (1): 04018058.

Mishra, A., E. Ahmadisharaf, B. L. Benham, M. L. Wolfe, S. C. Leman, D. L. Gallagher, et al. 2018. "Generalized likelihood uncertainty estimation and Markov chain Monte Carlo simulation to prioritize TMDL pollutant allocations." *J. Hydrol. Eng.* 23 (12): 05018025.

Moriasi, D. N., M. W. Gitau, N. Pai, and Daggupati, P. 2015. "Hydrologic and water quality models: Performance measures and evaluation criteria." *Trans. ASABE* 58 (6): 1763–1785.

Moriasi, D. N., B. N. Wilson, K. R. Douglas-Mankin, J. G. Arnold, and P. H. Gowda. 2012. "Hydrologic and water quality models: Use, calibration, and validation." *Trans. ASABE* 55 (4): 1241–1247.

Muñoz-Carpena, R., G. Vellidis, A. Shirmohammadi, and W. Wallender. 2006. "Evaluation of modeling tools for TMDL development and implementation." *Trans. ASABE* 49 (4): 961–965.

NRC (National Research Council). 2001. *Assessing the TMDL approach to water quality management.* Washington, DC: National Academy Press.

NWQMC (National Water Quality Monitoring Council). 2020. "National Water Portal." Accessed July 12, 2020. https://www.waterqualitydata.us/.

Pidot, J. 2020. "The Supreme Court rejects a narrow reading of the Clean Water Act in County of Maui vs. Hawaii Wildlife Fund." Accessed July 17, 2020. https://www.acslaw.org/expertforum/the-supreme-court-rejects-a-narrow-reading-of-the-clean-water-act-in-county-of-maui-v-hawaii-wildlife-fund/#:~:text=April%2024%2C%202020-,The%20Supreme%20Court%20Rejects%20a%20Narrow%20Reading%20of%20the%20Clean,Hawaii%20Wildlife%20Fund&text=United%20States%2C%20Justice%20Scalia%20rejected,direct%20discharges%20into%20jurisdictional%20waters.

Pritchard, D. W. 1969. "Dispersion and flushing of pollutants in estuaries." *J. Hydraul. Eng. Div.* HY1: 115–124.

Ritchie, J. C., and C. M. Cooper. 2001. *Remote sensing techniques for determining water quality: Applications to TMDLs.* Beltsville, MD: USDA Agriculture Research Service Hydrology and Remote Sensing Laboratory, and National Sedimentation Laboratory.

SCDHEC (South Carolina Department of Health and Environmental Control). 1998. *Implementation plan for achieving total maximum daily load reductions from nonpoint sources for the state of South Carolina.* Columbia, SC: SCDHEC.

Shoemaker, L., T. Dai, J. Koenig, and M. Hantush. 2005. *TMDL model evaluation and research needs.* Rep. No. EPA/600/R-05/149. National Risk Management Research Laboratory, Office of Research and Development. Cincinnati, OH: United States Environmental Protection Agency.

Shoemaker, L., Lahlou, M., Bryer, M., Kumar, D., and Kratt, K. 1997. *Compendium of tools for watershed assessment and TMDL development.* Rep. No. EPA 841-B-97-006. Office of Wetlands, Oceans, and Watershed. Washington, DC: EPA.

Sridharan, V. K., N. W. T. Quinn, S. Kumar, S. C. McCutcheon, E. Ahmadisharaf, X. Fang, et al. 2021. Selecting reliable models for total maximum daily load development: A holistic protocol. *J. Hydrol. Eng.* 26 (10): 1–22.

Stephen, C. E., D. I. Mount, D. J. Hansen, J. R. Gentile, G. A. Chapman, and W. A. Brungs. 1985. *Guidelines for deriving numerical national water quality criteria for the protection of aquatic organisms and their uses.* PB85-227049. Corvallis, OR: EPA Office of Research and Development Environmental Research Laboratories.

Thomann, R. V., and J. A. Mueller 1987. Principles of Surface Water Quality Modeling and Control. Pearson Inc., ISBN-13: 978-0060466770 / ISBN-10: 0060466774.

USEPA (US Environmental Protection Agency). 1991. *Guidance for water quality-based decisions: The TMDL process.* Rep. No. EPA 440/4-91-001. Washington, DC: EPA, Office of Water.

USEPA. 1992. *Compendium of watershed-scale models for TMDL development.* Rep. No. EPA 841-R-92-002. Washington, DC: Office of Science and Technology.

USEPA. 1995a. *Technical guidance manual for developing total maximum daily loads. Book II: Streams and rivers. Part 1: Biochemical oxygen demand/dissolved oxygen and nutrients/eutrophication.* Rep. No. EPA 823-B-95-007. Washington, DC: EPA, Office of Water.

USEPA. 1995b. *Watershed protection: A statewide approach.* Rep. No. EPA 841-R-95-004. Washington, DC: EPA, Office of Water.

USEPA. 1995c. *Watershed protection: A project focus.* Rep. No. EPA 841-R-95-004. Washington, DC: EPA, Office of Water.

USEPA. 1999a. *Draft guidance for water quality-based decisions: The TMDL process.* 2nd ed. Rep. No. EPA 841-D-99-001. Washington, DC: EPA.

USEPA. 1999b. *Protocol for Developing Sediment TMDLs.* 1st ed. Rep. No. EPA 841-B-99-004. Washington, DC: EPA.

USEPA. 1999c. *Protocol for developing nutrient TMDLs.* 1st ed. Rep. No. EPA 841-B-99-007, Washington, DC: EPA.

USEPA. 2000. Guidance manual and sample NPDES permit for concentrated animal feeding operations: Final internal review draft. Washington, DC: Office of Wastewater Management.

USEPA. 2001a. *The national costs of the total maximum daily load program.* Draft Rep. Rep. No. EPA 841-D-01-003. Washington, DC: Office of Water.

USEPA. 2001b. *The national costs to develop TMDLs.* Draft Rep. Support document #1. Rep. No. EPA 841-D-01-004. Washington, DC: Office of Water.

USEPA. 2001c. *Protocol for developing pathogen TMDLs.* 1st ed. Rep. No. EPA 841-R-00-002. Washington, DC: EPA.

USEPA. 2002a. *Guidelines for reviewing TMDLs under existing regulations issued in 1992.* Washington, DC: EPA.

USEPA. 2002b. *Establishing total maximum daily load (TMDL) wasteload allocations (WLAs) for storm water sources and NPDES permit requirements based on those WLAs.* Memorandum from Robert H. Wayland, III, Director, Office of Wetlands, Oceans and Watersheds and James A. Hanlon, Director. Washington, DC: Office of Wastewater Management.

USEPA. 2007a. *Watershed-based National Pollutant Discharge Elimination System (NPDES) permitting technical guidance.* Rep. No. EPA 833-B-07-004. Washington, DC: Office of Water, Office of Wastewater Management, Water Permits Division.

USEPA. 2007b. *Water quality trading toolkit for permit writers.* Rep. No. EPA-833-R-07-004. Washington, DC: Office of Water, Office of Wastewater Management.

USEPA. 2008a. *Handbook for developing watershed TMDLs.* Draft. Washington, DC: Office of Wetlands, Oceans and Watersheds.

USEPA. 2008b. "Incorporating green infrastructure concepts into total maximum daily loads (TMDLs)." Accessed July 30, 2020. https://www.epa.gov/sites/production/files/2015-07/documents/2008_12_12_tmdl_stormwater_tmdl_lid_final.pdf.

USEPA. 2010. *Chesapeake Bay total maximum daily load for nitrogen, phosphorous and sediment.* Chesapeake Bay TMDL document. Washington, DC: EPA.

USEPA. 2011. *Using microbial source tracking to support TMDL development and implementation.* Prepared by Tetra Tech, Inc. and Herrera Environmental Consultants for Region 10. Seattle, WA: EPA

USEPA. 2012. *Supplemental information for reviewing reasonable assurance in TMDLs.* Washington, DC: EPA.

USEPA. 2017. *Restoring the Long Island Sound while saving money: Lessons in innovation and collaboration.* Washington, DC: EPA.

USEPA. 2018a. *Overview of Total Maximum Daily Loads (TMDLs)*. Washington, DC: EPA.

USEPA. 2018b. *Effectively implementing TMDLs*. Washington, DC: EPA.

USEPA. 2020a. *History of the Clean Water Act*. Washington, DC: EPA.

USEPA. 2020b. *Watershed Web Academy: Introduction to the Clean Water Act*. Washington, DC: EPA.

USEPA. 2020c. *Milestones in EPA and environmental history*. Washington, DC: EPA.

Vellidis, G., P. Barnes, D. D. Bosch, and A. M. Cathey. 2006. Mathematical simulation tools for developing dissolved oxygen TMDLs. *Trans. ASABE* 49 (4): 1003–1022.

Wainger, L. A. 2012. Opportunities for reducing total maximum daily load (TMDL) compliance costs: Lessons from Chesapeake Bay. *Environ. Sci. Technol.* 46: 9256–9265.

Wallace, C. W., B. L. Benham, E. R. Yagow, and D. L. Gallagher. 2018. Comparison of two alternative methods for developing TMDLs to address sediment impairments. *J. Hydrol. Eng.* 23 (12): 05018023.

CHAPTER 2
WATERSHED MODELS

Deva K. Borah, Ebrahim Ahmadisharaf, G. Padmanabhan, Sanaz Imen,
Harry X. Zhang, Yusuf M. Mohamoud, Zhonglong Zhang

2.1 INTRODUCTION

Over the last several decades, with the advent and rapid progress of computational technologies, watershed models have increasingly become important and effective tools for tackling a wide range of water resources and environmental management issues and supporting regulatory compliances. Watershed models are fundamental to support the development and implementation of total maximum daily load (TMDL). Existing watershed models with hydrologic and water quality components have been comprehensively compiled and published in Singh (1995) and Singh and Frevert (2002a, b, 2006). Historically, watershed hydrologic models were developed to simulate the dynamic behavior of land surface hydrology and storage processes and generate water balance information. Water quality components have been developed and incorporated into some watershed models as the importance of quantifying nonpoint-source pollution was recognized. Most watershed nonpoint-source models simulate hydrologic, physical, and chemical processes involved in the entrainment and transport of sediment, nutrients, and pesticides.

Based on the time scale used in them, watershed hydrologic models can be classified into three types: event based, continuous, and the combination event-based-continuous (Borah and Bera 2003). Event-based models are used to simulate the hydrologic response of a watershed to a single hydrologic event or rainstorm. The event-based models use a time step in the order of minutes or seconds, depending on the numerical scheme and its stability during a model run, and are used to assess the impact on the study area from a single storm event. Thus, components of the model must deal with the characteristics of the input rainstorm, abstractions from the rainfall, routing of overland and shallow subsurface flow to the channel system, and finally, the routing of the channel flow to the watershed outlet. Event-based watershed hydrologic model emphasis is on simulating infiltration and surface runoff. Evapotranspiration is not important in event-based models and is commonly ignored. However, initial moisture content is considered important for event-based models.

Continuous models differ from event-based models in that they attempt to simulate the hydrologic response of a watershed to several rainstorm events and their cumulative effects over a longer period that includes both wet and dry conditions. Most of these models use time steps hourly or daily, and some subhourly, and others monthly, depending on the computational scheme, and can be used to simulate conditions over one season or over several years. Continuous models generate integrated responses by synthesizing hydrologic processes over a broad scope of hydroclimatic conditions. Inputs for the simulation include continuous time series of observed precipitation, real or stochastically generated climate data, soil–water content, groundwater storage, evaporation demand, stage of plant growth, and others. Continuous models require more parameters than event-based models. A large number of parameters imply a complex model structure to incorporate individual impacts from these parameters. Continuous watershed hydrologic models emphasize simulation of all the hydrologic processes. Unlike event-based models, evapotranspiration is very important in continuous models, and initial moisture content becomes less important. The use of warm-up periods minimizes the uncertainty in initial moisture content.

As is shown later, some models are combined event-based-continuous models having capabilities of both the event-based and continuous models. Each model has its own unique way of combining the processes and the routines. Most of these models use variable time steps, shorter during rain events, and longer during dry periods to keep the model run time down without compromising results.

In this chapter, 14 watershed models were selected based on their documentations, successful applications to watersheds, evaluations, and acceptances found in the literature (Borah and Bera 2003, 2004, Borah 2011, Borah et al. 2006, 2019, Obropta and Kardos 2007, Shoemaker et al. 2005, Singh and Frevert 2002a, b, 2006, Singh and Woolhiser 2002, Kalin and Hantush 2003, 2006, Breuer et al. 2009, Sharifi et al. 2017) and evaluated for their usefulness and applicability for TMDL development and implementation.

The 14 watershed models are briefly described in this chapter. Their key features, components, and capabilities are tabulated for evaluation and intercomparisons, focusing primarily on the mathematical basis of simulations of the physical processes. The routing procedures of the models, which are mathematically based, are compared, and the models are ranked. The procedures used in the models to simulate the water quality constituents are tabulated. Suitability of the models in the development and implementation planning of TMDLs are presented in a table, along with notable strengths and limitations of the models. Finally, recommendations are made toward advancing watershed modeling by improving existing models or developing improved modeling techniques and models, along with recent recommendations by Fu et al. (2020) in overcoming present challenges in watershed water quality modeling and potential improvements.

This chapter is developed from Borah et al. (2019). Notable changes from Borah et al. (2019) included in this chapter are the addition of the watershed assessment model (WAM) (SWET 2011a, b) to the review and removal of the review of the spreadsheet tool for the estimation of pollutant load (STEPL) (Tetra Tech 2011) for its addition to Chapter 5 "Simple Models and Methods" in this manual.

2.2 BRIEF DESCRIPTIONS OF THE SELECTED WATERSHED MODELS

2.2.1 Agricultural Nonpoint-Source and Annualized Agricultural Nonpoint-Source Models

The agricultural nonpoint-source (AGNPS) model is an event-based model that predicts runoff, nitrogen, phosphorus, sediment, and chemical oxygen demand (COD) from small- to medium-sized agricultural watersheds resulting from a single storm event (Young et al. 1987). The model represents a watershed as square grids and channels. It is supported by the United States Agricultural Research Service (ARS) and the Natural Resource Conservation Service (NRCS).

The annualized agricultural nonpoint-source (AnnAGNPS) model (Bingner and Theurer 2001) is the enhanced and continuous version of the AGNPS. The model simulates sheet, rill, and gully erosion, the fate and transport of chemicals (e.g., nitrogen, phosphorus, organic carbon, and many pesticides), and downstream sediment and chemical transport from watersheds dominated by croplands, feedlots, and other agricultural land uses. Water and sediment yields are predicted by particle-size class and source. A field pond water and sediment loading routine is included for rice and crawfish ponds. AnnAGNPS represents landscapes using classes of homogeneous land uses. The model routes water, eroded sediment, and chemicals after simulating any deposition of contaminated sediment in the fields and stream channels. For water quality and TMDL assessments, the model evaluates the effect of management decisions that control water, sediment, and chemical loadings within a watershed.

AGNPS has been found widely used for watershed studies. AnnAGNPS was used in a number of model evaluation studies (Shoemaker et al. 2005) followed by more watershed studies. In a literature search, Borah et al. (2019) found 140 reports and peer-reviewed articles on AGNPS and AnnAGNPS in the period 1996 to 2016.

2.2.2 ANSWERS-2000

The original version of this model is the areal nonpoint-source watershed environment response simulation (ANSWERS), an event-based watershed model, developed by Beasley et al. (1980) at Purdue University. It uses parameters distributed over square grids and channel reaches to simulate spatially varying runoff and infiltration, subsurface drainage, and upland erosion from small agricultural watersheds during a rainfall event discretized into time steps of seconds to several minutes. The enhanced and continuous version of the model, ANSWERS-2000, was developed by Bouraoui and Dillaha (1996, 2000) at the Virginia Polytechnic Institute and State University, Blacksburg, Virginia, which continuously simulates hydrologic responses and the fate of nutrients in the watershed. It can be used to evaluate agricultural and urban BMPs for reducing (a) sediment and nutrient delivery to streams by surface runoff, and (b) leaching of nitrogen through the root zone.

The model requires 10 to 12 parameters to be specified for each cell to simulate spatially varying breakpoint rainfall, interception, surface retention, surface detention, infiltration, percolation, surface runoff, channel flow, potential evapotranspiration (PET), crop growth, surface cover, erosion and sediment transport, as well as soil nitrogen and phosphorous cycles. It simulates up to 10 particle-size classes. Nitrogen and phosphorous cycles consist of organic and inorganic, dissolved, and adsorbed species, nitrate leaching, and nutrient losses in surface runoff. The model is recommended for use in medium-sized watersheds (500 to 3,000 ha) where upland processes dominate the hydrologic cycle. Simulations of 20 or more years are recommended using daily and 30 s time steps for dry and wet days, respectively. The most important information and parameters specified are the number of rain gauges, time interval and rainfall intensity, total porosity, field moisture capacity, steady-state infiltration rate, antecedent soil moisture, land-use and management measures, potential interception volume, Manning's roughness coefficient, and channel width. Runoff and sediment load, nitrate losses, dissolved ammonium losses, adsorbed ammonium losses, adsorbed total Kjeldahl nitrogen losses, and dissolved orthophosphate are simulated.

ANSWERS-2000 was applied and tested in small USDA watersheds near Watkinsville, Georgia, and in Owl Run and Nomini Creek watersheds in Virginia with simulations of 14 to 36 months (Bouraoui and Dillaha 1996, 2000). The model is not available for download, but requests can be made by contacting Dr. T. Dillaha via Biological Systems Engineering Department, Virginia Polytechnic Institute and State University.

2.2.3 Dynamic Watershed Simulation Model

The dynamic watershed simulation model (DWSM) (Borah et al. 2002) is a distributed model that simulates surface and subsurface runoff, flood wave, erosion of soil, and sediment and agricultural chemical transport in small to large agricultural and semiurbanized watersheds during a single or a series of rainfall events. A watershed is divided first into subwatersheds and reservoir units, if any exists, then each subwatershed is further subdivided into two homogeneous overland planes and one uniform channel segment configuration resembling an open book, both overland planes yielding water, sediment, and pollutants laterally into the channel that could be a stream or river reach. The model uses average hydraulic properties for each channel segment and area-weighted averages for each overland plane. Primary model input includes physical dimensions and hydrologic–hydraulic properties of the overland planes and the channel segments. Most of these data are measurable or available in the literature, with only a few parameters needing calibration. Other required data include stage–discharge tables for reservoirs and rainfall time series from distributed rain gauges. A subhourly or hourly time step is used depending on the resolution of the time series data and sizes of the overland planes and channel segments. There is no model stability issue as the computational schemes are analytic or explicit.

DWSM computes rainfall excess that generates runoff from rainfall, in excess of initial abstraction and infiltration, using two alternate procedures: (1) NRCS runoff curve number; and (2) an interception–infiltration procedure (Smith and Parlange 1978), described in Borah et al. (2002). The kinematic wave equation's analytical and approximate shock-fitting solutions (Borah et al. 1980) are used to route rainfall excess over overland planes and through channel segments. NRCS modified pulse method is used to route water through reservoir units. Lateral subsurface flow is routed using a kinematic storage approach (Sloan et al. 1983).

Raindrop-impacted soil detachment (erosion) is computed over the overland planes. Runoff-induced erosion, deposition, and sediment transport over overland planes and through channel segments are based on the transport capacities of different size groups (fine to coarse sand and silt to very fine sand) using established formulas. Mass balance (continuity) equation for sediment is solved analytically to route the sediment, track overland and channel bed elevation changes, and sediment discharges and yields. Pollutants mixing with surface and subsurface runoff and adsorbing to sediment are simulated, and routing of the liquid and solid phases of the pollutants is performed.

The model outputs are (a) a summary on yields, peaks, and times to peaks of runoff, sediment, and pollutants at the watershed outlet; (b) tabulated results on runoff, sediment, and pollutant yields for all the overland planes, channels, and reservoirs; and (c) time series (hydrographs) of flow, sediment, and pollutant fluxes at the outlet of the watershed and at the end (outfall) of selected channels and reservoirs.

Borah and Bera (2004) compiled 18 applications of DWSM on watersheds, experimental plots, and hypothetical planes. The tested watersheds range from 0.01 to 2,400 km² and are located in the United States and China. Some detailed applications are reported in Borah et al. (2002, 2004, 2007) and Gao et al. (2015). The primary advantages of DWSM are computational efficiency and parsimony of parameters. The disadvantages are a lack of a GUI for pre- and postprocessing. Only DWSM_HydroSed with hydrology and sediment simulations has been extensively tested and is available from the developer (Dr. Deva K. Borah) for applications. The DWSM_AgChem with additional chemical transport components needs further testing and refining.

2.2.4 Gridded Surface and Subsurface Hydrologic Analysis

The gridded surface and subsurface hydrologic analysis (GSSHA) model (Downer and Ogden 2004, Downer et al. 2006) was developed from the cascade of planes in two-dimensional (CASC2D) model (Ogden and Julien 2002). This is a USACE model for applying to small watersheds with mixed land uses. The model is available for download from the USACE for both Windows and Linux operating systems as part of the watershed modeling system (WMS) in 2D hydrology package, which is proprietary for anyone other than the federal employees.

The model simulates distributed precipitation, snowmelt, interception, infiltration, soil moisture, PET, surface water retention, overland flow, unsaturated lateral flow, saturated groundwater flow, erosion, deposition, and sediment transport. Both single-event and continuous simulations can be performed. Seconds to minute time steps are used. Overland and unsaturated lateral flows are simulated using 2D square grids. Channel flows simulated in 1D describe longitudinal changes. Coastal tides in channels are simulated using full dynamic wave routing in 1D or 2D. Research is in progress to add nutrient dynamics (Johnson et al. 2013) and simulate nonpoint-source pollution for the purposes of calculating TMDLs and designing abatement measures (Pradhan et al. 2014).

GSSHA has been mainly used internally by USACE in evaluating extreme flood events (Shoemaker et al. 2005). The developers and others have conducted a number of model evaluation studies on GSSHA (Kalin and Hantush 2006, Paudel et al. 2011, El Hassan et al. 2013, Downer et al. 2015). In a literature search, Borah et al. (2019) found 25 journal articles,

42 conference papers, and 20 technical notes/reports on GSSHA/CASC2D from 2000 to 2017.

2.2.5 Generalized Watershed Loading Function

The generalized watershed loading function (GWLF) model was originally developed by Haith et al. (1992) and later upgraded by Dai et al. (2000) with a Windows-based interface (BasinSim 1.0) and by Evans et al. (2001) with ArcView (AVGWLF) and Mapshed (GWLF-E) interfaces for Pennsylvania watersheds. This is a continuous spatially lumped parameter model. It simulates surface and subsurface flows, sediment, nitrogen, and phosphorus delivered to streams from a combination of point and nonpoint sources of pollution, including septic systems and channel erosion. It simulates on a daily time step using NRCS runoff generation method for rainfall events and an approximate daily water balance for continuous hydrologic simulations and estimations of infiltration, ET, and groundwater interactions.

The model simulates erosion from pervious areas (mostly agricultural lands) using the universal soil loss equation (USLE) modified by a daily rainfall factor and a sediment delivery factor. Monthly sediment loads are estimated from the annual sediment load using a monthly transport factor computed from monthly runoff. The model adds sediment contributed from impervious urban areas through a daily buildup and washoff routine. The sediment simulation procedure ignores any long-term net deposition and any carryover of detached sediment from one simulation year to the next (April to next March). The model also calculates loads from septic systems and point sources. For nutrient simulations, a loading function is used, where dissolved or particulate concentrations are associated with flow volumes or sediment loads, respectively, from various land uses or pollutant source inputs, such as groundwater, manure application, and septic system effluent.

The model has been used nationally for TMDL development, extensively in the northeast and mid-Atlantic regions (Shoemaker et al. 2005) primarily for nutrient loading–related TMDLs in mixed land-use or rural settings because of its simplicity and requiring a relatively small amount of input data. It has been adopted by the state of Pennsylvania for TMDL development and agricultural land management.

2.2.6 Hydrologic Engineering Center-Hydrologic Modeling System

The Hydrologic Engineering Center-Hydrologic Modeling System (HEC-HMS) (USACE 2016) is an upgraded version of one of the oldest and widely used models, HEC-1 (USACE 1968). This USACE model (HEC-HMS) is user-friendly and simulates rainfall-runoff responses of a watershed (small to large river basins) represented by a dendritic drainage network covering a wide range of geographic areas (small urban to natural basins) to address water supply and flooding. Simulated hydrographs can be interpreted directly or by transferring those to other software to estimate water availability, flood forecasting, floodplain mapping, or design reservoir spillways. The hydrologic modeling is based on watershed physical descriptions, meteorological datasets, and specifications of the parameters. A comprehensive library of simulation routines is available in HEC-HMS, from HEC-1 and other models, most of which have been modernized and combined with new algorithms. Recently released versions of HEC-HMS (latest 4.5) include a built-in uncertainty analysis module via the Monte Carlo method that addresses the uncertainty of hydrologic parameters.

In the sediment transport module of HEC-HMS, sediment yield is estimated from land surface erosion and sediment transport in channels and reservoirs based on noncohesive sediment-carrying capacity of flows by grain-size distribution. The module was evaluated by Pak et al. (2009, 2010) on the Upper North Bosque River Watershed in Texas while studying reservoir trap efficiencies.

Water quality simulation is included as an option in HEC-HMS and done through its basin module that uses an advection–diffusion equation. Mass balance equations are used to simulate nitrogen (organic, ammonia, nitrite, and nitrate), phosphorus, algae, dissolved oxygen, and carbonaceous biological oxygen demand in river reaches and reservoirs.

2.2.7 Hydrological Simulation Program-Fortran

The Hydrological Simulation Program-Fortran (HSPF) model (Bicknell et al. 1993, 2001) was developed by combining the Stanford Watershed Model (Crawford and Linsley 1966), a pioneering hydrologic model, with two water quality models: agricultural runoff management (ARM) and nonpoint-source (NPS) runoff, supported by USEPA. The model was later enhanced collaboratively with USGS by using its Watershed Data Management (WDM) system. In the 1990s, HSPF became the core watershed model in the USEPA's Better Assessment Science Integrating point and Nonpoint Sources (BASINS) modeling system, specifically developed for TMDLs.

HSPF is a comprehensive model capable of simulating water quantity and quality. It is a flexible, process-based, and semidistributed model. It divides a watershed into subwatersheds, which are further subdivided into pervious and impervious lands draining into a channel–stream–river–reservoir network. It is applicable to urban and rural watersheds. It has the capability to perform single-event and continuous long-period simulations at user-specified temporal and spatial scales. The model uses meteorological time-series input data and computes time-series hydrology and water quality variables (hydrographs). It simulates interception, soil moisture, surface runoff, interflow, base flow, snowpack depth and water content, snowmelt, ET, groundwater recharge (flux to deep aquifer), dissolved oxygen, chemical oxygen demand, temperature, pesticides, conservative constituents, fecal coliform, sediment detachment and transport, sediment routing by particle size, channel routing, reservoir routing, constituent routing, pH, total nitrogen, total phosphorus, ammonia, nitrite–nitrate, organic nitrogen, orthophosphate, organic phosphorus, phytoplankton, and zooplankton. HSPF is used to assess the effects of land-use changes, reservoir operations, management options of point- or nonpoint-source pollution, diversion of flows and water withdrawals, and setting TMDLs for water quality–impaired waterbodies in the United States.

HSPF is continually undergoing updates and advancements (version 12.5) including improvements in its channel hydraulic representation at the watershed scale (Mohamoud 2007), development of algorithms for BMP designs (Mohamoud et al. 2007, 2009, 2010) useful in TMDL implementation, and an enhanced expert system HSPF (HSPEXP+) for model calibration, output postprocessing, and performing sensitivity and uncertainty analyses. Model-independent Parameter ESTimation and uncertainty analysis (PEST) by Doherty (2016) can also be integrated with the HSPF for performing sensitivity and uncertainty analyses and calibration.

Borah and Bera (2004) compiled 12 early applications of HSPF from the literature, although many more applications are found today, including 166 TMDL studies in creeks, rivers, and lakes (Borah et al. 2019). HSPF application to the more than 166,000 sq. km (64,000 sq. mi) Chesapeake Bay Watershed began in the 1980s, and through subsequent iterations and enhancements, has resulted in the historical evolution of HSPF modeling applications for large regional TMDL implementation (Shenk and Linker 2013).

2.2.8 Kinematic Runoff and Erosion

The kinematic runoff and erosion (KINEROS) model developed by Woolhiser et al. (1990) is a USDA-ARS model simulating interception, infiltration, surface runoff, soil erosion, and sediment transport in small watersheds that are mostly agricultural and some with mixed land-use during a single rainfall event. The model uses one-dimensional kinematic wave equations to route flow over rectangular planes and through trapezoidal open channels, circular conduits, and small detention ponds using an implicit finite-difference solution. A physically based infiltration algorithm is used that interacts with both rainfall and surface water in transit. Soil erosion on overland surfaces consists of two major components—rainfall splash erosion on bare soil and hydraulics causing erosion (or deposition) from the interplay between water shear force on loose soil bed and settling of soil particles under gravitational force. Flow and erosion equations are numerically solved for each particle size and at each time step using a four-point finite-difference scheme.

KINEROS is a public-domain model. Its applications are available in the literature (Goodrich et al. 2012), including modeling of the processes of rainfall-runoff, erosion, transport of manure-borne bacteria, land cover impact, and flood risk prediction.

2.2.9 Loading Simulation Program in C++

The Loading Simulation Program in C++ (LSPC), a recoded version of the HSPF model by Tetra Tech (2002), is a watershed modeling system to determine watershed-scale TMDLs. LSPC was designed to facilitate the iterative analysis of TMDL allocations, scenario analysis, and subwatershed or nested watershed simulations unique to larger and more complex TMDLs. The preceding mining data analysis system is based on HSPF algorithms (Shen et al. 2005). Hydrology, sediment, and water quality constituent simulations on land and in waterbodies are also based on HSPF algorithms. The primary difference between the LSPC and the HSPF is the programming architecture. LSPC employs C++ to use common data management software (such as Microsoft Access) and avoid inherent limits on data array sizes and spatiotemporal resolution. LSPC automatically generates comprehensive subwatershed files for all land layers, river reaches, and simulated modules using hourly or daily time intervals help interpret each simulation result. Allocations of the pollutant source reductions can also be done in LSPC.

LSPC has been applied throughout the continental United States, Hawaii, and the Caribbean in TMDL studies. Although frequently used for watersheds, there are some applications of LSPC throughout the United States where it has been linked to receiving water models for complex multipoint TMDL allocations that address riverine and receiving water (i.e., lake, estuary, or coastal region) TMDLs.

2.2.10 MIKE Système Hydrologique Européen

MIKE SHE (Système Hydrologique Européen), developed and maintained by the Danish Hydraulic Institute (DHI 2014), is a proprietary watershed model. It is a fully integrated physically based and distributed parameter code for simulations of three-dimensional hydrologic systems (Refsgaard and Storm 1995). A broad range of hydrologic, hydraulic, and fate and transport processes are simulated in small and mixed land-use watersheds. The model simulates water flow in the entire land phase of the hydrologic cycle from rainfall to streamflow and various flow paths such as ET from vegetated land cover, evaporation from waterbodies, overland flow, infiltration into soils, flow through the unsaturated zone, groundwater flow, and interactions between groundwater and surface water through interflow and base flow. MIKE SHE can also simulate irrigation, crop growth, and nitrogen processes in the root zone. It can be applied to event-based or continuous simulations using time steps of seconds to minutes, which could be different in different simulation zones, such as overland hydrology, river hydraulics, groundwater, and water quality. MIKE SHE is linked with GIS for pre (input data) and post (simulated output) analysis. It can also be linked to external uncertainty analysis modules.

ECOLAB, a generic ecological modeling tool, can be linked with MIKE SHE for ecological modeling. The link allows simulations of a range of water quality and ecological processes in rivers, surface waters, soils, and groundwater systems. ECOLAB, a process equation solver, facilitates water quality and ecosystem response evaluations because of the exposure of various chemical constituents that degrade water quality in various uses. It calculates the rate of changes of any state variable (chemical constituent) for a given number of related variables and processes. ECOLAB depends on other models for flows and transport processes. It can also be used in postprocessing calculations of the process dynamics.

MIKE SHE has been used in research and applied projects on a wide range of climatologic and hydrologic regimes (Graham and Butts 2006). It has been applied in studies across the globe for various purposes, including conjunctive uses of surface and ground waters by municipalities and industries, and in agricultural irrigation. It has also been used in studies of the wetland processes and water quality in connection with point and nonpoint sources of pollution assessment and TMDL development. In the United States, most of its applications have been in Florida, having a strong interaction between surface water and groundwater aquifers.

2.2.11 Soil and Water Assessment Tool

The Soil and Water Assessment Tool (SWAT) model (Neitsch et al. 2011) was developed by Arnold et al. (1998) at the USDA-ARS Grassland, Soil and Water Research Laboratory, Temple, Texas, in collaboration with Texas A&M University. It simulates watershed hydrology, climate, erosion, sediment transport, crop growth, nutrients, pesticides, bacteria, and agricultural management. SWAT is incorporated into the USEPA BASINS for nonpoint-source pollution simulations and TMDL developments on agricultural lands.

The model and its GIS interface have been expanded or upgraded continually with the latest version as SWAT+ (Bieger et al. 2017) with its latest release in December 2019. The GIS interface has been evolved through ArcView (ArcSWAT) and MapWindow (MWSWAT) to its latest

QSWAT (Dile et al. 2016) written in an open-source GIS software QGIS that enables the users to run SWAT without the need for proprietary GIS software. SWAT has a number of pre- and postprocessing tools among which SWAT-CUP is a genetic interface to carry out automatic calibration and uncertainty analysis.

In SWAT, a watershed is divided into subwatersheds, which are further subdivided into user-specified hydrologic response units (HRUs), with unique soil, land cover, and land management characteristics. The channel network is divided at a chosen scale with a subwatershed containing one main channel or a tributary channel. Ponds, wetlands, reservoirs, and point sources are added as additional simulation units. It is a long-term yield model run in a daily time step and was not designed for detailed single-event flood routing, even though it has been modified for simple flood routing running with subdaily time steps.

Hydrologic simulations include surface runoff, snowmelt, infiltration, and components of subsurface flow as lateral flow, base flow, and percolation to a shallow aquifer, losses to a deep aquifer, and evaporation from the saturated zone. Daily soil temperatures at the surface and at the centers of soil layers are computed. ET is computed using several alternate methods. The model routes upland runoff through channels, wetlands, ponds, and impoundments; simulates upland soil erosion to estimate sediment yield from subwatersheds; and accounts for transport, deposition, and resuspension in channels and other waterbodies. The model simulates crop growth and computes usages of water and nutrients. Fate and transport of nutrients, carbon cycling, pesticides, and bacterial are simulated on the uplands and routed through channels, impoundments, reservoirs, and wetlands. Algal growth, dissolved oxygen, carbonaceous biological oxygen demand, urban runoff, and buildup and washoff from streets are also simulated.

Meteorological data required for simulation are daily precipitation, maximum and minimum air temperatures, relative humidity, and wind speed. A weather generator tool fills any missing records. Physical data required for SWAT modeling are (1) topographic data typically in the form of a digital elevation model (DEM) for watershed and subwatershed delineations; (2) morphology of the main channels, tributaries, wetlands, ponds, and reservoirs; (3) soil data typically from the NRCS maintained Soil Survey Geographic (SSURGO) database or the USDA State Soil Geographic (STATSGO) soil data; (4) land-use land cover data from the National Landcover Database (NLCD) (for the years 1992, 2001, 2006, 2011, and 2016) and the USDA Crop Data Layer (annual, USDA-NASS 2021) that can be automatically read and processed by ArcSWAT; (4) crop management and agricultural BMPs; (5) point-source locations and loads; and (6) water management practices.

Borah and Bera (2004) compiled 17 early applications of SWAT from the literature, although numerous applications are found today. In a recent literature search through a database for peer-reviewed journal articles (Iowa

State University 2021) for the period 2000 to 2021, 4110 articles have been found published on SWAT, out of which 7 are on TMDL applications. For an up-to-date count and more information, the reader is advised to visit the webpage, link provided in Iowa State University 2021. The application of SWAT in the Wabash River watershed, Ohio TMDL (USEPA 2004), is notable.

2.2.12 Storm Water Management Model

The Storm Water Management Model (SWMM) (Rossman 2015a, b, 2016) was originally developed in 1971 by Metcalf and Eddy (1971) for USEPA, who made several revisions and significant extensions. SWMM5 is the latest major extension made in 2005 and has been updated several times since then. It is a comprehensive hydrologic and hydraulic modeling package simulating stormwater runoff, storm and sanitary sewer flows, and combined sewer overflows for planning, analysis, and design of drainage systems and BMPs, and managing drainage systems in urbanized areas. SWMM is a public-domain model available from USEPA and included in the USEPA BASINS. SWMM5 is an FEMA–approved model for National Flood Insurance Program (NFIP) studies. PCSWMM (James et al. 2002) and XP-SWMM (XP Solutions 2014) are two widely used proprietary software packages based on SWMM5 with the additions of unique graphical user interfaces having capabilities such as time-series analysis, GIS integration, storm-event separation, and uncertainty analysis.

SWMM's simulation capabilities include (1) event-based or continuous runoff and subsurface flows, including groundwater exchange from rainfall and snowmelt using time steps ranging from seconds to hours; (2) full dynamic flow routings in streams and subsurface drainage networks and sanitary sewers, including surcharging, reverse flow, and surface ponding; (3) storage and treatment units with flow dividers, pumps, weirs, and orifices; (4) loading of up to 10 pollutants; (5) limited erosion and sediment transport; (6) pervious and impervious areas; and (7) various stormwater BMPs (e.g., permeable pavement, green roofs, rain barrels, vegetative swales, and others), which are also called low-impact developments (LIDs).

SWMM has been used in numerous urban stormwater and sewer studies worldwide. Stormwater applications include master drainage planning, collection system analysis and design, detention facility optimization, stormwater treatment analysis, BMP or LID evaluation, and hydro-modification simulations. Sewer master planning includes infiltration and inflow studies, wet weather flow analysis, designing pumping and pressure sewers, estimating overflows, controlling combined sewer overflows, green infrastructure (LID) planning, and planning and design of capital improvement projects. Applications in water quality planning include pollutant buildup and washoff assessments, street sweeping and pollutant loading and transport evaluations, treatment analysis and optimization, and TMDL modeling. In a literature search, Borah et al. (2019) found 51 TMDL studies in creeks, rivers, and lakes using SWMM.

2.2.13 Watershed Assessment Model

The Watershed Assessment Model (WAM), developed by Soil and Water Engineering Technology (SWET 2011a, b) is a GIS-based software to evaluate the relative impacts of alternate land-use and management practices on surface and subsurface hydrology and pollutant loads at a watershed scale. The model, first developed in the 1980s, is now fully integrated with ArcMap (ESRI 2011) application where watershed data are imported and edited, and model results viewed via the ArcMap interface.

WAM simulates surface water and groundwater flows and water quality constituents, including particulate and soluble phosphorus, particulate and soluble nitrogen (NO_3, NH_4, and organic N), TSS, and biochemical oxygen demand (BOD). The watershed is divided into user-defined rectangular source cells (typically 1 ha) and reaches. Cells with the same soil, land use, rain zone (Thiessen polygon of rain gauge), and wastewater utility service area are termed as unique cell type, simulation of which is done once and applied to all similar unique cell types to save computational time, an approach similar to SWAT's HRUs.

Three field-scale models are used to simulate the unique cells on a daily time step: (1) groundwater loading effects of agricultural management systems (GLEAMS) (Leonard et al. 1987) for well-drained soils; (2) Everglades agricultural area model (EAAMOD) (SWET, 2008) for high water table soils; and (3) a special-case model for wetlands, open waters, and mines (Bottcher et al. 2012). Models 1 and 2 are for the vegetative portions of the unique cells, although a BMP adjustment factor is applied to any impervious surface that may exist. Model 3 is a simplified daily water balance method where user-defined constituent concentrations are applied. Cell-generated daily flows and constituents are routed to the nearest reaches following flow paths from six unique flow paths and using user-inputted unit hydrograph and flow-path-dependent assimilation or attenuation procedures (SWET 2011a, b).

The resulting surface and subsurface water flow and constituent loads reaching the reaches are routed through the reach network to the watershed outfall using a modified linear reservoir routing technique developed by SWET (2011a, b) and Jacobson et al. (1998). The routing algorithm solves Manning's equation of uniform channel flow with a variable time step (maximum 10 min) depending on velocity and numerical stability. It incorporates in-stream assimilative capacity or attenuation for each reach type and accommodates complex water control structures such as gates, pumps, weirs, and culverts (Bottcher et al. 2012).

WAM was developed to handle unique hydrologic conditions in Florida such as abundance of wetlands, high groundwater table conditions, and complex water control structure operations (Khare 2014), and, thus, its main drawback is the requirements of intensive physical characterization data that may not be available for other areas (Yuan et al., 2020) as those were empirically derived.

2.2.14 Watershed Analysis Risk Management Framework

The Watershed Analysis Risk Management Framework (WARMF) is a decision support system developed by Systech Water Resources, Walnut Creek, California, sponsored by the Electric Power Research Institute (EPRI) and USEPA (Chen et al. 1998). As quoted in Shoemaker et al. (2005), the WARMF was based on an Integrated Lake-Watershed Acidification Study (ILWAS) that represents a watershed by land catchments, river segments, and lake layers. Meteorological data are input into the model for simulation of runoff and nonpoint loads as well as stream hydrology and water quality. Erosion and sediment/pollutant transport simulations were adopted from the ANSWERS (Beasley et al. 1980). The pollutant accumulation and washoff from urban areas was adopted from the SWMM. For stratified lakes or reservoirs, water quality in the waterbody is simulated as either a 1D vertically stratified, horizontally mixed reservoir or in 2D using an embedded CE-QUAL-W2 model (Environmental and Hydraulics Laboratories 1986). The theoretical basis of WARMF is mass balance, heat balance, reaction kinetics, and chemical equilibrium. The model is available for download from USEPA.

The US Bureau of Reclamation and the State of California Reclamation have actively supported the development of the San Joaquin River Salinity Forecasting Model, which utilizes the WARMF model to estimate daily river salt-assimilative capacity and to provide decision support for real-time salinity management at the watershed level (Quinn 2020, Quinn et al. 2010, 2018a, b). The model provides a framework for analysis of flow and salinity data from tributaries to the river and of water district diversions from the river. Salt-assimilative capacity forecasts require both the provision of real-time flow and salinity data and anticipated actions impacting flow and salinity in the river over a 2-week forecast period. The accuracy of these forecasts is indicative of the high level of stakeholder involvement and the sharing of information relevant to WARMF model input data.

2.3 ANALYSES OF MODELS: SUITABILITY FOR TOTAL MAXIMUM DAILY LOADS

Model review results are presented in three tables: Table 2-1 lists model key characteristics and capabilities, Table 2-2 presents hydrologic simulation procedures of the models emphasizing mathematical bases, and Table 2-3 presents formulations used in the water quality simulations

Table 2-1. Watershed Models: Characteristics and Capabilities.

Watershed model	Dominant land use	Event or continuous simulation	Variables simulated	Uncertainty analysis	Graphical user interface	Availability
AGNPS and AnnAGNPS	Agricultural	Event (AGNPS) and continuous (AnnAGNPS)	Surface flow, sediment, nutrients, COD and pesticides	No	Yes	Public
ANSWERS-2000	Agricultural	Event and continuous	Surface and subsurface flows, sediment, nutrients and crop growth	No	No	Developer
DWSM	Agricultural	Event	Surface and subsurface flows, sediment, nutrients and pesticides	No	No	Developer
GSSHA	Agricultural	Event and continuous	Surface and subsurface flows, snowmelt, tidal, hydraulic structures and sediment	No	Yes, proprietary	Public and proprietary

GWLF	Mixed	Continuous	Surface and subsurface flows, sediment, nutrients, COD and pesticides	No	Yes	Public
HEC-HMS	Mixed	Event and continuous	Surface and subsurface flows, snowmelt, sediment, nutrients, algae, dissolved oxygen and CBOD	Yes, inbuilt	Yes	Public
HSPF/LSPC	Agricultural and Urban	Event and continuous	Surface and subsurface flows, snowmelt, sediment, nutrients, pesticides, temp, dissolved oxygen, BOD, pH, phytoplankton, zooplankton and fecal coliform	Yes, external, HSPEXP+ and PEST	Yes	Public
KINEROS	Agricultural	Event	Surface flow and sediment	No	Yes	Public
MIKE SHE	Agricultural	Event and continuous	Surface and subsurface flows, sediment, and link to ECOLAB for water quality (nitrogen, geochemical processes, and crop growth)	Yes, external	Yes	Proprietary

(Continued)

Table 2-1. (*Continued*).

Watershed model	Dominant land use	Event or continuous simulation	Variables simulated	Uncertainty analysis	Graphical user interface	Availability
SWAT	Agricultural	Event and continuous	Weather, surface and subsurface flows, sediment, temp, crop growth, nutrients, pesticides, bacteria, and agricultural management	Yes, with SWAT-CUP	Yes	Public
SWMM	Urban	Event and continuous	Surface and subsurface flows, tidal, sanitary sewer; sediment, and conservative pollutants	No	Yes	Public and proprietary
WAM	Agricultural and Urban	Event and Continuous	Surface and subsurface flows, sediments, nutrients, and BOD	No	Yes	Proprietary
WARMF	Agricultural	Continuous	Surface flow, sediment, nutrients, temp, dissolved oxygen, pH, coliform bacteria, cations and anions, algal species, periphyton, and metal	No	Yes	Public and proprietary

Source: Adapted from Borah et al. (2019).

Table 2-2. Mathematical Bases of Hydrologic Simulations in the Models.

Watershed model	Watershed representation	Temporal resolution	Rainfall excess/infiltration	Overland/sheet flow routing	Stream/pipe flow routing	Subsurface flow simulation
AGNPS and AnnAGNPS	Square cells and channels/reaches	Storm duration (AGNPS) and subdaily (AnnAGNPS)	NRCS runoff curve number	Rational formula or its modifications	Rational formula or its modifications for peak flow and Manning's equation for water depth and velocity	No
ANSWERS-2000	Square cells and channels	Subhourly (event) and daily (continuous)	Modified Holton–Overton	Nonlinear reservoir equations	Nonlinear reservoir equations	Huggins and Monke drainage
DWSM	Overland planes, channels, and reservoirs	Subhourly	NRCS runoff curve number or Smith and Parlange	Kinematic wave analytical solution	Kinematic wave analytical and shock-fitting solutions	Kinematic storage equation

(*Continued*)

Table 2-2. (*Continued*).

Watershed model	Watershed representation	Temporal resolution	Rainfall excess/infiltration	Overland/sheet flow routing	Stream/pipe flow routing	Subsurface flow simulation
GSSHA	2D overland, 1D channel and 2D subsurface grids	Subhourly	Richard's or Green and Ampt	Diffusive wave numerical solution	Dynamic wave or diffusive wave numerical solutions	2D groundwater flow equations
GWLF	Single unit	Monthly loadings using daily steps	NRCS runoff curve number	No routing	No routing	From approximate daily water balance
HEC-HMS	Subwatersheds, reaches, and junctions	Subhourly and daily	NRCS runoff curve number, Green and Ampt, or initial loss and constant rate	Kinematic wave numerical solution or unit hydrographs	Kinematic wave numerical solution, Muskingum method, or nonlinear reservoir equations	Baseflow recession curve

HSPF/LSPC	Catchments (pervious and impervious), channels, and reservoirs	Hourly/subhourly	Philip's	Nonlinear reservoir equations	Function of reach volume or demand; limited dynamic wave upgrades	Empirical relations
KINEROS	Overland planes and channels	Subhourly	Smith and Parlange	Kinematic wave numerical solution	Kinematic wave numerical solution	No
MIKE SHE	2D overland, 1D channel, 1D unsaturated and 3D saturated grids	Subhourly	Richard's	Diffusive wave numerical solution	Diffusive wave numerical solution	3D groundwater flow equations
SWAT	Subwatersheds, channels, and ponds	Subdaily (event) and daily (continuous)	NRCS runoff curve number or Green and Ampt	Lag coefficient	Muskingum method or variable storage coefficient	Empirical parameters to partition shallow and deep aquifer recharges and volume of daily base flow

(Continued)

Table 2-2. (Continued).

Watershed model	Watershed representation	Temporal resolution	Rainfall excess / infiltration	Overland / sheet flow routing	Stream/pipe flow routing	Subsurface flow simulation
SWMM	Catchments (% impervious), stream and sewer network and storages	Subhourly	NRCS runoff curve number, Green and Ampt, or Horton's	Nonlinear reservoir equations	Dynamic wave numerical solution	Mass balance and empirical fluxes
WAM	Cells and reaches	Daily/hourly	NRCS runoff curve number and water balance	User-inputted unit hydrograph	Modified linear reservoir routing	Simple subsurface flow equation
WARMF	Land catchments, stream segments, and lake layers	Daily	Modified Holton–Overton	Nonlinear reservoir equations	Kinematic wave numerical solution	Simple conceptual: partitioning precipitation between surface runoff, intercepted tile drainage, and groundwater flow

Source: Adapted from Borah et al. (2019).

Table 2-3. Formulations Used in the Water-Quality Simulations of the Models.

Watershed model	Overland sediment transport method	Stream/sewer sediment transport method	Chemical/pathogen constituents simulated	Overland/stream/sewer Chemical/pathogen transport methods
AGNPS and AnnAGNPS	USLE/RUSLE, delivery ratio and particle fall velocities	Modified Einstein and Bagnold equations	Nitrogen (N), phosphorus (P), chemical oxygen demand (COD), pesticides, and organic carbon	Soil moisture, nutrients, and pesticides in each cell are tracked using NRCS soil databases and crop info. N and P in runoff using extraction coefficients and in sediment using enrichment ratios; COD in runoff water assuming accumulative without loss. Reach routing includes fate and transport of N, P, pesticides, and organic carbon
ANSWERS-2000	USLE and modified Yalin's equation	Not simulated	Nitrate, dissolved ammonium, adsorbed ammonium, adsorbed total Kjeldahl N, and dissolved orthophosphate	N and P transport and transformations through mineralization, ammonification, nitrification, and denitrification; and losses through uptake, runoff, and sediment

(Continued)

Table 2-3. (*Continued*).

Watershed model	Overland sediment transport method	Stream/sewer sediment transport method	Chemical/pathogen constituents simulated	Overland/stream/sewer Chemical/pathogen transport methods
DWSM	Raindrop detachment by Meyer and Wischmeier; Mutchler and Young and sediment transport by Yalin's equation and continuity by particle-size groups	Bed scour, deposition, and transport of sediment by continuity and transport capacity of size groups using Yang and Laursen's formulas	Nutrients (N and P) and pesticides	Nutrients and pesticides are simulated in dissolved and adsorbed phases with water and sediment, respectively, through mixing and exchange between rainfall, runoff, soil, and pore water and routing through overland and stream segments using approximate analytical solutions of spatially and temporarily varying continuity equations
GSSHA	Modified Kilinc–Richardson equation with USLE factors and mass conservation	Yang's equation for sand particles and silt clay as wash loads	No	N/A

GWLF	USLE modified by a daily rainfall factor and delivery ratio	Empirical bank erosion prediction; watershed monthly load from annual load multiplied by a monthly runoff-based transport factor	N and P	Daily buildup and washoff using a procedure from the SWMM
HEC-HMS	MUSLE	Partheniades–Krone formula	Optional; N (organic, ammonium, nitrite and nitrate), algae, dissolved oxygen, and CBOD	Solves the advection–diffusion equation and apply mass balances to channel reaches and reservoirs
HSPF/LSPC	Rainfall splash detachment, scour, and washoff as functions of water storage and outflow	Noncohesive sand transport using Toffaleti or Colby methods; cohesive silt and clay transport using shear stress and settling velocity	Temperature, dissolved oxygen, BOD, pH, ammonia, nitrite–nitrate, organic nitrogen, orthophosphate, organic phosphorus, phytoplankton, zooplankton, fecal coliform (FC), and pesticides	Atmospheric deposition, dieoff, buildup, and washoff

(Continued)

Table 2-3. (*Continued*).

Watershed model	Overland sediment transport method	Stream/sewer sediment transport method	Chemical/pathogen constituents simulated	Overland/stream/sewer Chemical/pathogen transport methods
KINEROS	Raindrop detachment, scour, sediment transport by transport capacity, and continuity for one-particle-size group	Streambed scour, deposition, and transport of sediment by continuity and transport capacity of one-size group	No	N/A
MIKE SHE	Soil erosion add-on module using EUROSEM	Simulated in MIKE 11 using cohesive and noncohesive transport modules	Link to ECOLAB for water-quality simulations: N processes, dissolved oxygen	Dissolved conservative solutes in surface, soil, and ground waters by solving numerically the advection–dispersion equation for the respective regimes

SWAT	MUSLE	Bagnold's stream power adjusted with USLE and particle fall velocity (other options include simplified Bagnold, Kodatie, Molinas, and Wu, and Yang formulas / models)	Soil temperature, crop growth, nutrients, pesticides, bacteria, and agricultural management	Nitrate-N based on water volume and average concentration, runoff P based on partitioning factor, daily Organic N and sediment adsorbed. P losses using loading functions, crop N and P use from supply and demand, and pesticides based on plant leaf-area index, application efficiency, washoff fraction, organic carbon adsorption coefficient, and exponential decay according to half lives
SWMM	MUSLE	Assumed the same as from overland (RUNOFF module) and no stream process simulated	Up to 10 conservative pollutants	Atmospheric deposition, buildup, and washoff

(Continued)

Table 2-3. (*Continued*).

Watershed model	Overland sediment transport method	Stream/sewer sediment transport method	Chemical/pathogen constituents simulated	Overland/stream/sewer Chemical/pathogen transport methods
WAM	USLE	Assimilative capacity	Particulate and soluble phosphorus, particulate and soluble nitrogen, and BOD	Assimilative capacity
WARMF	Adopted from ANSWERS (USLE and modified Yalin equation) with further modifications	Sand, silt, and clay scour and deposition are based on shear stress	pH, temperature, dissolved oxygen, ammonia, nitrate, phosphate, coliform bacteria, major cations, and anions, three algal species, periphyton, iron, zinc, manganese, and copper	Atmospheric deposition, washoff, mass balance, heat balance, kinetic reactions, and chemical equilibrium

Source: Adapted from Borah et al. (2019), Borah and Bera (2003).

of the models. These review results concur with those of previous reviews by Singh and Woolhiser (2002), Borah and Bera (2003), Shoemaker et al. (2005), USEPA (2008), Borah (2011), and Daniel et al. (2011). Some up-to-date model information were gathered by contacting the model developers. Finally, the models were evaluated by listing notable strengths and limitations found on the models and commenting on the suitability of the models for TMDL development and implementation in Table 2-4.

2.3.1 Key Characteristics and Capabilities of the Models

Table 2-1 summarizes some general information on the 14 watershed models that are useful for narrowing the number of models for selecting the most desirable model for a TMDL or any other project. Information includes (1) the watershed type based on dominant land use, such as agricultural or urban, for which the model was originally developed, although all the models can simulate all the land uses to some extent; (2) simulation types such as event or continuous; (3) simulation variables (capabilities), such as surface and subsurface flows, sediment, and water quality constituents, which will be reported in the model results or outputs in various forms; (4) capability of performing uncertainty analysis; (5) whether the model has a graphical user interface (GUI); and finally, (6) availability of the models in the public domain for free, proprietary and commercially available for a fee, or available from only the developer. The basic algorithms of the HSPF and LSPC models are the same, and, therefore, information on these two models is presented on a single row in Tables 2-1 through 2-4.

More discussions on the contents of Table 2-1 can be found in Borah et al. (2019). Dominant land-use (Column 2) and single-event or continuous simulation (Column 3) capabilities of the models are important factors to consider toward selecting a model to fit the specific situations, such as watershed land uses, and to achieve the intended goals, such as extreme event or continuous average responses. The variables simulated (Column 4) are also a key factor in selecting a model for the TMDL as the model capability must "match" the relevant pollutant for which the TMDL is developed.

The uncertainty analysis (Column 5) emphasizes the growing recognition to include uncertainty analysis in TMDL modeling. Although many of these models can have "extensions" for uncertainty analysis, only HEC-HMS model has an inbuilt capability for uncertainty analysis. Experienced modelers can test uncertainty and evaluate accuracy of any of the other models facilitated by external tools. Some are easier to link externally through the use of time-series outputs. Chapter 9 of this manual covers model uncertainty analysis in detail, including its recent advances.

Table 2-4. Notable Strengths and Limitations of the Models and Suitability for TMDLs.

Watershed model	Notable strengths	Notable limitations	Suitability for TMDLs
AGNPS and AnnAGNPS	• Model is spatially distributed and simulates water yield, sediment yield by particle-size class and source, nitrogen, phosphorus, COD, organic carbon, and pesticides.	• Empirically based model algorithms • No subsurface flow simulation • AGNPS is temporally lumped predicting storm-event yields • AnnAGNPS is limited to small watersheds as all the runoff and associated sediment, nutrients, and pesticide loads for a single day are routed to the watershed outlet before the next-day simulation begins • AGNPS is also limited to small watersheds as it uses uniform rainfall over the watershed	• Both the AGNPS and AnnAGNPS are useful in predicting sediment and nutrient loads from small watersheds for TMDL development, provided model limitations are recognized and considered.

ANSWERS-2000	• Model is spatially distributed simulating both event and continuous surface and subsurface flows, sediment, nitrate, dissolved ammonium, adsorbed TKN, and dissolved orthophosphate	• Less accurate for intense events owing to the leveled water surface approximation and nonlinear reservoir routing • Sediment and chemical simulations are limited to upland areas or subwatersheds and not done for the channels/streams, thus limiting applications to small watersheds	• Model is suitable for predicting sediment and nutrient loads from small watersheds in TMDL development, provided model limitations are recognized and considered.
DWSM	• Physically based hydrologic and nonpoint-source pollution model for storm events with small number of calibration parameters • Analytical solutions–based routing algorithms are unique and robust, making the model suitable for small to large watersheds • It is a balanced physically based model ranging from simple to computationally intensive models • Other models can take advantage of its robust algorithms	• Event simulations only • No user interface • Only the hydrology and sediment (DWSM_HydroSed) model is available for use • DWSM_AgChem with agricultural chemical routines require further testing and refinements	• Available DWSM_HydroSed version is suitable for use in TMDL development and implementation planning.

(Continued)

Table 2-4. (*Continued*).

Watershed model	Notable strengths	Notable limitations	Suitability for TMDLs
GSSHA	• Physically based hydrologic, hydraulic, and sediment transport model suitable for detailed studies	• Because of the numerical solutions in the routing algorithms, the model is computationally intensive and practically limited to small areas or watersheds with model grid cells limited to 100,000. • Current version is limited to sediment only without other water-quality processes and transport.	• Model is suitable for the development and implementation of sediment TMDLs. • Recommended for TMDLs requiring higher precision of sediment transport.

GWLF	• This continuous model estimates runoff, sediment, nitrogen, and phosphorus loads delivered to streams from a combination of point and nonpoint sources of pollution, including septic systems and channel erosion. • Model is popular because of its simple concept and algorithms, and minimum data requirement.	• Assuming that the watershed as a single unit limits its use to small watersheds only. • Not an event model, predictions are monthly or yearly averages or totals. • Model algorithms are empirically based.	• Model is useful in predicting sediment and nutrient loads from small watersheds for TMDL development. • Model is limited for TMDL implementation planning because of the aggregated nature of watershed simulation, a lack of ability to simulate impoundments, and other limitations.
HEC-HMS	• It is a comprehensive watershed hydrology model derived from HEC-1, an original model of the 1960s, with recent additions of basin water quality and stream-reservoir network sediment transport. • Allows wide selections of hydrologic procedures • Recent version (4.5) includes uncertainty analysis for hydrologic and meteorological parameters.	• Model may become inefficient or limited to small watersheds while using its physically based kinematic wave routing algorithm because of its numerical solutions.	• Model has been tested in sediment transport through streams and reservoirs and, thus, would be useful in certain sediment TMDLs.

(Continued)

Table 2-4. (Continued).

Watershed model	Notable strengths	Notable limitations	Suitability for TMDLs
HSPF/LSPC	• Comprehensive process-based hydrologic and nonpoint-source pollution model for mixed urban, agricultural, and rural watersheds for event and continuous simulations. • Snowmelt simulation is unique. • External programs HSPEXP and PEST are available for calibration, output post processing, sensitivity, and uncertainty analyses. • LSPC based on the 2000 version of the HSPF has an advanced programing architecture and flexibility using C++, widely used in conjunction with receiving water models.Part of the BASINS model system and its online users' group.	• It is an extremely data-intensive and overempirical parameterized model that requires a large amount of site information to accurately represent hydrology and water quality in a watershed. • Daily predictions of extreme events are less reliable than monthly and yearly predictions because of less precise (physically based) routing algorithms. • LSPC does not have the latest upgrades of the HSPF.	• HSPF and LSPC are widely used and appropriate models for developing sediment, nutrients, and bacteria TMDLs. • Latest 12.5 version of the HSPF includes explicit BMPs and facilitates TMDL implementations plan developments through quantitative evaluations of BMPs.

KINEROS	• Physically based hydrologic and sediment transport model	• Storm-event simulations only. • Model is practically limited to small areas or watersheds (up to 1,000 ha) because of the numerical solutions in the routing algorithms.	• Model is suitable for the development and implementation of sediment TMDLs. • Model has been used in manure-borne bacteria modeling and, thus, may have supplemental use in bacteria TMDL developments using other required continuous models.
MIKE SHE	• Physically based event and continuous hydrologic and nonpoint-source pollution (sediment and chemical) model. • Interactions between surface and groundwater flows is unique. • Model has auto calibration and sensitivity analysis capabilities. • External module for uncertainty analyses of various model parameters and results is available.	• Because of the multidimensional numerical solutions in the routing algorithms, the model is very inefficient, taking a long time to run and practically limited to small areas or watersheds (a little extra detail or a slightly smaller grid size or time step could lead to double-triple run times).	• Suitable for detailed studies of small areas or watersheds and for the development and implementation of sediment and nutrient TMDLs. • Recommended for TMDLs requiring higher precision of sediment and nutrient predictions or strong surface and groundwater interactions.

(Continued)

Table 2-4. (*Continued*).

Watershed model	Notable strengths	Notable limitations	Suitability for TMDLs
SWAT	• It is a comprehensive watershed model simulating hydrology, climate, erosion, sediment, crop growth, nutrients, pesticides, bacteria, and agricultural management in the uplands, main channels, and waterbodies of small to large agricultural and rural watersheds. • A recent version SWAT+ has its own GIS interface and is independent of commercial software. • Online user group	• Model is mostly empirically based requiring a significant amount of data and empirical parameters to run. • It is not suitable for intense storm-event routings of flow, sediment, and chemicals. • It is mostly a continuous simulation model using daily time steps, reliably predicting at monthly and yearly intervals only.	• SWAT is suitable for developing sediment, nutrient, bacteria, and pesticide TMDLs and evaluating agricultural management practices for implementation planning. • Because of the empirical algorithms, it may not be suitable for evaluating structural BMPs in the implementation phase.

SWMM

- This is a physically based hydrologic and hydraulic model for urban watersheds with impervious/pervious areas and storm and sanitary sewer networks, applicable to rural watersheds as well.
- It also simulates sediment and up to 10 conservative pollutants on the subcatchments (overland planes) of the watershed, including stormwater treatments/BMPs/LIDs on the subcatchments.
- Online user group

- Because of the numerical solution–based flow-routing algorithms, the model is subject to instabilities and sensitive to spatial and temporal resolutions, needing caution in running the model and interpreting the results, also limiting the size of the watershed for efficient and reliable model runs.
- No sediment and pollutant processes are simulated in the conduits (pipes and open ditches/streams) assuming the same as received from the subcatchments.

- Model can be used to estimate sediment and nutrient (assuming conservative) loads from the subcatchments to the conduits and reservoirs, the receiving waterbodies, which must be analyzed using another appropriate model for TMDL development and implementation.

(Continued)

Table 2-4. (*Continued*).

Watershed model	Notable strengths	Notable limitations	Suitability for TMDLs
WAM	• Proved to be the best-suited hydrologic and nonpoint-source pollution model for the unique hydrologic conditions of Florida. • It is a GIS-based model with a fully integrated ArcMap interface.	• Limited to Florida hydrologic conditions only • Not suitable for short-term storm events • Simplified representation of urban impervious land conditions • Limited documentation on model assumptions, methodologies, and sensitivity and uncertainty analyses	• Suitable for particulate and soluble phosphorus, particulate and soluble nitrogen (NO3, NH4, and organic N), TSS, and BOD TMDLs in Florida or similar hydrologic conditions.
WARMF	• Model simulates surface flow, sediment, nutrients, temp, dissolved oxygen, pH, coliform bacteria, cations and anions, algal species, periphyton and metal. • It can simulate water quality in the receiving waterbody as either a 1D vertically stratified, horizontally mixed reservoir or in 2D.	• Lack of perspective of modeling hydrologic and water-quality processes at the watershed scale.	• Suitable for certain sediment, nutrient, bacteria, and metal TMDL development and implementation.

2.3.2 Hydrologic Simulations in the Models

Table 2-2 presents key components of the hydrologic simulations in the models along with listings of the mathematical formulations used in the computational schemes following Borah (2011) where reviews of all the formulas and the procedures can be found. The second column of Table 2-2 lists the way a watershed is represented in the model, such as dividing its surface by subwatersheds, overland planes, or square/rectangular grids and their resolutions and connections to the channels/streams and reservoirs forming the drainage network. Approximations made in the watershed representations have effects on the performance and accuracy of the models and, therefore, must be made with care. The third column in Table 2-2 lists the temporal resolution (time step) used by the models, which is a sensitive input dictated by the mathematical condition for achieving numerical stability and the desired precision of outputs. This is not the case for empirically based models such as the GWLF generating monthly/yearly loading results, although the hydrologic calculations are done daily on a continuous basis. The rest of Table 2 includes listings of the simulation procedures for rainfall excess or infiltration (Column 4), overland or sheet flow routing (Column 5), stream or pipe flow routing (Column 6), and finally subsurface flow simulation (Column 7) used in the models.

Table 2-2 is helpful in further distinguishing the models based on discretization of the watershed to homogeneous pieces (spatial resolution), temporal resolution (subhourly to annual) adopted in computations, and the hydrologic simulation procedures. The spatial resolution or homogeneity assumption indicates whether the model is lumped (representing the watershed as a single unit), semidistributed (dividing the watershed into multiple subwatersheds), or fully distributed (using small grids to represent the watershed). The infiltration approaches adopted in the models for rainfall excess simulation shown in Table 2-2 are helpful to understand the models' runoff generating concepts and assumptions. Subsurface flows are simulated in some of the models, not all, and the approaches vary from simple to the most complex. A model simulating subsurface flows has an advantage over one without as it could be a significant part of the hydrologic cycle.

The overland or sheet and stream or pipe flow-routing procedures of the models (Table 2-2) can be objectively compared as those are mathematically based. Flow-routing provides the base to the rest in a model and, thus, can be called its backbone. Key model results such as peak flows and times to the peaks and simulations of sediment and water quality constituents depend on flow or movement of the water, which is simulated through the flow-routing procedures adopted in the models. Thus, flow routing has a great bearing on the model performance and accuracy of the results and can be used to compare the models.

Following Borah (2011), Figures 2-1 and 2-2 compare and rank the models based on the level of physical bases or accuracies against the level of complexities of the procedures used, respectively, in overland and channel/pipe flow routings. As previously discussed, HSPF and LSPC procedures are the same and, therefore, only the HSPF is shown in Figures 2-1 and 2-2, making the total number of models 13. Some models provide options among different procedures (Table 2-2), and for those models, the comparisons are based on the most physically based or accurate procedure used in the model. Physically based procedures are expected to yield more accurate results, provided measurements of physical parameters are available. As the

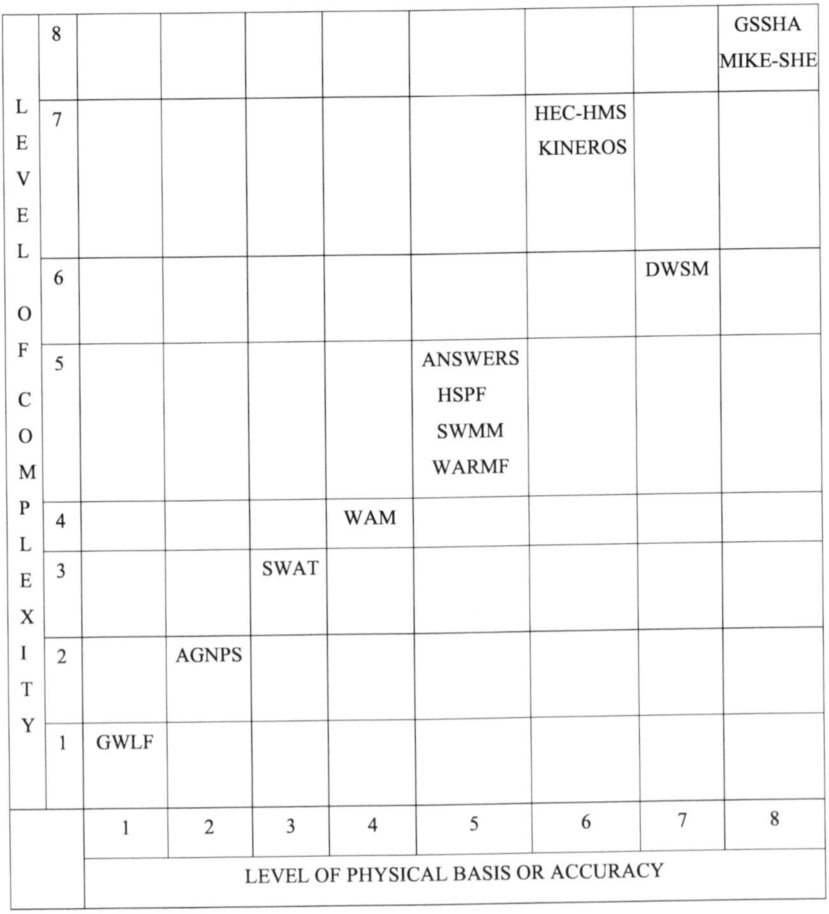

LEVEL OF COMPLEXITY	1	2	3	4	5	6	7	8
8								GSSHA MIKE-SHE
7					HEC-HMS KINEROS			
6							DWSM	
5					ANSWERS HSPF SWMM WARMF			
4				WAM				
3			SWAT					
2		AGNPS						
1	GWLF							

LEVEL OF PHYSICAL BASIS OR ACCURACY

Figure 2-1. Watershed models' overland runoff routing procedure comparison or ranking.
Source: Adapted from Borah et al. (2019).
Note: Level of physical basis or accuracy and complexity increase from 1 to 8.

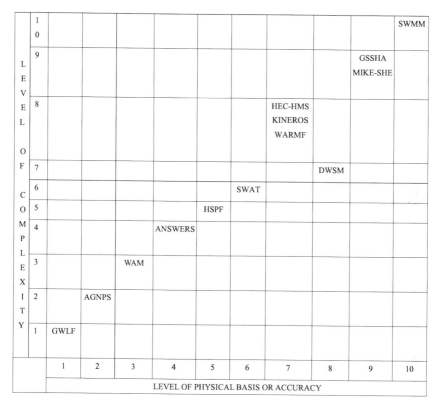

Figure 2-2. Watershed models' channel or pipe flow-routing procedure comparison or ranking.
Source: Adapted from Borah et al. (2019).
Note: Level of physical basis or accuracy and complexity increase from 1 to 10.

procedure is more physically based, the governing equations have more mathematical terms, and the solution gets more numerically complex. Therefore, the trends in Figures 2-1 and 2-2 are positive where accuracy or complexity increases with the numerical-level numbers. The physical basis of a model is critical in modern hydrology, which is undergoing extensive land-use changes and where traditional empirical parameters are becoming less credible, especially in evaluating BMPs.

More discussions on comparisons and rankings related to Figures 2-1 and 2-2 can be found in Borah (2011) and Borah et al. (2019). These comparisons or rankings are helpful in better understanding of some of the basic differences of the models toward selecting a suitable model for a TMDL or another related project with the desired, required, or tolerable accuracy and efficiency or to know these inherent characteristics of already selected model(s).

2.3.3 Water Quality Simulations in the Models

Table 2-3 summarizes water quality simulation approaches (formulations) used by the models by expanding most of those presented in Borah and Bera (2003). The simulation categories/components or terms listed are (1) the overland sediment transport methods including soil erosion from raindrop impact and runoff and transport of the eroded particles; (2) methods used for simulating stream/sewer erosion of the bed and bank and transport of the sediment; (3) the chemical constituents simulated by the models (repeated or expanded from Table 2-1 as those are relevant here); and (4) the approaches or procedures to simulate the transport of the chemicals through overland, stream/channel, and/or sewer.

Table 2-3 has the most relevant and useful information for TMDL development and implementation as the sediment and chemical or pathogen constituents are the various impairment agents for which the TMDLs are required. In most cases, water quality simulation procedures have been added to watershed models already established for simulating hydrologic, erosion, and sediment transport processes. Progress in the understanding and modeling of water quality processes is far behind that of hydrologic processes. Therefore, water quality modeling formulations are primarily empirical.

Erosion and sediment transport modeling formulations, although extensively studied, developed, and combined with hydrologic models, are also mostly empirical. Inappropriate uses are common as pointed out by Boomer et al. (2008), who concluded, "USLE-based sediment delivery models provide an inadequate framework for managing land and water resources at the catchment scale" and pointed to HSPF, GWLF, and SWAT models. AGNPS/AnnAGNPS, HEC-HMS, SWMM, and WAM using USLE/RUSLE/MUSLE also fall into this category (the second column of Table 2-3). Therefore, modelers must understand the physical processes and the modeling approaches to be able to best apply the models (limiting to its applicable conditions, choosing appropriate parameter values, etc.) and properly interpret the results.

2.3.4 Strengths and Limitations of the Models and Suitability for Total Maximum Daily Loads

Table 2-4 presents notable strengths and limitations found in the 14 models. The suitability or usefulness of the models in TMDL development and implementation is also included to provide some guidance in comparing and making informed selections of the models.

All 14 models have potential uses in developing and implementing TMDLs depending on the project-specific circumstances. SWMM was developed and continually supported by USEPA for urban stormwater and pollution management, thus having applications in urban TMDL development and implementation. The multipurpose HSPF model, although not originally developed for TMDL assessment, has been adapted through the ground-breaking application to the Chesapeake Bay TMDL assessment. HSPF was specifically modified for its first TMDL application (temperature impairment) in eastern Oregon (Chen et al. 1998a, b). SWMM focuses primarily on urban areas, and HSPF focuses on predominantly rural environments.

Using the TMDL Report Selection (TRS) tool developed by ASCE (2017), also described in Chapter 10, Borah et al. (2019) found the following models used in TMDL studies (from the most to least used): HSPF/LSPC, GWLF, SWAT, SWMM, WARMF, AGNPS, ANSWERS, HEC-HMS, and KINEROS. Although these models have been used in various TMDL developments, caution must be exercised on interpreting their validities in those applications. A general tendency is to choose a model that is easily accessible and user-friendly, although it may be inappropriate for the project, resulting in the misuse of the model. Such cases are often found in TMDL study reports (Borah et al. 2016). User familiarity or experience on only a limited number of models and having model user-support groups can play a role in making good or bad selection of models. In addition, all the models are not capable of evaluating BMPs and useful for TMDL implementation planning. Physically based models using measured data have the potential to be more effective in evaluating BMPs than empirically based models. It should be noted that the WAM is not a part of the TRS tool, although it has been applied to TMDL studies in Florida, such as on three lakes of the Upper Peace River by SWET (2009) for Tetra Tech and USEPA and on Lake Okeechobee (Khare et al. 2019). Similarly, MIKE SHE has also been reported to be applied primarily in Florida with strong surface and groundwater interactions and in TMDL developments such as for the city of Kissimmee in Central Florida (ASCE 2017).

Watershed hydrologic model capability distinction as continuous, single event, or both continuous and single-event simulations, as shown in Table 2-1, is an important factor to consider in selecting a model for a TMDL that may need only one of these capabilities to be effective and successful. For example, public domain event–based watershed models, KINEROS and CASC2D (Ogden and Julien 2002), the predecessor of GSSHA, are suitable for sediment TMDLs and evaluating the performances of BMPs (Kalin and Hantush 2003). Public domain continuous watershed models, HSPF, SWAT, and AnnAGNPS, are suitable for TMDLs on nutrients. The HEC-HMS, SWMM, GSSHA, HSPF, and SWAT are among the few watershed models having both event and continuous simulation capabilities and, thus, suitable for a wide variety of TMDLs.

It must be noted that there are other factors to consider toward selecting a model for a TMDL. A TMDL is being performed to address an impairment.

Therefore, the model capability must "match" the relevant pollutant and the associated expression of the standard that triggered the listing of the impairment. The variables simulated in the 14 models as listed in Table 2-1 and chemical/pathogen constituents simulated listed in Table 2-3 are helpful in screening the models for such an investigation. It is important to know the ability of a model to evaluate the TMDL target or end point that is based on the pollutant and the associated water quality (WQ) standard. Some TMDLs may have a "load" allocation to meet an end point such as nutrient load that is linked to lake eutrophication and might be measured by an algal concentration target. If the TMDL is for a concentration of a toxic pollutant in a stream (say arsenic), then the loading might need to address daily loads and associated in-stream targets as related to the WQ standard. Bacteria have another set of loading/counts/ and frequency conditions to be met. Thus, further investigations and evaluations of the models must be conducted in relation to this hierarchy of computational needs prior to model selection.

2.4 SUMMARY, CONCLUSIONS, AND RECOMMENDATIONS

Fourteen prevalent watershed models were critically reviewed for use in TMDL development and implementation, and the results are presented here in four tables. The tables compile key characteristics and capabilities of the models, mathematical bases in simulating various watershed processes, notable strengths and limitations of the models, and suitability of the models in developing and implementing TMDLs. In addition, the flow-routing procedures of the models, which are the models' backbones, are compared and ranked in terms of their physical basis and complexity levels or degrees. All these provide valuable factual information on the models to compare and help determine the relative applicability of the models and to make informed selections of those for developing TMDLs and implementation plans for a variety of impaired waters. This information is also useful for other watershed management studies.

Among the 14 models reviewed, HSPF/LSPC, GWLF, SWAT, SWMM, WARMF, AGNPS, ANSWERS, HEC-HMS, KINEROS, WAM, and MIKE SHE are found to be used in TMDL studies; however, caution must be exercised in regard to their appropriate applicability in those applications as misuses of models are commonly found in TMDL study reports (Borah et al 2016).

The review results presented here are helpful in distinguishing the valid and invalid applications. HSPF/LSPC, SWAT, and WARMF are the most comprehensive models for TMDL studies, although primarily meant for agricultural and rural watersheds. As shown here, these models are not highly physically based and, therefore, have room for improvements by developing and employing more physically based procedures. SWMM is the only physically based urban watershed model with strong hydraulic (channel/pipe flow-routing) procedures, however with poor sediment and pollutant simulations along with numerical instabilities and inefficiencies of the hydraulic routines. Therefore, further improvements to SWMM to overcome these weaknesses are desirable. SWMM's overland flow routings can be improved as well with more physically based procedures such as kinematic wave equations analytically solved as in the DWSM.

Although DWSM and GSSHA have not been found to be used in TMDL studies, these two models have been extensively evaluated and used in other watershed management and evaluation studies and, therefore, are suitable for TMDL studies as well. As shown here, GSSHA is one of the most physically based models and also one of the most numerically complex models. With a more accurate representation of the physical processes, DWSM is an efficient model among the kinematic wave routing models whose robust algorithms can be utilized and taken advantage of in other watershed models as well.

The physical basis of a model is critical in modern hydrology in which extensive land-use changes are undergoing, and traditional empirical parameters are becoming less credible, especially in evaluating BMPs. Models are ranked here based on physical bases of the flow routing procedures, the backbones of the models. GSSHA and MIKE SHE models ranking top on overland flow routing and SWMM ranking top on channel/pipe flow routing have the most physically based (expecting high accuracy) and also the most numerically complex routing procedures. GWLF ranks at the bottom on both these aspects. The rest of the models falls in between, although the DWSM is exceptionally efficient among the kinematic wave models.

There are also other important factors to consider in selecting a model for a TMDL. The model capability must "match" the relevant pollutant and the associated expression of the standard that triggered the listing of the impairment. The list of variables simulated (Table 2-1) and chemical/pathogen constituents simulated (Table 2-3) are helpful in finding this "match," although further evaluations and extensions of the models may have to be conducted.

A modeler must understand the physical processes and the modeling approaches to be able to best apply the models (limiting to the applicable conditions, choosing the appropriate parameter values, etc.) and interpret the results. This chapter is a valuable resource for a modeler toward those goals.

The watershed model reviews conducted by Borah et al. (2019) and also presented in this chapter provide a basis for future research recommending and improving existing models by strengthening the weaknesses found or developing better models. Robust physically based algorithms, the use of remotely sensed and high-resolution data, and uncertainty analysis capabilities are recommended to be part of model improvements.

In a recent synthesis of present watershed water quality modeling, Fu et al. (2020) outlined future research and potential improvements in the representation of freshwater systems pertaining to water quality, including the representation of environmental interfaces, in-stream water quality and process interactions, soil health and land management, and (peri-) urban areas. According to these researchers, the current challenges are quality control of monitoring data, model parameterization and calibration, uncertainty management, scale mismatches, and provisioning of modeling tools. To overcome these challenges, Fu et al. (2020) recommended building stronger collaborations between experimentalists and modelers, bridging gaps between modelers and stakeholders, and cultivating and applying procedural knowledge to better govern and support water quality modeling processes within organizations.

2.5 STATE-OF-THE-ART AND STATE-OF-THE-PRACTICE

As discussed, 12 (HSPF, LSPC, GWLF, SWAT, SWMM, WARMF, AGNPS, ANSWERS, HEC-HMS, KINEROS, WAM, and MIKE SHE) of the 14 models selected and evaluated are found to be used in TMDL studies and, therefore, can be labeled as state-of-the-practice. However, caution must be exercised in regard to their applicability in those applications as misuses and inappropriate applications of models in a number of ways are often found in TMDL study reports (Borah et al. 2016). One important factor of successful TMDL modeling is to "match" model capabilities with the pollutant of concern and the TMDL formulation. Although DWSM and GSSHA have not been found to be used in TMDL studies, these two models have been extensively evaluated and used in other watershed management and evaluation studies and, therefore, are potentially suitable for TMDL studies, especially where a higher resolution of sediment modeling is needed.

In the case of watershed modeling, which has been researched and developed for over half a century, state-of-the-practice, in general, has almost caught up with state-of-the-art. The ongoing challenge is to avoid inappropriate uses of models and appropriately aligning models with the pollutant of linkage of the pollutant sources to the receiving water. This chapter serves as a valuable resource to understand the key features of the 14 models that are essential to selecting appropriate models. There are many other considerations in the selection of appropriate models that are discussed in further detail in Chapter 11.

REFERENCES

Arnold, J. G., R. Srinivasan, R. S. Muttiah, and J. R. Williams. 1998. "Large area hydrologic modeling and assessment part I: Model development." *J. Am. Water Resour. Assoc.* 34 (1): 73–89.

ASCE. 2017. *Total maximum daily load analysis and modeling: Assessment of the practice.* Prepared by TMDL Analysis and Modeling Task Committee of the Environmental and Water Resources Institute of ASCE. Reston, VA: ASCE.

Beasley, D., L. Huggins, and A. Monke. 1980. "ANSWERS: A model for watershed planning." *Trans. ASABE* 23 (4): 938–944.

Bicknell, B. R., J. C. Imhoff, J. L. Kittle Jr., A. S. Donigian Jr., and R. C. Johanson. 1993. *Hydrologic simulation program − FORTRAN (HSPF) user's manual for release 10.* EPA/600/R-93/174. Athens, GA: USEPA Environmental Research Laboratory.

Bicknell, B., J. Imhoff, J. Kittle Jr., T. Jobes, A. Donigian Jr., and R. Johanson. 2001. *Hydrological simulation program-Fortran: HSPF version 12 user's manual.* Mountain View, CA: AQUA TERRA Consultants.

Bieger, K., J. G. Arnold, H. Rathjens, M. J. White, D. D. Bosch, P. M. Allen, et al. 2017. "Introduction to SWAT+, a completely restructured version of the soil and water assessment tool." *J. Am. Water Resour. Assoc.* 53 (1): 115–130.

Bingner, R., and F. Theurer. 2001. *AnnAGNPS technical processes: Documentation version 3.* Oxford, MS: Agricultural Research Service, USDA.

Boomer, K. B., D. E. Weller, and T. E. Jordan. 2008. "Empirical models based on Universal Soil Loss Equation fail to predict sediment discharges from Chesapeake Bay catchments." *J. Environ. Qual.* 37 (1): 79–89.

Borah, D. K. 2011. "Hydrologic procedures of storm event watershed models: a comprehensive review and comparison." *Hydrol. Processes* 25 (22): 3472–3489.

Borah, D. K., E. Ahmadisharaf, G. Padmanabhan, S. Imen, and Y. M. Mohamoud. 2019. "Watershed models for development and implementation of total maximum daily loads." *J. Hydrol. Eng.* 24 (1): 03118001.

Borah, D. K., J. G. Arnold, M. Bera, E. C. Krug, and X.-Z. Liang. 2007. "Storm event and continuous hydrologic modeling for comprehensive and efficient watershed simulations." *J. Hydrol. Eng.* 12 (6): 605–616.

Borah, D., and M. Bera. 2003. "Watershed-scale hydrologic and nonpoint-source pollution models: Review of mathematical bases." *Trans. ASAE* 46 (6): 1553–1566.

Borah, D. K., and M. Bera. 2004. "Watershed-scale hydrologic and nonpoint-source pollution models: Review of applications." *Trans. ASAE* 47 (3): 789–803.

Borah, D., M. Bera, and R. Xia. 2004. "Storm event flow and sediment simulations in agricultural watersheds using DWSM." *Trans. ASAE* 47 (5): 1539–1559.

Borah, D. K., J. L. Martin, and G. Padmanabhan. 2016. "Model selections for TMDL development: Simple analytical to complex hydrodynamic and water quality models." In *Presentation at ASCE EWRI World Environmental & Water Resources Cong.*, West Palm Beach, Florida, May 22–26, 2016. ASCE, Reston, VA.

Borah, D. K., S. N. Prasad, and C. V. Alonso. 1980. "Kinematic wave routing incorporating shock fitting." *Water Resour. Res.* 16 (3): 529–541.

Borah, D., R. Xia, and M. Bera. 2002. "DWSM—A dynamic watershed simulation model." In *Mathematical models of small watershed hydrology and applications*, edited by V. P. Singh and D. K. Frevert, 113–166. Highlands Ranch, CO: Water Resources Publications.

Borah, D. K., G. Yagow, A. Saleh, P. L. Barnes, W. Rosenthal, E. C. Krug, et al. 2006. "Sediment and nutrient modeling for TMDL development and implementation." *Trans. ASABE* 49 (4): 967–986.

Bottcher, A. B., B. J. Whiteley, A. I. James, and J. G. A. Hiscock. 2012. "Watershed assessment model (WAM) applications in Florida." In *Proc., 2012 Esri Int. User Conf. (ESRI)*, San Diego, California, July 23–27, 2012: 1–17.

Bouraoui, F., and T. A. Dillaha. 1996. "ANSWERS-2000: Runoff and sediment transport model." *J. Environ. Eng.* 122 (6): 493–502.

Bouraoui, F., and T. A. Dillaha. 2000. "ANSWERS-2000: Non-point-source nutrient planning model." *J. Environ. Eng.* 126 (11): 1045–1055.

Breuer, L., J. A. Huisman, P. Willems, H. Bormann, A. Bronstert, B. F. W. Croke, et al. 2009. "Assessing the impact of land use change on hydrology by ensemble modeling (LUCHEM). I: Model intercomparison with current land use." *Adv. Water Resour.* 32 (2): 129–146.

Chen, C. W., J. Herr, and L. Ziemelis. 1998. *Watershed analysis risk management framework—A decision support system for watershed approach and TMDL calculation.* Palo Alto, CA: Electric Power Research Institute.

Chen, D. Y., R. F. Carsel, S. C. McCutcheon, and W. L. Nutter. 1998a. "Stream temperature simulation of forested riparian areas: I. Watershed-scale model development." *J. Environ. Eng.* 124 (4): 304–315.

Chen, D. Y., S. C. McCutcheon, D. J. Norton, and W. L. Nutter. 1998b. "Stream temperature simulation of forested riparian areas: II. Model application." *J. Environ. Eng.* 124 (4): 316–328.

Crawford, N. H., and R. K. Linsley. 1966. *Digital simulation on hydrology: Stanford Watershed Model IV.* Tech. Rep. No. 39. Palo Alto, CA: Stanford University.

Dai, T., R. L. Wetzel, T. R. L. Christensen, and E. A. Lewis. 2000. *BasinSim 1.0: A Windows-based watershed modeling package.* Special Report in Applied Marine Science and Ocean Engineering. Gloucester Point, VA: Virginia Institute of Marine Science.

Daniel, E. B., J. V. Camp, E. J. LeBoeuf, J. R. Penrod, J. P. Dobbins, and M. D. Abkowitz. 2011. "Watershed modeling and its applications: A state-of-the-art review." *Open Hydrol. J.* 5: 26–50.

DHI (Danish Hydraulic Institute). 2014. *MIKE SHE User manual Vol. 1: User guide*. Horsholm: Danish Hydraulic Institute Water and Environment.

Dile, Y. T., P. Daggupati, C. George, R. Srinivasan, and J. Arnold. 2016. "Introducing a new open source GIS user interface for the SWAT model." *Environ. Modell. Software* 85: 129–138.

Doherty, J. 2016. *PEST: Model-Independent Parameter Estimation, User manual Part II PEST utility support software*. Brisbane: Watermark Numerical Computing.

Downer, C. W., and F. L. Ogden. 2004. "GSSHA: A model for simulating diverse streamflow generating processes." *J. Hydrol. Eng.* 9 (3): 161–174.

Downer, C. W., F. L. Ogden, J. Niedzialek, and S. Liu. 2006. "Gridded surface/subsurface hydrologic analysis (GSSHA) model: A model for simulating diverse streamflow producing processes." In *Watershed models*, edited by V. Singh, and D. Frevert. Boca Raton, FL: CRC Press, 131–158.

Downer, C. W., N. R. Pradhan, F. L. Ogden, and A. R. Byrd. 2015. "Testing the effects of detachment limits and transport capacity formulation on sediment runoff predictions using the US Army Corps of Engineers GSSHA model." *J. Hydrol. Eng.* 20 (7): 040140.

El Hassan, A. A., H. O. Sharif, T. Jackson, and S. Chintalapudi. 2013. "Performance of a conceptual and physically based model in simulating the response of a semi-urbanized watershed in San Antonio, Texas." *Hydrol. Process.* 27: 3394–3408.

ESRI (Environmental Systems Research Institute). 2011. *ArcMap geographic information systems software*. Redlands, CA: Trademarked by Environmental Systems Research Institute.

Evans, B. M., S. A. Sheeder, K. J. Corradini, and W. S. Brown. 2001. *AVGWLF version 3.2: Users guide*. Environmental Resources Research Institute, Pennsylvania State University, State College, PA, and Pennsylvania Dept. of Environmental Protection, Bureau of Watershed Conservation, Harrisburg, PA.

Fu, B., J. S. Horsburgh, A. J. Jakeman, C. Gualtieri, T. Arnold, and L. Marshall et al. 2020. "Modeling water quality in watersheds: From here to the next generation." *Water Resour. Res.* 56: e2020WR027721.

Gao, P., D. Borah, and C. Yi. 2015. "Storm event flow and sediment simulations in a Central New York watershed: model testing and parameter analyses." *Trans. ASABE* 85 (5): 1241–1252.

Goodrich, D., I. Bums, C. Unkrich, D. Semmens, D. Guertin, M. Hernandez, et al. 2012. "KINEROS 2/AGWA: Model use, calibration, and validation." *Trans. ASABE* 55 (4): 1561–1574.

Graham, D., and M. Butts. 2006. "Flexible, integrated watershed modelling with MIKE SHE." In *Watershed models*, edited by V. Singh and D. Frevert, 833–882. Boca Raton, FL: CRC Press.

Haith, D. A., R. Mandel, and R. S. Wu. 1992. *GWLF, generalized watershed loading functions, version 2.0, user's manual*. Ithaca, NY: Cornell University.

Iowa State University. 2021. "SWAT literature database for peer-reviewed journal articles." Accessed November 5, 2021. https://www.card.iastate.edu/swat_articles/.

Jacobson, B. M., A. B. Bottcher, N. B. Pickering, and J. G. Hiscock. 1998. *Unique routing algorithm for watershed assessment model*. ASAE Paper, No. 98-2237. St. Joseph, MI: American of Society of Agricultural Engineers.

James, W., W. Huber, R. Pitt, R. Dickinson, and R. James. 2002. *Water systems models: User's guide to SWMM5*. Guelph, Canada: Computational Hydraulics International.

Johnson, B. E., Z. Zhang, and C. W. Downer. 2013. "Watershed scale physically based water flow, sediment and nutrient dynamic modeling system." Chap. 8 in *Landscape ecology for sustainable environment and culture*, edited by B. Fu and K. B. Jones, 145–171. New York, NY: Springer.

Kalin, L., and M. M. Hantush. 2003. *Evaluation of sediment transport models and comparative application of two watershed models*. EPA/600/R-03/139. Cincinnati, OH: USEPA-NRMRL.

Kalin, L., and M. M. Hantush. 2006. "Comparative assessment of two distributed watershed models with application to a small watershed." *Hydrol. Processes* 20 (11): 2285–2307.

Khare, Y. P. 2014. *Hydrologic and water quality model evaluation with global sensitivity analysis: Improvements and applications*. Gainesville, FL: Univ. of Florida.

Khare, Y., G. M. Naja, G. A. Stainback, C. J. Martinez, R. Paudel, and T. V. Lent. 2019. "A phased assessment of restoration alternatives to archive phosphorous water quality targets for Lake Okeechobee, Florida, USA." *Water* 11 (2): 327.

Leonard, R. A., W. G. Knisel, and D. A. Still. 1987. "GLEAMS: Groundwater loading effects on agricultural management systems." *Trans. ASAE* 30 (5): 1403–1428.

Metcalf and Eddy, Inc., University of Florida, and Water Resources Engineers, Inc. 1971. *Storm water management model, Vol. I*. Final Rep. EPA Rep. 11024. Washington, DC: Environmental Protection Agency.

Mohamoud, Y. M. 2007. "Enhancing Hydrological Simulation Program-Fortran model channel hydraulic representations." *J. Am. Water Resour. Assoc.* 43 (5): 1280–1292.

Mohamoud, Y. M., R. Parmar, and K. Wolfe. 2007. *Web-based HSPF toolkit to support low impact development (LID) and other urban stormwater modeling applications*. BASINS Technical Note 9. Washington, DC: EPA, Office of Water.

Mohamoud, Y. M., R. Parmar, and K. Wolfe. 2009. *Infiltration BMP tutorial for HSPF*. Basins Technical Note 11. Washington, DC: United States Environmental Protection Agency, Office of Water.

Mohamoud, Y. M., R. Parmar, and K. Wolfe. 2010. *Modeling best management practices (BMPs) with HSPF*, 892–898. Innovations in Watershed Management Under Land Use and Climate Change. Madison, WI: ASCE.

Neitsch, S. L., J. G. Arnold, J. R. Kiniry, and J. R. Williams. 2011. *Soil and water assessment tool theoretical documentation, version 2009*. College Station, TX: Texas Water Resources Institute. https://swat.tamu.edu/software.

Obropta, C., and J. Kardos. 2007. "Review of urban stormwater quality models: Deterministic, stochastic, and hybrid approaches." *J. Am. Water Resour. Assoc.* 43 (6): 1508–1523.

Ogden, F., and P. Julien. 2002. "CASC2D: A two-dimensional, physically-based, Hortonian hydrologic model." In *Mathematical models of small watershed hydrology and applications*, edited by V. Singh and D. Frevert, 69–112. Highlands Ranch, CO: Water Resources Publications.

Pak, J., M. Fleming, W. Scharffenberg, and P. Ely. 2009. "Evaluation of sediment transport module within the hydrologic modeling system (HEC-HMS) for the Upper North Bosque River Watershed in Central Texas." In *Proc., 33rd Int. Association of Hydraulic Engineering and Research (IAHR) Biennial Cong.*, Vancouver, British Columbia, August 9–14.

Pak, J., M. Fleming, W. Scharffenberg, and S. Gibson. 2010. "Assessment of reservoir trap efficiency methods using the hydrology modeling system (HEC-HMS) for the Upper North Bosque River Watershed in Central Texas." In *Proc., Joint 9th Federal Interagency Sedimentation Conf. and 4th Federal Interagency Hydrologic Modeling Conf.*, Las Vegas, Nevada. June 27–July 1, 2010.

Paudel, M., J. E. Nelson, C. W. Downer, and R. Hotchkiss. 2011. "Comparing the capability of distributed and lumped hydrologic models for analyzing the effects of land use change." *J. Hydroinf.* 13 (3): 461–473.

Pradhan, N. R., C. W. Downer, and B. E. Johnson. 2014. "A Physics Based Hydrologic Modeling Approach to Simulate Non-point Source Pollution for the Purposes of Calculating TMDLs and Designing Abatement Measures." *Chap. 9 in Practical Aspects of Computational Chemistry-III*, edited by J. Leszczynski and M. K. Shukla. New York: Springer.

Quinn, N. W. T. 2020. "Policy innovation and governance for irrigation sustainability in the Arid, Saline San Joaquin River Basin." *Sustainability J.* 12 (11): 4733.

Quinn, N. W. T., B. Hughes, A. Osti, J. Herr, and J. Wang. 2018a. "Real-time, web-based decision support for stakeholder implementation of basin-scale salinity management." In *Environmental Software Systems, Computer Science for Environmental Protection, ISESS 2017*, edited by J. Hrebicek, R. Denzer, G. Schimak and T. Pitner. Berlin: Springer. IFIP AICT 507. Keynote Lecture. 3–18.

Quinn, N. W. T., R. Ortega, and L. Holm. 2010. "Environmental sensor networks and continuous data quality assurance to manage salinity within a highly regulated river basin." In *Decision support systems in agriculture, food and the environment: Trends, applications and advances*, edited by Basil Manos (Aristotle University of Thessaloniki, Greece), Nikolaos Matsatsinis (Technical University of Crete, Greece), Konstantinos Paparrizos (University of Macedonia, Greece) and Jason Papathanasiou (University of Macedonia, Greece): IGI Global: 420–436.

Quinn, N. W. T., A. Osti, J. Herr, E. Raley, and J. Wang. 2018b. "WARMF-Online – A web-based portal supporting real-time salinity management in the San Joaquin River Basin." *Open Water* 1 (1): 4.

Refsgaard, J., and B. Storm. 1995. "MIKE SHE." In *Computer models of watershed hydrology*, edited by V. Singh, 809–846. Highlands Ranch, CO: Water Resources Publications.

Rossman, L. A. 2015a. *Storm water management model reference manual*. Vol. I. Cincinnati, OH: National Risk Management Research Laboratory, Office of Research and Development, EPA.

Rossman, L. A. 2015b. *Storm water management model user's manual, version 5.1*. Cincinnati, OH: National Risk Management Research Laboratory, Office of Research and Development, EPA.

Rossman, L. A. 2016. *Storm water management model reference manual*. Vol. III. Cincinnati, OH: National Risk Management Research Laboratory, Office of Research and Development, EPA.

Sharifi, A., H. Yen, K. Boomer, L. Kalin, X. Li, and D. Weller. 2017. "Using multiple watershed models to assess the water quality impacts of alternate land development scenarios for a small community." *Catena* 150: 87–99.

Shen, J., A. Parker, and J. Riverson. 2005. "A new approach for a Windows-based watershed modeling system based on a database-supporting architecture." *Environ. Modell. Software* 20 (9): 1127–1138.

Shenk, G. W., and L. C. Linker. 2013. "Development and application of the 2010 Chesapeake Bay watershed total maximum daily load model." *J. Am. Water Resourc. Assoc.* 49 (5): 1042–1056.

Shoemaker, L., T. Dai, J. Koenig, and M. Hantush. 2005. *TMDL model evaluation and research needs*. EPA/600/R-05/149. Cincinnati, OH: National Risk Management Research Laboratory, Office of Research and Development, EPA.

Singh, V. P. 1995. *Computer models of watershed hydrology*. Highlands Ranch, CO: Water Resources Publications.

Singh, V. P., and D. K. Frevert. 2002a. *Mathematical models of large watershed hydrology*. Highlands Ranch, CO: Water Resources Publication.

Singh, V. P., and D. K. Frevert. 2002b. *Mathematical models of small watershed hydrology and applications*. Highlands Ranch, CO: Water Resources Publication.

Singh, V. P., and D. K. Frevert. 2006. *Watershed models*. Boca Raton, FL: CRC Taylor & Francis.

Singh, V. P., and D. A. Woolhiser. 2002. "Mathematical modeling of watershed hydrology." *J. Hydrol. Eng.* 7 (4): 270–292.

Sloan, P. G., I. D. Moore, G. B. Coltharp, and J. D. Eigel. 1983. *Modeling surface and subsurface stormflow on steeply-sloping forested watersheds*. Water Resources Institute Rep. 142. Lexington, KY: University of Kentucky.

Smith, R. E., and J. Y. Parlange. 1978. "A parameter-efficient hydrologic infiltration model." *Water Resourc. Res.* 14 (3): 533–538.

SWET (Soil and Water Engineering Technology). 2008. *EAAMOD technical and user manuals*. Final Rep. to the Everglades Research and Education Center. Belle Glade, FL: University of Florida.

SWET. 2009. *Upper Peach River – Three lakes modeling report using WAM and WASP: WAM setup and results for the development of total maximum daily load (TMDL) estimation for lakes Alfred, Arianna, and Crystal in the Upper Peach River basin, Florida*. Tetra Tech under contract to USEPA. Gainesville, FL: SWET.

SWET. 2011a. *Watershed assessment model technical and user manuals*. http://www.swet.com/wam-for-arcmap-100. Gainesville, FL: SWET.

SWET. 2011b. *Watershed assessment model documentation and validation: Model calibration and validation*. West Palm Beach, FL: Final Rep. Submitted to the South Florida Water Management District.

Tetra Tech. 2002. *The loading simulation program in C++ (LSPC) watershed modeling system—Users' manual*. Athens, GA: United States Environmental Protection Agency.

Tetra Tech. 2011. *Spreadsheet Tool for the Estimation of Pollutant Load (STEPL): Version 4.1*. Fairfax, VA: Tetra Tech, Inc.

USACE (United States Army Corps of Engineers). 1968. *HEC-1 flood hydrograph package: User's manual*. Davis, CA: HEC.

USACE. 2016. *Hydrologic modeling system HEC-HMS: User's manual*. Davis, CA: HEC.

USDA-NASS. 2021. CropScape – Cropland Data Layer. USDA National Agricultural Statistic Service. Accessed November 5, 2021. https://nassgeodata.gmu.edu/CropScape/.

USEPA. 2004. *Total maximum daily load (TMDL) for the Wabash River watershed*, Ohio. Chicago: USEPA, Region 5.

USEPA. 2008. *Handbook for developing watershed plans to restore and protect our waters*. Washington, DC: Nonpoint Source Control Branch, Office of Water.

Woolhiser, D. A., R. Smith, and D. C. Goodrich. 1990. *KINEROS: a kinematic runoff and erosion model: Documentation and user manual*. Fort Collins, CO: USDA-ARS-77.

XP Solutions. 2014. *XP-SWMM: Stormwater and wastewater management model: Getting started manual.* Portland, OR: XP Solutions.

Young, R. A., C. A. Onstad, D. D. Bosch, and W. P. Anderson. 1987. *AGNPS, Agricultural Non-Point-Source Pollution Model: A watershed analysis tool.* Albany, CA: Agricultural Research Service, Western Utilization Research and Development Div.

Yuan, L., T. Sinshaw, and K. J. Forshay. 2020. "Review of watershed-scale water quality and non-point source pollution models." *Geosciences* 10 (1): 1–36.

CHAPTER 3
RECEIVING WATER QUALITY MODELS

Rene A. Camacho-Rincon, Zhonglong Zhang, Xiaobo Chao

3.1 INTRODUCTION

The excess of nutrients and organic matter and the presence of toxic chemicals and metals are primary causes of contamination in aquatic ecosystems (Table 3-1). These contaminants, generated by natural and anthropogenic processes, enter waterbodies as loads originating from point sources and nonpoint sources (ASCE 2017, Chapra 2003, USEPA 1991). Examples of point sources include municipal and industrial facilities that have a well-defined effluent discharge point to the waterbody. Nonpoint sources, on the contrary, are areas that generate contaminant loads that reach waterbodies in a diffuse way that can change in time and space. Nonpoint-source contaminant load is typically transported through surface runoff over watersheds (Chapter 2).

Existing modeling approaches to simulate the impacts of point and nonpoint sources on waterbodies typically consist of coupling watershed and receiving waterbody models (Figure 3-1). A watershed model (Chapter 2) is used to calculate the magnitude of nonpoint-source loadings generated in a watershed, and the results are used as load inputs to the receiving waterbody model (Chapra 2003, Shoemaker et al. 2005). A receiving water model uses the loading information and simulates the major physical, chemical, and biological processes in a waterbody by calculating the mass balances and biokinetic transformations occurring among contaminants (Camacho et al. 2019). The linkage allows a quantitative assessment of water quality responses to external loadings. This integrated modeling approach is used by states to determine total maximum daily load (TMDL) allocations of point and nonpoint loads of contaminants.

Table 3-1. List of Top 16 Causes of Impairment from the National Summary of Impaired Waters.

Pollutant	Number of impairments	% of Total
Pathogens	9,874	13.6
Nutrients	7,092	9.8
Metals (other than mercury)	7,066	9.7
Organic enrichment and oxygen depletion	6,602	9.1
Polychlorinated biphenyls	6,060	8.3
Sediment	5,964	8.2
Mercury	4,860	6.7
pH, acidity, and caustic conditions	4,450	6.5
Cause unknown—impaired biota	4,741	6.1
Temperature	3,007	4.1
Turbidity	2,869	3.9
Salinity, total dissolved solids, chlorides, and sulfates	1,996	2.7
Pesticides	1,774	2.4
Cause unknown	1,151	1.6
Algal growth	1,057	1.5
Habitat alterations	882	1.2
Other	3,222	4.4
Total	72,667	100

Note: Information as of January 10, 2021.

Source: http://iaspub.epa.gov/waters10/attains_nation_cy.control?p_report_type=T #causes_303d.

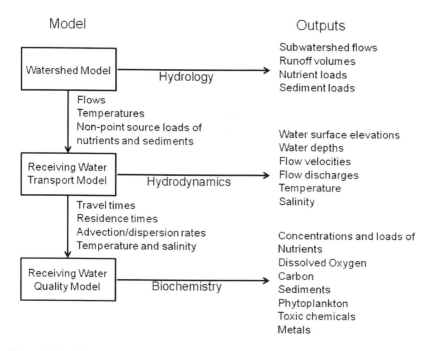

Figure 3-1. Schematic representation of linkage between watershed, hydrodynamic, and water quality models for TMDL development.
Source: Camacho et al. (2019).

Multiple watershed and receiving water quality models can be linked to support TMDL studies (Chapter 4). However, the task of selecting a set of models for a particular application is challenging, given the vast range of mathematical approaches, input data requirements, model capabilities, and limitations of the models available at present. To help water resource professionals identify appropriate modeling approaches and technologies to support a particular study, the ASCE/EWRI TMDL Analysis and Modeling Task Committee has compiled a review of multiple watershed and receiving water quality models to document their capabilities and applicability for TMDL studies (ASCE 2017, Borah et al. 2019, Camacho et al. 2019).

This chapter presents a review of some of the most widely used receiving water quality models used in TMDLs to simulate eutrophication processes, including carbon and nutrient cycling, phytoplankton dynamics, dissolved oxygen, and fate and transport of toxic chemicals and mercury (Camacho et al. 2019). The models discussed in this chapter have been identified by the ASCE/EWRI TMDL Analysis and Modeling Task Committee as a representative subset of models that can illustrate the main capabilities and approaches currently used to support TMDL studies (ASCE 2017).

Table 3-2. Summary of Selected Receiving Waterbody Models.

Model	Public license	In-Build Transport			Water Quality									Applicability			
		1D	2D	3D	Temp	Sal	DO	Algae	C, N, P,	Sediments	Pathogens	Toxics	Metals	Rivers	Lakes	Reservoirs	Estuaries
CE-QUAL-ICM[a]	X			X	X	X	X	X	X	X	X	X	X	X	X	X	X
WASP[a]	X	X	X		X	X	X	X	X	X	X	X	X	X	X	X	X
EFDC	X	X	X	X	X	X	X	X	X	X	X	X	X	X	X	X	X
CE-QUAL-W2	X		X		X	X	X	X	X	X	X				X	X	
HEC-RAS	X	X			X	X	X	X	X	X	X			X			
CCHE-1D/2D/3D	X	X	X	X	X	X	X	X	X	X		X	X	X	X	X	X
EPD_RIV1	X	X			X	X	X				X			X			
QUAL2K	X	X			X	X	X	X			X			X			
MINTEQA2 and Visual MINTEQ	X													X	X			
OTEQ	X	X												X	X			
MIKE11 – ECOLAB		X			X	X	X	X	X	X	X			X			

*Can be linked to hydrodynamic models to simulate 2D and 3D transport.

Source: Camacho et al. (2019).

A summary of the models discussed in this chapter is presented in Table 3-2. Because a comprehensive review of the large number of existing software packages used for water quality studies is unpractical, details of other models used in water quality studies can be found elsewhere (e.g., Shoemaker et al. 2005).

Sources of data for model setup as well as methodologies for model calibration, validation, and uncertainty analysis, including recommended statistics for model performance evaluation, are discussed in detail in Chapters 7 and 8.

3.2 RECEIVING WATER QUALITY MODELS FOR TOTAL MAXIMUM DAILY LOAD APPLICATIONS

3.2.1 Corps of Engineers Integrated Compartment Water Quality Model

3.2.1.1 Model Background and Capabilities. Corps of Engineers Integrated Compartment Water Quality Model (CE-QUAL-ICM), or simply referred to as ICM, is a multidimensional water quality model developed by US Army Corps of Engineers (USACE 2014)-Engineer Research and Development Center (ERDC). The model can be applied to lakes, rivers, estuaries, and coastal ecosystems (Cerco and Cole 1993, Cerco et al. 2004, 2006). ICM simulates multiple biogeochemical cycles, including the cycles of carbon, nitrogen, phosphorus, and oxygen, in addition to physical variables such as salinity, temperature, and suspended solids. The model has been subject to many refinements and improvements since the initial development efforts in the late 1980s and early 1990s. Some notable model improvements include the addition of capabilities to simulate multiple zooplankton groups, submerged aquatic vegetation, and benthos. The model has also been subject to specific modifications to address the unique environment of the Lower St. Johns River, Florida. The ICM simulates mass transport and biokinetic cycles of 36 water quality state variables, including dissolved oxygen, nitrogen, phosphorus, multiple phytoplankton groups, zooplankton, carbon, and silica. Water quality variables can be activated or deactivated in ICM depending on the needs of a particular project. One of the features of the ICM is that it uses unstructured grid finite volume. The unstructured grid feature allows the linkage of ICM with various hydrodynamic models, including the CH3D and EFDC. Figure 3-2 provides an overview of ICM representation of water quality state variables. Additional details of the CE-QUAL-ICM and download options can be found at USACE (2014).

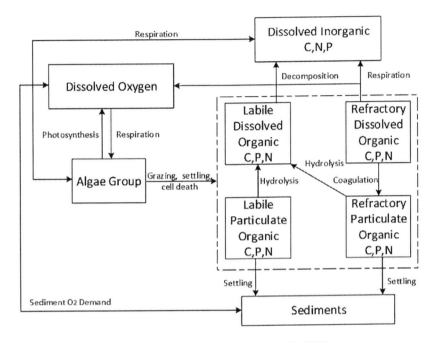

Figure 3-2. Schematic representation of the CE-QUAL-ICM.
Source: USACE (2014).

3.2.1.2 Applicability to Total Maximum Daily Load Studies. The ICM can simulate water quality responses to point and nonpoint-source loads and can be used as part of TMDL modeling. The model has been applied in the environmental restoration projects of Chesapeake Bay, Green Bay, New York Harbor, San Juan Bay, Florida Bay, Lower St. Johns River, Mississippi Sound, Lake Washington, and many other systems (Cerco and Noel 2013, Mark et al. 1993, Martin et al. 2002).

3.2.2 Water Quality Analysis Simulation Program

3.2.2.1 Model Background and Capabilities. The Water Quality Analysis Simulation Program (WASP) was initially developed as a transport code with water quality subroutines. After Di Toro (1983) applied the WASP model to simulate nutrient cycling in the Great Lakes, Ambrose et al. (1986) created a publicly available WASP code that has evolved during the last few decades to simulate complex water quality processes. The WASP model can simulate dissolved oxygen, nutrient, and carbon cycling, including organic and inorganic speciation, sediment oxygen demand, sediment digenesis, multiple phytoplankton groups, detritus, periphyton, organic toxicants, metals, and mercury. Cope et al. (2020) describe an assessment of the body of literature related to the modeling applications for the prediction of nutrients and related parameters using the WASP.

The WASP model is one of the most extensively used water quality models worldwide and has a user database with over 15,000 users. The latest model version WASP 8.32 (as of 2021) can be downloaded from USEPA (2021). The WASP model includes a graphical user interface (GUI) that allows the preprocessing of data for the model. The GUI can be used to create and edit model segments, activate and deactivate water quality variables, specify model parameter values, and read inputs such as loading time series and atmospheric information from different databases or excel workbooks. Early versions of WASP included MOVEM, a postprocessor system to visualize model results and generate comparison plots between simulations and observations. Latest model versions include GRAPH, which is a more recent postprocessing GUI with GIS and database capabilities. WASP allows the simulation results to be also written to spreadsheets as *.CSV files and plotted or animated two-dimensionally in GRAPH. In addition to the WASP model interface, input information and generation of WASP modeling segments can be assisted with tools available from the Better Assessment Science Integrating Point and Nonpoint Sources system (Chapter 4).

The WASP model is typically coupled to hydrologic and hydrodynamic models to simulate complex, large-scale ecosystems. Watershed models such as SWAT, SWMM, HSPF, and LSPC (Chapter 2) are used to calculate nonpoint-source inputs for the model (Mandel et al. 2008). Meanwhile, hydrodynamic models such as EFDC are used to simulate hydrodynamic and physical transport variables, including velocities, depths, water temperatures, and others needed for mass balance and advective and dispersive transport calculations. The hydrodynamic information is passed to WASP by means of a linkage hydrodynamic file.

3.2.2.2 Applicability to Total Maximum Daily Load Studies. The WASP model is widely used in conjunction with other transport hydrodynamic models to simulate complex water quality processes in rivers, lakes, reservoirs, estuaries, and coastal waters. The WASP model has been applied to support TMDL studies in the Neuse River Estuary, North Carolina; Sawgrass Lake Florida; and Wissahickon Creek, Pennsylvania, among others (USEPA 2009, Wool et al. 2003b, Zou et al. 2006).

3.2.3 Environmental Fluid Dynamics Code

3.2.3.1 Model Background and Capabilities. The Environmental Fluid Dynamics Code (EFDC) is a surface water model with hydrodynamic and water quality modeling capabilities. The EFDC model was originally developed at the Virginia Institute of Marine Science (Hamrick, 1992) and is currently maintained by Tetra Tech. The EFDC is available for download from USEPA (2021).

The EFDC uses a structured, curvilinear-orthogonal horizontal grid to simulate ecosystems in one, two, and three dimensions. Vertical model discretization uses uniform segmentation based on sigma stretching or variable discretization depending on bathymetric variability. An optional HEC-type cross-section description can be used for 1D applications. The hydrodynamic model solves the fundamental hydrostatic equations of mass and momentum conservation using a semi-implicit, conservative finite-volume solution scheme with either two- or three-level time stepping. Salinity and heat transport are dynamically coupled and calculated using high-accuracy advection schemes, including multidimensional positive-definite advection transport algorithm and COSMIC. Additional model capabilities include wetting and drying, hydraulic control structures, vegetation resistance, and wave-induced currents. In addition, the model includes a single port buoyant jet module for the simulation of near- and far-field mixing.

The EFDC water quality model is based on the modules and subroutines included in the US Army Corps of Engineers' CE-QUAL-ICM model, including the eutrophication module for the simulation of nutrient and carbon cycling, dissolved oxygen, multiple phytoplankton groups, and sediment diagenesis. In addition to the EFDC water quality model, EFDC can generate hydrodynamic transport files for WASP and CE-QUAL-ICM.

In addition to the water quality module, the EFDC model includes a sediment transport model to simulate cohesive and noncohesive sediments of variable sizes. Multiple sediment transport functions are included in the model to facilitate a wide range of currently accepted parameterizations for settling, deposition, resuspension, and bed load transport. The sediment bed is modeled with multiple layers, and multiple armoring options for noncohesive sediment and consolidation formulation for dynamic simulation of bed layer thickness, void ratio, and pore-water advection are available. The sediment transport module can simulate morphological changes fully coupled with the hydrodynamic module to represent a dynamic evolution of bed topography.

EFDC can simulate the fate and transport of unconventional contaminants, including metals and organic compounds adsorbed to sediments, and to dissolved and particulate organic carbon, using a three-phase equilibrium partitioning formulation. A contaminant processes function library allows the simulation of various degradation and transformation processes.

3.2.3.2 Applicability to Total Maximum Daily Load Studies.   The EFDC model has been widely used in more than 100 modeling studies of aquatic ecosystems around the world and in multiple TMDL studies. TMDL applications include the Peconic Bay in New York (USEPA 2007), Klamath Estuary in California (Tetra Tech 2009), Charles River in Massachusetts (Tetra Tech 2005), Mobile Bay in Alabama (Wool et al. 2003a), Christina River in Pennsylvania–Maryland–Delaware, Los Angeles Harbor in California (Tetra Tech 2010), and Charleston Harbor in South Carolina (Cantrell 2013).

3.2.4 CE-QUAL-W2

3.2.4.1 Model Background and Capabilities. The CE-QUAL-W2 model is a two-dimensional (2D), laterally averaged hydrodynamic and water quality model. The hydrodynamic model capabilities include the simulation of water levels and depths, flow velocities, temperature, density, and a conservative tracer. The CE-QUAL-W2 model evolved from the laterally averaged reservoir model (Edinger and Buchak 1975) originally developed in the 1970s for hydrodynamic applications. In the last three decades, development and maintenance of the CE-QUAL-W2 model has been carried out by Portland State University (PSU) and USACE (Cole and Wells 2016, Wells and Berger 2016). The CE-QUAL-W2 model can be applied to reservoirs with multiple branches and river reaches. The model can simulate nutrient cycling with detailed nitrogen and phosphorus speciation, dissolved oxygen, and multiple phytoplankton and CBOD groups (Figure 3-3). The CE-QUAL-W2 model also includes a sediment diagenesis module to represent sediment–water nutrient exchanges (Zhang et al. 2015, Cole and Wells 2016). The CE-QUAL-W2

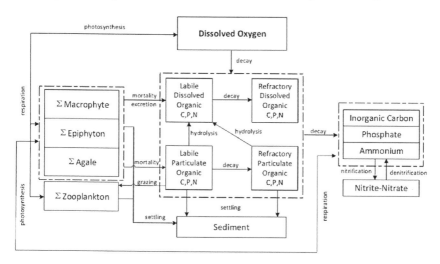

Figure 3-3. Schematic representation of the CE-QUAL-W2 model.

model can be downloaded from the PSU website (PSU, 2021). In addition, Cope et al. (2020) describe an assessment of the body of literature related to the modeling applications for the prediction of nutrients and related parameters using CE-QU2L-W2.

3.2.4.2 Applicability to Total Maximum Daily Load Studies. The CE-QUAL-W2 model has been widely used as a management tool to evaluate effects from various stressors, including temperature, nutrients, and organic loads in waterbodies (Bowen and Hieronymus 2003, O'Donnell et al. 2011, Singleton et al. 2013, Sullivan et al. 2003, Zhang et al. 2008), by several US federal and local agencies, including USEPA, USGS, USACE, US Bureau of Reclamation, and Tennessee Valley Authority, and numerous state, county, and local agencies. Recent model applications include studies in the Lower Minnesota River (Minnesota), Lost Creek Lake (Oregon), and Applegate Lake (Oregon) (Smith et al. 2012, Threadgill et al. 2017).

3.2.5 Hydrologic Engineering Center-River Analysis System

3.2.5.1 Model Background and Capabilities.   HEC-RAS is a 1D and 2D hydraulic and water quality model for riverine ecosystems developed by the USACE Hydrologic Engineering Center (HEC). HEC-RAS is an extensively used model worldwide designed to perform hydraulic analysis of open channel systems with capabilities to simulate the impacts of a wide variety of hydraulic structures such as spillways, culverts, bridges, and weirs. The HEC-RAS model contains several modules: (1) 1D steady flow module, (2) 1D dynamic flow module, (3) 2D dynamic flow module, (4) movable boundary sediment transport module, and (5) water quality module. The HEC-RAS model includes a GUI to facilitate the manipulation and entry of input data and the processing and display of model results. The HEC-RAS model can be downloaded from the HEC website at http://www.hec.usace.army.mil.

The HEC-RAS 1D model incorporates several water quality submodules developed at the USACE Environmental Laboratory. The submodules include nutrient simulation module I (NSMI), nutrient simulation module II (NSMII), water temperature (TEMP), solids (SED), contaminants (CSM), mercury (HgSM), and a general constituent. A detailed description of these modules is provided by Zhang and Johnson (2016a, b). Water quality processes represented in the NSMI (Figure 3-4) submodule include nutrient and carbon cycling, dissolved oxygen, and phytoplankton groups. The water quality submodule solves internal sources and sinks and main biochemical processes associated with each state variable in a unit volume of water and benthic sediments. The kinetics for the water column and active sediment layer are fully coupled.

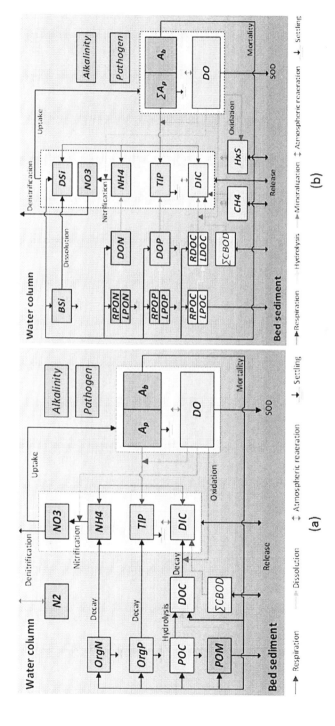

Figure 3-4. Schematic representation of the nutrient simulation modules in the HEC-RAS model: (a) NSMI and (b) NSMII.

3.2.5.2 Applicability to Total Maximum Daily Load Studies.   The HEC-RAS water quality model has been used to support TMDLs and environmental impact statement studies. Recent studies include the lower Minnesota River (Zhang and Johnson 2014), Missouri River (Zhang and Johnson 2017), and the Columbia River and Snake River.

3.2.6 Center for Computational Hydroscience and Engineering-1D/2D/3D

3.2.6.1 Model Background and Capabilities.   The numerical models CCHE-1D/2D/3D have been developed by the National Center for Computational Hydroscience and Engineering at the University of Mississippi. This development was supported by the USDA Agricultural Research Service by means of funds appropriated by the US Congress.

CCHE-1D is a one-dimensional channel network model that has been designed to simulate unsteady flows, sediment transport, water quality, and pollutant transport in streams. This model considers the influence of hydraulic structures, including culverts, measuring flumes, bridge crossings, and drop structures. The CCHE-1D water quality module simulates the physical, chemical, and biological processes in the stream as well as the bed sediment layers. The temporal and spatial variations of the concentrations of nonconservative chemicals, phytoplankton, dissolved oxygen, biological oxygen demand, nutrients, and others can be obtained. This model can also be applied to simulate toxic chemicals and heavy metals (Inthasaro 2010, Wu and Vieira 2002). An ArcView-based GUI has been developed to operate the CCHE-1D model, including the generation of a channel network based on digital elevation data, parameter setting, and model simulation.

CCHE2D/3D are integrated software packages that have been developed to simulate free surface flow hydrodynamics, nonuniform sediment transport, morphologic processes, water quality, and pollutant distribution in rivers, lakes, and coastal waters (Chao et al. 2007, Jia et al. 2013). The CCHE2D/3D water quality model simulates the physical, chemical, and biological processes of water quality constituencies in waterbodies. It can also be applied to simulate the chemical contaminates in the water column and bed sediment layers. In this model, the sediment-associated water quality processes, including the effect of sediment on the light intensity for the growth of phytoplankton, the adsorption–desorption of nutrients by sediment, and the release of nutrients from the bed sediment layer, are taken into account. A mesh generator (CCHE_MESH) and a GUI (CCHE_GUI) have been developed to operate CCHE2D/3D models, including the generation of computational mesh, parameter setting, model simulation, and result visualization (Zhang 2013).

3.2.6.2 Applicability to Total Maximum Daily Load Studies. CCHE-1D/2D/3D models are applicable to TMDL studies for nutrients, sediment, toxic chemicals in channel networks, rivers, lakes, and coastal waters. The CCHE-1D model has been applied to simulate flow fields, sediment transport, water quality, and pollutant transport in the East Fork River, Hudson River, Chattahoochee River, dendritic channels in Goodwin Creek watershed, Dan River, and so on (Chao et al. 2016, Inthasaro 2010, Wu and Vieira 2002). CCHE2D/3D models have been applied to simulate free surface hydrodynamics, sediment transport, water quality, and chemical contaminants in the Deep Hollow Lake, Beasley Lake, Pelahatchie Bay, Lake Pontchartrain, Enid Lake, Hudson River, Yangtze River, Jialing River, and so on (Chao et al. 2007, 2012, Zhu 2006). The model results provide useful information for establishing and implementing TMDL plans for nutrients, sediments, and chemical contaminants.

3.2.7 Environmental Protection Division-RIV1

3.2.7.1 Model Background and Capabilities. The EPD-RIV1 model is a 1D, cross-sectional-averaged, hydrodynamic, and water quality model for rivers and streams. The EPD-RIV1 model was originally developed for the Georgia Environmental Protection Division (EPD) to simulate hydrodynamics and water quality processes in the Chattahoochee River (Martin and Wool 2002). The EPD-RIV1 code is based on modifications and improvements to subroutines from CE-QUAL-RIV1 to increase their performance and modeling capabilities, particularly to perform an analysis of waste load allocations (WLAs). Model improvements were performed to simplify model manipulation and facilitate the model linkage to pre- and postprocessing tools. Powerful pre- and postprocessing modules for the EPD-RIV1 model are included in the Water Resources Database (WRDB), a program also developed for the Georgia EPD and USEPA Region IV, to organize and process environmental information for model inputs and to process simulation outputs. The EPD-RIV1 model can be downloaded from the repository website (Wilson Engineering, 2021).

The hydrodynamic module included in the EPD-RIV1 model simulates the advective and dispersive transport of pollutants. The water quality module simulates the fate and transport of up to 16 state variables, including water temperature, nutrient cycling including organic and inorganic speciation, dissolved oxygen, two types of carbonaceous oxygen demand, phytoplankton and macrophytes, coliform bacteria, and metals such as iron and manganese.

3.2.7.2 Applicability to Total Maximum Daily Load Studies. The EPD-RIV1 model can be used in 1D river systems subject to dynamic hydrodynamics. EPD-RIV1 provides time-varying simulations of water temperature and water quality with a primary focus on processes impacting dissolved oxygen. The pre- and postprocessing capabilities and database capabilities included in the EPD-RIV1 model and WRDB interface facilitate the processing of model data to evaluate existing conditions and perform WLAs, including allocations for TMDLs. The EPD-RIV1 model has been used, among others, by USEPA to support TMDL studies in the Savannah Harbor, Georgia (USEPA 2010), and by the Alabama Department of Environmental Management for TMDL studies in the Cahaba River Watershed (ADEM 2006).

3.2.8 QUAL2K

3.2.8.1 Model Background and Capabilities.   The QUAL2K model is a 1D water quality model for river and stream networks. The model is based on the algorithms and routines originally included in the QUAL2E model with improvements in the representation of biochemical processes and numerical efficiency (Chapra and Pelletier 2003, Chapra 2003, 2008). Improvements in the QUAL2E subroutines available in QUAL2K include algorithms for slow and fast carbonaceous biochemical oxygen demand, detritus, periphyton, sediment diagenesis, pH, and alkalinity. QUAL2K has user-friendly Excel spreadsheets formatted for the manipulation of model inputs and outputs. Several QUAL2K functionalities are coded in VBA to write and read files for use in a FORTRAN executable code. The QUAL2K model can be downloaded from USEPA (2021).

In addition, Cope et al. (2020) describe an assessment of the body of literature related to the modeling applications for the prediction of nutrients and related parameters using QUAL2K.

3.2.8.2 Applicability to Total Maximum Daily Load Studies.   QUAL2K has been used to support WLAs and TMDL studies of rivers and streams. Typical applications are related to pollution caused by pathogens, excess nutrients such as nitrogen and phosphorus, dissolved oxygen depletion owing to eutrophication processes, biochemical oxygen demand, sediment oxygen demand, phytoplankton blooms, benthic algae, and pH. Example applications include TMDL studies for nutrients and dissolved oxygen in the Blanchard River Watershed and the Ottawa River Watershed (Ohio EPA 2009, 2013).

3.2.9 MINTEQA2 and Visual MINTEQ

3.2.9.1 Model Background and Capabilities.   The MINTEQA2 model (Allison et al. 1991) is a geochemical equilibrium-speciation model for the fate and transport of metals in aqueous systems. MINTEQA2 and Visual MINTEQ simulate the equilibrium and mass distribution among adsorbed, dissolved, and multiple chemical solid phases under different conditions, including a gas phase with constant partial pressure. The simulations use input concentrations and loadings of a substance of interest. The chemical distribution and partitioning among solid, dissolved, and adsorbed phases are then computed from known chemical equilibrium models, including in a series of chemical databases, with databases available for gas reactions, sorption, thermodynamics, and other chemical reactions and transformations.

MINTEQA2 was developed at the Battelle Pacific Northwest Laboratory by incorporating the mathematical subroutines of MINEQL with a thermodynamic database. The MINTEQA2 model can be obtained from USEPA (2020).

Visual MINTEQ was originally developed in 2000 as a Windows GUI to the USEPA model MINTEQA2. The model gradually diverged from MINTEQA2, such as in expanding and revising the thermodynamic database and including new options. A copy of the Visual MINTEQ model can be obtained directly from the developer (Gustafsson, 2013), from the Royal Institute of Technology (KTH) (Stockholm, Sweden).

3.2.9.2 Applicability to Total Maximum Daily Load Studies. Simulation of the fate and transport and speciation of dissolved metals, free metal ions, sorbed metals, metal precipitates, and metal complexes is a difficult task. Speciation is driven by multiple chemical reactions that must be captured to accurately represent the biological exposure and toxicity of metals. MINTEQ and MINTEQA2 can be used to evaluate most of these processes and to determine the necessary controls on sources of metal pollution that must be applied for a particular TMDL. Example applications of MINTEQ to support the development of TMDLs for metals and pH in the West Fork River Watershed, West Virginia, can be found in USEPA (2002).

3.2.10 One-Dimensional Transport with Equilibrium Chemistry

3.2.10.1 Model Background and Capabilities. The One-Dimensional Transport with Equilibrium Chemistry (OTEQ) model is a reactive transport model that simulates the fate and transport of solutes and speciation and transport of metals in rivers and streams (Runkel et al. 1999). The model couples a chemical equilibrium model based on MINTEQ with a solute transport model. The transport model simulates advection, dispersion, transient solute storage, and the transport and deposition of waterborne solid particles. The chemical module simulates acid–base reactions, complexation, precipitation or dissolution, and sorption. The OTEQ model is developed and distributed by the United States Geological Survey (USGS 2016).

3.2.10.2 Applicability to Total Maximum Daily Load Studies. OTEQ can be applied to support TMDLs and WLA studies related to the fate and transport of metals in rivers and streams. The model has been previously used to support the evaluation of remediation alternatives in an acid mine drainage stream (Runkel and Kimball 2002).

3.2.11 MIKE 11

3.2.11.1 Model Background and Capabilities. MIKE 11 is a River Hydraulics and Sediment Transport model developed by the Danish Hydraulic Institute (DHI) Water and Environment which is currently in the MIKE+ platform (DHI 2021). The MIKE 11 model has been widely used in projects around the world for real-time forecasting of flood warnings and river flows, including projects in the United States, Bangladesh, Italy, United Kingdom, Czech Republic, Thailand, China, Iran, and Denmark.

MIKE 11 is a 1D river hydraulics model, but it can also be dynamically linked to other DHI software such as ECO-Lab for water quality studies, MIKE SHE for surface–groundwater interactions, and MIKE 21 to perform 2D simulations of river and floodplain hydraulics. The linkage alternatives allow the use of MIKE 11 in complex projects requiring an integrated evaluation of hydrologic, hydraulic, and hydrogeological processes. The linking of MIKE 11 and ECO-Lab allows the user to perform water quality simulations and TMDL studies for different constituents. Integrated modeling capabilities include floodplain analysis and mapping, analysis and design of hydraulic structures, design and analysis of flood-mitigation systems, dam break analysis, channel restoration, real-time flood optimization of river and reservoir operations, water quality analysis, TMDL development and sediment transport, and dredging impacts (Sørensen et. al 1999, Cook 2012).

3.2.11.2 Applicability to Total Maximum Daily Load Studies. MIKE 11 is typically linked to ECO-Lab for water quality studies involving eutrophication of waterbodies, nutrient transport and cycling, and to support TMDL projects (e.g., Liang et al. 2015, Long 2014).

3.3 STATE-OF-THE-ART AND STATE-OF-THE-PRACTICE

This chapter presents reviews of 11 receiving water quality models commonly used in TMDL development and implementation. Capabilities and limitations of each of the models are discussed. Like watershed modeling, receiving water quality modeling has been a topic of active research and developed for over half a century, and the advances in water quality modeling, including better representation of biochemical processes or advances in computational efficiency and parallel processing, are typically incorporated in models such as WASP and released to the public. In some cases, the state-of-the-practice has caught up with the state-of-the-art. However, the state-of-the-practice is at present limited by the cost of monitoring data to set up, calibrate, and validate receiving water quality models. This chapter serves as a valuable resource to understand the generalities and limitations of 11 models commonly used in water quality applications. This information can help modelers to make informed receiving water quality model selections in TMDL studies.

REFERENCES

ADEM (Alabama Department of Environmental Management). 2006. *Final nutrient total maximum daily loads (TMDLs) for the Cahaba River Watershed.* Montgomery, AL: Alabama Dept. of Environmental Management.

Allison, J., D. S. Brown, and K. J. Novo-Gradac. 1991. *MINTEQA2/ PRODEFA2, a geochemical assessment model for environmental systems: Version 3.0 user's manual.* Washington, DC: EPA.

Ambrose, R. B., S. B. Vandergrift, and T. A. Wool. 1986. *WASP3, A hydrodynamic and water quality model—Model theory, user's manual and programmer's guide.* Athens, GA: USEPA.

ASCE. 2017. *Total maximum daily load analysis and modeling: Assessment of the practice.* Prepared by TMDL Analysis and Modeling Task Committee of the Environmental and Water Resources Institute of ASCE. Reston, VA: ASCE.

Borah, D. K., E. Ahmadisharaf, G. Padmanabhan, S. Imen, and Y. M. Mohamoud. 2019. "Watershed models for development and implementation of total maximum daily loads." *J. Hydrol. Eng.* 24 (1): 03118001.

Bowen, J., and J. Hieronymus. 2003. "A CE-QUAL-W2 model of neuse estuary for total maximum daily load development." *J. Water Resour. Plann. Manage.* 129 (4): 283–294.

Camacho, R. A., Z. Zhang, and X. Chao. 2019. "Receiving water quality models for TMDL development and implementation." *J. Hydrol. Eng.* 24 (2): 04018063.

Cantrell, W. 2013. *Total maximum daily load revision Charleston Harbor, Cooper, Ashley, and Wando Rivers.* Prepared for the South Carolina Department of Health and Environmental Control. Columbia. SC: South Carolina Dept. of Health and Environmental Control.

Cerco, C. F., and T. Cole. 1993. "Three-dimensional eutrophication model of Chesapeake Bay." *J. Environ. Eng.* 119 (6): 1006–1025.

Cerco, C. F., and M. R. Noel. 2013. "Twenty-one-year simulation of Chesapeake Bay water quality using the CE-QUAL-ICM eutrophication model." *J. Am. Water Resour. Assoc.* 49 (5): 1119–1133.

Cerco, C. F., M. R. Noel, and S.-C. Kim. 2006. "Three-dimensional management model for Lake Washington, Part II: Eutrophication modeling and skill assessment." *Lake Reservoir Manage.* 22 (2): 115–131.

Cerco, C. F., M. R. Noel, and L. Linker. 2004. "Managing for water clarity in Chesapeake Bay." *J. Environ. Eng.* 130 (6): 631–642.

Chao, X., M. Altinakar, and R. Marsooli. 2016. "Numerical modeling of the fate and transport of contaminants due to a coal ash spill accident in the Dan River." In *Proc., ASCE World Water & Environmental Resources Cong.* West Palm Beach, Florida. Reston, VA: ASCE.

Chao, X., Y. Jia, F. D. Shields, S. S. Wang, and C. M. Cooper. 2007. "Numerical modeling of water quality and sediment related processes." *Ecol. Modell.* 201 (3): 385–397.

Chao, X., Y. Jia, S. S. Wang, and A. A. Hossain. 2012. "Numerical modeling of surface flow and transport phenomena with applications to Lake Pontchartrain." *Lake Reserv. Manage.* 28 (1): 31–45.

Chapra, S. C. 2003. "Engineering water quality models and TMDLs." *J. Water Resour. Plann. Manage.* 129 (4): 247–256.

Chapra, S. C. (2008). "Surface water-quality modeling." Waveland press.

Chapra, S.C., Pelletier, G.J., 2003. "QUAL2K: A modeling framework for simulating river and stream water quality: documentation and users manual." Tufts University, Civil and Environmental Engineering Dept.

Cole, T. M., and S. A. Wells. 2016. *CE-QUAL-W2: A two-dimensional, laterally averaged, hydrodynamic and water quality model, version 4.0.* Portland, OR: Portland State University, Dept. of Civil and Environmental Engineering.

Cook, A. 2012. "Development of an integrated surface and subsurface model of Everglades National Park." FIU Electronic Thesis, University Graduate School. Accessed November 17, 2021. https://digitalcommons.fiu.edu/etd/

Cope, B., T. Shaikh, R. Parmar, S. Chapra, and J. Martin. 2020. *Literature review on nutrient-related rates, constants, and kinetics formulations in surface water quality modeling.* USEPA/600/R-19/241. Washington, DC: USEPA.

DHI (Danish Hydraulic Institute). 2021. MIKE+: River Networks. Accessed November 11, 2021. https://www.mikepoweredbydhi.com/products/mikeplus/river-networks.

Di Toro, D. M. 1983. *Documentation for water quality analysis simulation program (WASP) and model verification program (MVP).* 600/3-81-044. Washington, DC: USEPA.

Edinger, J. E., and E. M. Buchak. 1975. *A hydrodynamic, two-dimensional reservoir model: The computational basis.* Cincinnati, Ohio: US Army Engineer Division, Ohio River.

Gustafsson J. P. 2013. Visual MINTEQ. http://vminteq.lwr.kth.se/. Accessed November 11, 2021.

Hamrick, J. M. 1992. *A three-dimensional environmental fluid dynamics computer code: Theoretical and computational aspects.* Williamsburg, VA: College of William and Mary, Virginia Institute of Science.

Inthasaro, P. 2010. "A one-dimensional aquatic ecology and ecotoxicology model in river system." Ph.D. thesis, National Center for Computational Hydroscience and Engineering, University of Mississippi.

Jia, Y., X. Chao, Y. Zhang, and T. Zhu. 2013. *Technical manual of CCHE2D, Version 4.1.* NCCHE-TR-02-2013. University, MS: University of Mississippi.

Liang, J., Q. Yang, T. Sun, J. Martin, H. Sun, and L. Li. 2015. "MIKE 11 model-based water quality model as a tool for the evaluation of water quality management plans." *J. Water Supply: Res. Technol.-Aqua* 64 (6): 708–718.

Long, S. 2014. "Simulating Everglades National Park hydrology and phosphorus transport under existing and future scenarios using numerical modeling." FIU electronic thesis, University Graduate School. Accessed November 17, 2021. https://digitalcommons.fiu.edu/etd/

Mandel, R., S. Kim, A. Nagel, J. Palmer, C. Schultz, and K. Brubaker. 2008. *The TAM/WASP Modeling Framework for Development of Nutrient and BOD TMDLs in the Tidal Anacostia River.* ICPRB Rep. 000-7. Washington, DC: Interstate Commission on the Potomac River Basin Modeling.

Mark, D. J., N. W. Scheffner, H. L. Butler, B. W. Bunch, and M. S. Dortch. 1993. *Hydrodynamic and water quality modeling of Lower Green Bay, Wisconsin.* Vol. 1. Main Text and Appendixes A–E. Tech. Rep. CERC-93. Rep. E-83-11. Vicksburg, MS: US Army Engineer Waterways Experiment Station.

Martin, J. L., D. Tillman, C. Cerco, J. Hendrickson, and M. Dortch. 2002. "A three-dimensional water quality model for estimating TMDLs in a Blackwater river estuary, the lower St. Johns River, FL." In *Estuarine and Coastal Modeling (2001)*, edited by M. L. Spaulding, 227–245. Reston, VA: ASCE.

Martin, J. L., and T. Wool. 2002. *A dynamic one-dimensional model of hydrodynamics and water quality EPD-RIV1, Version 1.0.* Atlanta, Georgia: Course Materials prepared by ASCI Corporation for Robert Olson NRE.

O'Donnell, S., R. Gelda, S. Effler, and D. Pierson. 2011. "Testing and application of a transport model for runoff event inputs for a water supply reservoir." *J. Environ. Eng.* 137 (8): 678–688.

Ohio EPA. 2009. *Total maximum daily loads for the Blanchard River Watershed.* Columbus, OH: Ohio EPA, Division of Surface Water.

Ohio EPA. 2013. *Total maximum daily loads for the Ottawa River (Lima Area) Watershed.* Columbus, OH: Ohio EPA, Division of Surface Water.

PSU (Portland State University). 2021. Water Quality Research Group – CE-QUAL-W2: Hydrodynamic and Water Quality Model. Accessed November 11, 2021. http://www.ce.pdx.edu/w2.

Runkel, R. L., and B. A. Kimball. 2002. "Evaluating remedial alternatives for an acid mine drainage stream: Application of a reactive transport model." *Environ. Sci. Technol.* 36 (5): 1093–1101.

Runkel, R. L., B. A. Kimball, D. M. McKnight, and K. E. Bencala. 1999. "Reactive solute transport in streams: a surface complexation approach for trace metal sorption." *Water Resour. Res.* 35 (12): 3829–3840.

Shoemaker, L., T. Dai, J. Koenig, and M. Hantush. 2005. *TMDL model evaluation and research needs.* Washington, DC: National Risk Management Research Laboratory, USEPA.

Singleton, V., B. Jacob, M. Feeney, and J. Little. 2013. "Modeling a proposed quarry reservoir for raw water storage in Atlanta, Georgia." *J. Environ. Eng.* 139 (1): 70–78.

Smith, D. L., T. L. Threadgill, and C. E. Larson. 2012. *Modeling the hydrodynamics and water quality of the Lower Minnesota River using CE-QUAL-W2: A report on the development, calibration, verification, and application of the model.* Vicksburg, MS: US Army Engineer Research and Development Center.

Sørensen, H. R., T. V. Jacobsen, J. T. Kjelds, J. Yan, and E. Hopkins. 1999. "Application of MIKE SHE and MIKE 11 for Integrated Hydrological Modelling in South Florida." In *Proc., 3rd DHI Software Conf.* Helsingør, Denmark.

Sullivan, A. B., H. I. Jager, and R. Myers. 2003. "Modeling white sturgeon movement in a reservoir: the effect of water quality and sturgeon density." *Ecol. Modell.* 167 (1–2): 97–114.

Tetra Tech. 2005. *A hydrodynamic and water quality model for the Lower Charles River Basin, Massachusetts.* Washington, DC: USEPA.

Tetra Tech. 2009. *Model configuration and results Klamath River model for TMDL development.* Washington, DC: USEPA Region 9, USEPA Region 10, North Coast Regional Water Quality Control Board, Oregon Dept. of Environmental Quality.

Tetra Tech. 2010. *Los Angeles-Long Beach Harbors and San Pedro Bay hydrodynamic and sediment-contaminant transport model report.* Washington, DC: USEPA Region 9 Los Angeles Regional Water Quality Control Board.

Threadgill, T. L., D. F. Turner, L. A. Nicholas, B. W. Bunch, D. H. Tillman, and D. L. Smith. 2017. *Temperature modeling of lost creek lake using CE-QUAL-W2: A report on the development, calibration, verification, and application of the model.* Vicksburg, MS: US Army Engineer Research and Development Center.

USACE (US Army Corps of Engineers). 2014. CE-QUAL-ICM (ICM). US Army Corps of Engineers Engineer Research and Development Center,

Published October 29, 2014. Accessed November 11, 2021. https://www.erdc.usace.army.mil/Media/Fact-Sheets/Fact-Sheet-Article-View/Article/547416/ce-qual-icm-icm/.

USEPA (US Environmental Protections Agency). 1991. *Guidance for water quality-based decisions: The TMDL process.* Washington, DC: USEPA.

USEPA. 2002. *Metals and pH total maximum daily loads (TMDLs) for the West Fork River Watershed, West Virginia.* Philadelphia: USEPA.

USEPA. 2007. *Total maximum daily load for nitrogen in the peconic estuary program study area, including waterbodies currently impaired due to low dissolved oxygen: The Lower Peconic River and Tidal Tributaries; Western Flanders Bay and Lower Sawmill Creek; and Meetinghouse Creek, Terrys Creek and Tributaries.* Yaphank, NY: Peconic Estuary Program, Suffolk County Depaartment of Health Services, Office of Ecology.

USEPA. 2009. *Proposed total maximum daily loads for the Sawgras Lake WBID 28931 nutrients and dissolved oxygen.* Washington, DC: USEPA.

USEPA. 2010. *Total maximum daily load for dissolved oxygen in Savannah Harbor Savannah River Basin.* Washington, DC: USEPA.

USEPA. 2020. Environmental Modeling Community of Practice: Multimedia Models to Assess Exposures. Accessed November 11, 2021. http://www2.epa.gov/exposure-assessment-models/multimedia.

USEPA. 2021. Environmental Modeling Community of Practice: Surface Water Models to Assess Exposures. Accessed November 11, 2021. https://www.epa.gov/exposure-assessment-models/surface-water-models-assess-exposures.

USGS. 2016. One-Dimensional Transport with Equilibrium Chemistry (OTEQ): A Reactive Transport Model for Streams and Rivers. Accessed November 11, 2021. http://water.usgs.gov/software/OTEQ.

Wells, S. A., and C. J. Berger. 2016. "Modeling the response of dissolved oxygen to phosphorus loading in Lake Spokane." *Lake Reserv. Manage.* 32 (3): 270–279.

Wilson Engineering. 2021. Georgia EPD: Environmental Software. Accessed November 11, 2021. http://epdsoftware.wileng.com/.

Wool, T. A., S. R. Davie, Y. M. Plis, and J. Hamrick. 2003a. *The development of a hydrodynamic and water quality model to support TMDL determinations and water quality management of a stratified shallow estuary: Mobile Bay, Alabama.* Washington, DC: USEPA-Region 4.

Wool, T. A., S. R. Davie, and H. N. Rodriguez. 2003b. "Development of three-dimensional hydrodynamic and water quality models to support total maximum daily load decision process for the Neuse River Estuary, North Carolina." *J. Environ. Eng.* 129 (4): 295–306.

Wu, W., and D. A. Vieira. 2002. *One-dimensional channel network model CCHE1D 3.0-Technical manual.* Tech. Rep. No. NCCHETR-2002-1. University, MS: University of Mississippi.

Zhang, H., D. A. Culver, and L. Boegman. 2008. "A two-dimensional ecological model of Lake Erie: Application to estimate dreissenid impacts on large lake plankton populations." *Ecol. Modell.* 214 (2–4): 219–241.

Zhang, Y. 2013. *CCHE-GUI – Graphical users interface for NCCHE model quick start guide—Version 4.x.* NCCHE-TR-2013-03. University, MS: University of Mississippi.

Zhang, Z., and B. E. Johnson. 2014. *Application and evaluation of the HEC-RAS—Nutrient simulation module (NSMI).* Vicksburg, MS: US Army Engineer Research and Development Center.

Zhang, Z., and B. E. Johnson. 2016a. *Aquatic contaminant and mercury simulation modules developed for hydrological and hydraulic models.* Vicksburg, MS: US Army Engineer Research and Development Center.

Zhang, Z., and B. E. Johnson. 2016b. *Aquatic nutrient simulation modules (NSMs) developed for hydrologic and hydraulic models.* Vicksburg, MS: US Army Engineer Research and Development Center.

Zhang, Z., and B. E. Johnson. 2017. *Hydrologic engineer center-river analysis system (HEC-RAS) water temperature models developed for the Missouri River recovery management plan and environmental impact statement.* Vicksburg, MS: US Army Engineer Research and Development Center.

Zhang, Z., B. Sun, and B. E. Johnson. 2015. "Integration of a benthic sediment diagenesis module into a two-dimensional hydrodynamic and water quality model—CE-QUAL-W2." *Ecol. Modell.* 297 (2015): 213–231.

Zhu, T. 2006. "A depth-averaged two-dimensional water quality model as a research and management tool." Ph.D. thesis, University of Mississippi.

Zou, R., S. Carter, L. Shoemaker, A. Parker, and T. Henry. 2006. "Integrated hydrodynamic and water quality modeling system to support nutrient total maximum daily load development for Wissahickon Creek, Pennsylvania." *J. Environ. Eng.* 132 (4): 555–566.

CHAPTER 4

INTEGRATED MODELING SYSTEMS AND LINKED MODELS

Harry X. Zhang, Yusuf M. Mohamoud, Seshadri S. Iyer

4.1 INTRODUCTION

The choice of a model for total maximum daily load (TMDL) development for impaired waterbodies depends mainly on the modeling objectives and the system complexity. System complexity and modeling objectives, in turn, determine the required model complexity. Linking of different models is necessary to represent complex natural systems such as watersheds and their estuaries when such a system cannot be represented by a single model (Mohamoud and Zhang 2019). In TMDL studies, representation of sources and receiving water often require linking a watershed model with a receiving water model. Even for watersheds with multiple land and water features, such as urban centers, rural areas, flow-regulated rivers and canals, reservoirs, and estuaries, more than one model is often needed because the multiple features of the system cannot be sufficiently described by one model. Other scenarios include a need to achieve environmental management goals such as understanding the interactions between surface and groundwater resources to protect drinking water supply sources from pollutants, necessitating linking with a suite of models.

Modelers often connect or "link" models together to describe an entire system. Linkages can be accomplished through a simple file transfer system or using a common database through available modeling software systems or customized systems. Linkages can be static or dynamic. A static linkage takes the output from one model and uses it as input to a second model. A dynamic linkage can be bidirectional, where information from each time step transfers back and forth among the models and affects both simulations. Some models or modeling software systems provide software-enabled linkages so that all file exchange requirements are automatically performed as the models are applied (USEPA 2005).

Integrated modeling systems are also available to facilitate linking models by providing software for data exchanges using common spatial and point data formats and preparing input files for the linked models (Mohamoud and Zhang 2019). The tools used in integrated modeling systems or other model linking software support data management, web-based data downloads, model setup, and postprocessing. Some modeling systems are based on independent models with an open set of supporting tools. Others provide a unified system with a single interface that launches and manages several models concurrently (USEPA 2005).

This chapter provides an overview of integrated modeling systems and linked models used in TMDL studies (Mohamoud and Zhang 2019). A widely used integrated modeling system, called the Better Assessment Science Integrating point and Nonpoint Sources (BASINS), developed by USEPA (2019), is presented with descriptions of its origin and history, tools and models included, and a listing of example TMDLs. Another integrated modeling system, the watershed modeling system (WMS) of the US Army Corps of Engineers (Dellman et al. 2002, Aquaveo 2020), is presented with brief descriptions of a few example applications. Three major applications of linked models are presented: Chesapeake Bay TMDL, the Saugahatchee Creek Watershed in Alabama, and the Lynnhaven River Watershed in Virginia. Finally, an important discussion on performance evaluations of integrated modeling systems and linked models in TMDL applications is presented.

4.2 INTEGRATED MODELING SYSTEMS

This section summarizes two widely used integrated modeling systems: USEPA's (2019) BASINS and USACE's WMS (Dellman et al. 2002, Aquaveo 2020) with listings or brief descriptions of some of the applications.

4.2.1 BASINS Modeling System

The BASINS modeling framework was developed with the objective to expedite TMDL development for impaired waterbodies on the 303(d) lists of the Clean Water Act (Whittemore and Beebe 2000). The BASINS modeling system facilitates the examination of environmental information at the watershed level and provides a modeling framework that integrates point sources (e.g., sewage treatment plant discharges) and nonpoint sources (e.g., sediment, nutrients, and pathogens from agricultural lands) at the watershed scale (Battin et al. 1998). In addition, the BASINS modeling system brings together data from various sources, environmental analysis tools, and models to facilitate the modeling process through the development of an efficient user interface, web-based data download, analysis tools, and geographic information system (GIS) tools.

4.2.1.1 BASINS Model Releases. The BASINS version 1 was released in 1996 and consisted of various data sets (e.g., land use, water quality, digital elevation, river reach network, streamflow, and meteorological data), models such as HSPF, QUAL2E, and TOXIROUTE, and watershed assessment tools such as TARGET, ASSESS, and DATA MINING. BASINS version 2, released in 1999, added new utilities and watershed delineation, expanded data sets, and enhanced nonpoint-source modeling capabilities. USEPA released BASINS version 3 in 2001 (USEPA 2001). It introduced gridded data, watershed delineation enhancements, Soil and Water Assessment Tool (SWAT), National Hydrography Data sets (NHDs), watershed data management utilities (WDMutil), and PLOAD. Note that BASINS 3 and all preceding versions used proprietary geographic information systems software (e.g., Arcview 3.x and Spatial Analyst) from the Environmental Systems Research Institute (ESRI).

In May 2007, BASINS 4.0 was released with a nonproprietary open-source geographic information system (MapWindow) (Ames et al. 2008). BASINS 4 discontinued the water assessment tools, TARGET, ASSESS, and DATA MINING, and, instead, BASINS 4.0 introduced a Watershed Characterization Reports Tool as an alternative to the water assessment tools. Recent additions to BASINS include the storm water management model (SWMM) (Rossman 2010), the water quality analysis simulation program (WASP) (Wool et al. 2006), and the generalized watershed loading function (GWLF) (Haith and Shoemaker 1987) and were introduced as plug-ins for BASINS 4.0. USEPA released BASINS 4.1 in July 2012 (USEPA 2012) and BASINS 4.5 in January 2019 (USEPA 2019).

BASINS 4.1 is built on the latest stable release of the nonproprietary, open-source GIS MapWindow GIS system. The major functionality of two utilities, GenScn and WDMUtil, has been incorporated into the BASINS user interface. BASINS 4.1 now includes DFLOW, a tool to estimate design stream flows for use in water quality studies. Furthermore, the Version 4.5 core of the BASINS system is a maintenance release that builds on Version 4.1 and previous versions of the system. Table 4-1 list the key BASINS components (Version 4.1 and above).

The latest version BASINS 4.5 released in 2019 is available for download (USEPA 2019).

4.2.1.2 Data and Supported Models in BASINS Modeling System. The BASINS modeling system has four data categories: base cartographic, environmental background, environmental monitoring, and point-source data. The base cartographic data include administrative boundaries, ecoregions,

Table 4-1. Key BASINS Components (Version 4.1 and Above).

Components in the BASINS Modeling System			
Data sets	Base cartographic data	Eco regions Urbanized areas Major roads	USEPA Region Boundaries State Boundaries, County Boundaries Tiger Lines (detailed roads and US census boundaries)
	Environmental Background data	Land use and land cover (shape and grid) Digital Elevation Model (DEM) (shape and grid) National Elevation Data set (NED)	National Hydrology Data (NHD) USGS Hydrologic Unit Boundaries USGS NAQWA Study Boundaries Reach file 1 Soils (STATSGO)
	Environmental Monitoring Data	Bacteria monitoring station summaries Permit Compliance System sites and computed annual loadings	USGS NWIS daily streamflow values, water quality, and streamflow measurements USEPA STORET water-quality data, meteorological data
	Point Source Data	Permit Compliance System Sites and Computed Annual Loadings	

Analysis tools, Utilities, and Plug-ins	Watershed delineation (annual, automatic, advanced functions) TauDEM	Watershed Characterization System
	WDMUtil, GenScn	Lookup Tables
	Parameter Estimation Software (PEST)	Time series
	HSPF PARM Tool	Model Segmentation
	Climate Assessment Tool (CAT)	GIS toolbox
Models	AQUATOX	SWAT
	GLWF-E	SWMM
	HSPF	WASP
	PLOAD	
Model Linkages	HSPF-AQUATOX	

Source: USEPA (2019).

hydrologic boundaries (HUC8 layers), and major road systems. The base data are important for locating study areas and watershed drainage areas. Environmental background data include soil, land-use layers, digital elevation data, and stream hydrography. Their main role is to support watershed delineation, watershed characterization, and environmental analyses. The environmental monitoring data include streamflow, meteorological, and water quality data. Monitoring data are, in general, used for model input (e.g., meteorological data), model calibration and testing (e.g., streamflow data), and analysis of current and historical data trends. Point-source data provide information on pollutant loading from point-source discharges such as location, type of facility, and estimated loading. Point-source data establish watershed-based loading summaries that combine point and nonpoint sources.

The BASINS model system supports the use of seven models: AQUATOX, GWLF-E, HSPF, PLOAD, SWMM, SWAT, and WASP. These models are used for TMDL development applications. Over the years, models in BASINS have changed with user community preferences and the geographic information system software platform. Table 4-2 shows the list of models available in BASINS, model categorization, and an example TMDL study for each model.

The BASINS interface provides access to many utilities, analysis tools, and plug-ins. In general, BASINS utilities support model input data preparation efforts and watershed delineation using the environmental background and environmental monitoring data (Table 4-3). Analysis tools include a climate assessment tool (CAT) (USEPA 2009), DFLOW, and the United States Geological Survey surface water statistics (SWSTAT). Plug-ins are categorized into geographic information system–related, data analysis–related, and model setup and processing categories. In general, the plug-ins facilitate the selection of BASINS tools by allowing users to choose specific functionalities that are needed for their modeling project. For example, BASINS users who want to use the SWMM must first turn on the SWMM setup plug-in. HSPF and AQUATOX are the only loosely linked models in BASINS. When linked, these models are used for assessing the effect of pollutant loading on the health of aquatic ecosystems.

4.2.2 Watershed Modeling System

4.2.2.1 Overview of Watershed Modeling System. The watershed modeling system (WMS) is a comprehensive graphical modeling environment for all phases of watershed hydrology and hydraulics, which was used to support TMDL development. It was developed by the Environmental Modeling Research Laboratory of Brigham Young University in cooperation with the USACE Waterways Experiment Station (Dellman et al. 2002, Aquaveo 2020).

Table 4-2. Models and Model Descriptions in the BASINS Modeling Framework (Version 4.1 and Above).

Model and Category	Common Modeling Uses	Model Category and Example TMDLs
AQUATOX—AQUATOX is an ecosystem simulation model that predicts the fate of various pollutants, such as excess nutrients and organic chemicals, and their effects on aquatic ecosystems, including fish, invertebrates, and aquatic plants. AQUATOX is an in-stream model that is loosely linked with the HSPF model. **Category**: Receiving water model	Ecological impact assessment—Predicts the fate of various pollutants, such as nutrients and organic chemicals, and their effects on the ecosystem, including fish, invertebrates, and aquatic plants	Onondaga Lake, New York, Phosphorus TMDL
GWLF-E—The Generalized Watershed Loading Function. The GWLF is a watershed loading model that simulates flow, sediment, and nutrient for agricultural, forested, and developed land. **Category**: Simple loading model	Mainly for TMDLs in the eastern United States	Plum Run Watershed, Pennsylvannia sediment TMDL
HSPF—The Hydrological Simulation Program Fortran. The HSPF is the core watershed model in BASINS (Bicknell et al. 2011), and it is widely used for TMDL development and implementation plans. **Category**: Watershed loading and receiving water model	Worldwide—TMDL and general hydrology and water-quality modeling	Chesapeake Bay Watershed sediment and nutrient TMDL

(Continued)

Table 4-2. (*Continued*).

Model and Category	Common Modeling Uses	Model Category and Example TMDLs
PLOAD—PLOAD is a screening-level GIS-based, point and non-point-source pollutant load estimator. **Category:** Simple analytical model	Screening-level pollutant load estimator	Arroyo Seco Watershed, California Fecal coliform and Metals
SWAT—The Soil and Water Assessment Tool (SWAT) is a watershed simulation model that simulates flow and water quality at various spatial scales. **Category:** Watershed loading and receiving water model	General hydrology and water-quality modeling	Wabash River Watershed, Ohio nutrient TMDL
SWMM—The Storm Water Management Model (SWMM) is a dynamic rainfall-runoff simulation model used for single-event or long-term (continuous) simulation of runoff quantity and quality from primarily urban areas. **Category:** Watershed loading and water-quality model	Design, planning, and analysis related to stormwater runoff	Cedar River, Florida nutrients and DO TMDL
WASP—The Water Quality Analysis Simulation Program (WASP) is an in-stream receiving compartmental model that examines the water column and the underlying benthos. **Category:** Instream or receiving water model	Eutrophication of waterbodies (e.g., lakes and estuaries) model that simulates water-quality processes in rivers, lakes, estuaries, and coastal areas	Weiss Lake, AL nutrient TMDL

Source: USEPA (2019).

Table 4-3. BASINS Utilities (Version 4.1 and Above).

GenScn: *GenScn* facilitates the display and interpretation of output data derived from model applications. *GenScn* is not a model by itself. It serves as a postprocessor for both the *HSPF* and the *SWAT* models, as well as a tool for visualizing observed water-quality data and other time-series data.

WDMUtil: *WDMUtil* is a utility program for managing Watershed Data Management (WDM) files that contain input and output time-series data for the *HSPF*.

Manual Delineation Tool: The BASINS Manual Watershed Delineation tool allows the user to delineate sub-watersheds manually. It allows the user to subdivide a watershed into several smaller hydrologically connected watersheds based on the user's knowledge of that watershed's drainage topography. The tool also provides users the flexibility to edit the shapes and attributes of manually delineated watersheds, outlets, and generating stream networks.

Automatic Delineation Tool: The BASINS Automatic Watershed Delineation tool allows the user to delineate sub-watersheds based on an automatic procedure using Digital Elevation Model (DEM) data. User-specified parameters provide limits that influence the size and number of sub-watersheds created.

Land-Use Reclassification: The Land-Use Reclassification tool assists the user in grouping or renaming land-use categories as needed to support modeling and analysis. Land uses can be reclassified in one of two ways: reclassification of the entire layer (all land uses) or reclassification of selected layers (single or multiple land uses from within an entire layer).

Lookup Tables: The Lookup Tables provide users quick access to relevant reference information on data products included within BASINS. Information is provided for products such as the map projection, definition of agency codes for monitoring data, Standard Industrial Classification (SIC) codes, and the water quality criteria and threshold values of selected pollutants.

PEST: The parameter optimization program, PEST, may be accessed to assist in the estimation of HSPF parameters. PEST is not included in BASINS. More information about PEST can be obtained here. PEST can be made to work with an HSPF model developed using BASINS.

(Continued)

Table 4-3. (*Continued*) BASINS Utilities (Version 4.1 and Above).

Climate Assessment Tool (CAT): BASINS CAT provides flexible capabilities for creating climate change scenarios, allowing users to quickly assess a wide range of *what if* questions about how weather and climate could affect their systems.

DFLOW: A tool developed to estimate user-selected design stream flows for low-flow analysis and water-quality standards.

SWSTATS: The USGS surface-water statistics (SWSTAT) contains several options for statistically analyzing time-series data.

WMS supports hydrologic modeling with HEC-1/HEC-HMS, TR-20, TR-55, rational method, National Flood Frequency Program (NFF), and HSPF. It also supports hydraulic models such as HEC-RAS and CE-QUAL-W2. WMS consists of tools that automate modeling processes such as automated basin delineation, geometric parameter calculations, and GIS overlay computations (e.g., curve number, rainfall depth, and roughness coefficients). WMS is designed to be modular, enabling the user to select only those modules and hydrologic modeling capabilities that are required. Additional WMS modules can be added at any time.

Two-dimensional integrated hydrology (including channel hydraulics and groundwater interaction) can now be modeled with GSSHA (Downer et al. 2003). GSSHA is a distributed two-dimensional hydrologic model developed for the analysis of surface runoff, channel hydraulics, and groundwater interaction. Water quality and sediment transport are also supported. It was developed by the USACE Engineer Research and Development Center (ERDC) (refer to Chapter 3 "Watershed Models").

In WMS, a subwatershed is delineated based on a DEM grid or triangular irregular networks (TINs). Several small subwatersheds and representative streams may be networked together to represent a larger watershed drainage area. Various hydrological and hydraulic models are supported by WMS and can be used through WMS to simulate the various land and stream processes (USEPA 2005).

WMS provides GIS style tools and functionality that make it easy to build models and view results. All modeling parameters are entered through interactive graphics and easy-to-use dialog boxes. The system reads and writes native model input/output files through a graphical user interface (USEPA 2005). To facilitate data transfer between ArcView GIS and WMS, an extension called WMSHydro has been developed. All this in a GIS-based data-processing framework will make the task of watershed modeling and mapping easier than ever before.

Furthermore, WMS provides the interface linkage to various popular and tested models such as HSPF, which is a continuous simulation watershed model. HSPF is one of the models recommended by the USEPA for complex TMDL studies. The HSPF model has been used widely and the applications have been documented for the last 40 years.

4.2.2.2 Applications of the Watershed Modeling System. WMS was used in support of the Phosphorus TMDL for Conesus Lake within Livingston County, New York (USEPA Region 2, NYSDEC 2019). The nuisance aquatic plant growth is because of excess nutrient loading from the lake's watershed and its many tributaries. Phosphorus and oxygen demand were identified as the causes of nonattainment of water quality standards in Conesus Lake. As part of the TMDL development process, the CE-QUAL-W2 model was used to represent a lake as a two-dimensional grid consisting of multiple longitudinal segments and multiple vertical layers within each segment. The model grid for Conesus Lake was developed using geospatial bathymetric data for the lake and WMS software.

In addition, WMS was used for the delineation of boundaries of a watershed located southwest of Turkey at the Mediterranean Sea coast. Typical properties such as drainage areas and the characteristic length and slope of subdrainage areas have also been determined to be used as model inputs in hydrological and diffuse pollution modeling. The application of WMS in the study has shown that it is capable of visualizing the results in establishing watershed management strategies (Erturk et al. 2006).

Furthermore, the WMS modeling system was integrated with other models to identify the groundwater potential areas in the Sinai Peninsula, Egypt (Elewa and Qaddah 2011). Related data layers considered as part of GIS-based watershed modeling were rainfall, net groundwater recharge, lithology or infiltration, lineament density, slope, drainage density, depth to groundwater, and water quality.

4.3 LINKED MODEL APPLICATIONS

Many examples are available where multiple models are dynamically linked for applications in TMDL and water quality studies. One example of dynamically linked models is the Tampa Bay-integrated hydrological model (IHM), which consists of a dynamically coupled surface water model (HSPF) and groundwater model (MODFLOW). Other notable model linkages include economic and hydrologic models (Rosegrant 2000, Bharati et al. 2008), surface and groundwater models (Ross et al. 2004), and ecological and economic models (Costanza et al. 2002).

The following sections describe three linked model examples in TMDL development and implementation, briefly the Chesapeake Bay in the US Mid-Atlantic (USEPA 2010a), the Saugahatchee Creek Watershed in Alabama (USEPA 2015) and at length the Lynnhaven River watershed in Virginia (VIMS 2009).

4.3.1 Linked Models in Chesapeake Bay Total Maximum Daily Load

The Chesapeake Bay watershed is an example of a complex modeling system that consists of a large watershed (166,000 km^2 or 64,000 mi^2) with flow-regulated rivers, large urban centers, and expansive rural areas, and an estuary (USEPA 2010a). The Chesapeake Bay TMDL allocates total nitrogen, total phosphorus, and sediment loads to reduce the size of the oxygen-depleted zones in the bay to restore its living resources. As such, estimating nutrient loads from all sources (air and land) and assessing their effect on the bay's aquatic life requires the use of an integrated modeling framework. Because of the areal extent and system complexity of the watershed and the estuary, the Chesapeake Bay TMDL is one of the most complex TMDLs conducted in the United States.

The Chesapeake Bay TMDL uses a complex set of loosely linked models that consist of an air-shed model, watershed model, and an estuary model, which are briefly described subsequently. We present herein a brief description of each model.

- Air-shed model [community multi-scale air quality (CMAQ)] simulates atmospheric deposition predictions for nutrients and other constituents. CMAQ runs on a fine grid in the Chesapeake Bay region.
- The Watershed loading model is a modified version of the Hydrological Simulation Program-FORTRAN (HSPF). The loading model predicts sediment and nutrient loadings generated within watersheds and discharge to the estuary (Linker et al. 2000). Phase 6 is the latest version of the Chesapeake Bay Watershed Model, now called the Chesapeake Bay Suite of Modeling Tools. To facilitate a better understanding of this complex watershed, 10 additional years of water quality monitoring data doubles the amount of real-time data and provides more insight into how pollution loads have changed as best management practices, which are practices used to control pollution entering the environment, have been implemented. Furthermore, high-resolution land cover data allow for a $1 \times 1 \, m^2$ resolution, providing 900 times the amount of information that was previously available. This ground-breaking improvement enabled the prioritization and targeting of restoration, conservation, education, and public outreach efforts.

- Estuary model: The Water Quality Model and Sediment Transport Model (WQSTM) consists of three linked models, namely, a hydrodynamic model (Johnson et al. 1993), a eutrophication model (Cerco and Cole 1993), and a sediment diagenesis model (DiToro 2001). WQSTM is a three-dimensional model of the tidal bay, which represents transport processes, eutrophication processes, and living resources such as submerged aquatic vegetation and benthos.

Given the size and the complexity of the system, and overall performance evaluation of the air-shed, watershed and the estuary models cannot be estimated. Only performance measures of the watershed model are available for selected watersheds. Average Nash Sutcliff efficiency (NSE) (Krause et al. 2005) values for selected Chesapeake Bay watersheds were 0.72 for flow, −9.73 for total nitrogen, −5.25 for total phosphorus, and −0.66 for total suspended solids. It is noteworthy that NSE values range between −∞ and +1. For practical purposes, the range of NSE values between 0 (no correlation) and +1 (perfect fit) can be interpreted in a meaningful way. Lower than zero efficiency values indicate that the mean value of the observed time series would have been a better predictor than the model (Krause et al. 2005). The average coefficient of determination (R^2) of simulated and logarithms of observed quantities of time-series data were 0.78 for flow, 0.17 for total nitrogen, 0.16 for total phosphorus, and 0.38 for total suspended sediments (Mohamoud and Zhang 2019) (also refer to Chapter 8 "Model Calibration and Validation").

Modeling watersheds with lakes and reservoirs is a major challenge because they store inflows, trap sediments, and cause nutrient enrichment that does not always occur in free-flowing streams and rivers. Lower efficiencies of the HSPF model can be attributed to the presence of flow-regulated rivers. In general, watersheds with reservoirs and lakes require an accurate representation of operational rules, outflows, and water surface elevations that frequently change with management scenarios for better model prediction accuracy. However, the existing report presents model performance statistics only for the watershed loading model (USEPA 2010b). The model performance statistics are unavailable for the air-shed and the estuary models.

The linked models address a limitation of the more generalized watershed models, by explicating considering and estimating the impacts of "internal" impoundments such as lakes/reservoirs. Separately calibrating and evaluating these components can increase the understanding of dominant behavior in the system. There is a trade-off between the added value and the increased complexity that must be carefully assessed in specific TMDL modeling circumstances.

In summary, the Chesapeake Bay TMDL is one of the most complex examples for using several interlinked models to support management decisions. Although there is certainly room for continuous improvement in the future, the linked model system in the Chesapeake Bay TMDL has demonstrated its great utility in TMDL development and implementation.

4.3.2 LSPC-EFDC-WASP Models Applied to the Saugahatchee Creek Watershed (Alabama)

The following section presents an application of linked models, which provides an exchange of information between the models through common linkages (USEPA 2015). The modeling toolbox consists of the Loading Simulation Program in C++ (LSPC), Environmental Fluid Dynamics Code (EFDC), and Water Quality Analysis Simulation Program (WASP). LSPC was used as the watershed-loading model, EFDC was used as the hydrodynamic model, and WASP was used as the water quality model for the receiving waterbodies. The primary need for the models is to provide an accurate representation of dissolved oxygen (DO) and sources of DO depletion in the simulation of nutrient species and chlorophyll-*a*. Calibration data for the water quality model were collected at an ambient monitoring station.

As presented in Chapter 2, LSPC is a watershed model that includes streamlined HSPF model algorithms for simulating flow, sediment, and general water-quality simulation. LSPC was used to predict streamflow and total phosphorus loadings. LSPC predicted flow and water-quality constituent loadings were used as input into the EFDC.

As described in Chapter 3, EFDC is a single-source-code three-dimensional modeling system with linked hydrodynamic, water-quality-eutrophication, sediment transport, and toxic contaminant transport components. In this TMDL, the hydrodynamic module of the EFDC model was used. The simulated reservoir was the Saugahatchee Creek embayment. EFDC inputs include model grid and geometry, hourly upstream boundary discharges, monthly temperatures from the upstream boundary, meteorological data, and flows from the upstream boundary. The model grid was developed from USGS topographic maps and cross-sectional information from USEPA. The grid coverage extends from the mouth of Saugahatchee Creek at the Tallapoosa River (Yates Reservoir) to the bridge crossing (Lovelady Bridge) located on Lovelady Road in the city of Opelika, Alabama. The EFDC model was externally linked to the WASP through a hydrodynamic forcing file that contains the flows, volumes, and exchange coefficients between adjacent cells.

As also described in Chapter 3, WASP is a generalized instream model that simulates the fate and the transport of water quality variables in surface waters. As an instream model, WASP requires the linkage to a watershed loading model such as LSPC or HSPF model. Water quality output from the watershed loading model is used as input into the WASP model. WASP simulated DO, ultimate carbonaceous biochemical oxygen demand (CBODu), ammonia as nitrogen (NH_3-N), nitrate/nitrite as nitrogen (NO_3-N/NO_2-N), organic nitrogen (ON), organic phosphorus (OP), orthophosphate (PO_4-P), and chlorophyll-a.

To simulate water quality constituents, WASP was operated using the EFDC spatial grid. In contrast to the hydrodynamic model, the WASP water quality model contains parameters that are typically determined through calibration. The general modeling strategy adopted for the TMDL study was to reduce the total phosphorus content to achieve the 12 μg/L chlorophyll-a target for the Saugahatchee Creek embayment. The study set a growing season (April to October) for a total phosphorus concentration limit of 0.20 mg/L from point sources (WLA continuous sources) and a 50% total phosphorus reduction from stormwater sources (MS4 and LA) within the watershed. The study concluded that the total phosphorus reductions would lead to a chlorophyll-a target of 12 μg/L. Achieving the chlorophyll-a target would allow the TMDL to meet the water quality standards.

The Alabama Department of Environmental Management (ADEM) identified two segments within the Saugahatchee Creek watershed of the Lower Tallapoosa River basin as being impaired for nutrients and organic enrichment/DO (ADEM 2008). The Pepperell Branch, a tributary of Saugahatchee Creek watershed, is impaired for nutrients and the Saugahatchee embayment (Yates Reservoir) is impaired for nutrients and organic enrichment (OE)/DO. The ADEM selected chlorophyll-a, an early indicator of nutrient enrichment, as a candidate variable for the TMDL study because it is considered as a surrogate for phytoplankton biomass estimation. ADEM set a chlorophyll-a concentration of 12 μg/L as the nutrient target for the protection of aquatic life. The target nutrient concentration was developed using a "reference condition" approach that is based on the appropriate levels of nutrients necessary to support the designated uses from nutrient over-enrichment. The report stated that controlling nitrogen in the system is unnecessary because managing phosphorus could prevent nitrogen from becoming the limiting nutrient (ADEM 2008, USEPA 2000). The study concluded that total phosphorus control rather than total nitrogen control is an effective strategy for controlling nutrient enrichment.

Model scenarios were run from January 2000 to December 2002 to represent seasonal trends. Data collected by Auburn University and ADEM were used to calibrate the total phosphorus in the watershed. The case study report (ADEM 2008) presents graphical comparisons of measured and WASP-simulated chlorophyll-a and DO with no quantitative performance measures. The report does not indicate if LSPC was used to simulate sediment loadings, but it acknowledges that LSPC was used to simulate the total phosphorus loading. WASP model was calibrated to DO, total phosphorus (TP), and chlorophyll-*a* using data measured by ADEM at the Saugahatchee embayment during the 2000 and 2002 growing seasons (April through October). The TMDL report shows time-series plots that compare observed and simulated DO, TP, and chlorophyll-*a*. Despite the use of linked models and the extended effort of using three linked models, the plots show only seven observed DO, TP, and chlorophyll-a data points. This case study report does not present quantitative model performances (e.g., Nash–Sutcliffe efficiency) for LSPC, WASP, and EFDC. Without quantitative performance metrics of each linked model, based on this case study alone, the performance and, consequently, the utility of linked models cannot be determined.

4.3.3 HSPF, UnTRIM, and CE-QUAL-ICM Applied to the Lynnhaven River Watershed (Virginia)

The Lynnhaven River watershed encompasses 70 mi^2 (or 181 km^2) and is an urban watershed comprising 23 land uses but primarily residential (40%) and streets, commercial, and office space (35%). The Lynnhaven River system comprised of Linkhorn Bay, Broad Bay, Long Creek, Buchanan Creek, Bayville Creek, Brown Cove, and Eastern and Western Branch along with the main stem, is a shallow-water coastal system located near the southwest corner of the Chesapeake Bay and in the northeast corner edge of the city of Virginia Beach, Virginia.

Over the last several decades, the water quality of Lynnhaven River has degraded on account of increased runoff volume and decreased stormwater runoff quality. Nonpoint sources and urban stormwater runoff, soil erosion, lawn fertilizer, street litter, estuarine sediments, animal wastes, and failing septic systems have caused the most degradation. Additional causes of Lynnhaven River water quality degradation include the loss of wetland buffers associated with shoreline hardening and erosion, degradation of riparian buffers near stormwater outfalls, increased siltation from land-based construction, and increased stormwater runoff owing to more developments and roadways. Additional concerns regarding water quality in the Lynnhaven include water clarity and the levels of total suspended solids measured throughout the branches of the Lynnhaven as well as seasonally low-DO and high fecal coliform levels measured in the upper Western and Eastern Branches, where the river's flushing capacity diminishes. As a result, segments of the river are impaired for fecal coliform, nutrients–nitrogen, phosphorus, and sediment.

The principal objectives of the modeling study were to evaluate and identify potential sources, quantities, relative magnitude, and seasonal differences of pollutant loadings to the Lynnhaven River and its associated tributaries from point and nonpoint pollution sources. Sources addressed include both point and nonpoint sources from sanitary sewer overflows

(SSOs), septic system discharges, domestic animal loadings, and wildlife loadings.

Three models listed and described subsequently were selected and used on the project. An analysis of the model results helped in providing recommended actions to the city of Virginia Beach, Virginia, to minimize the impacts of land-based processes of runoff and nutrients on water quality (Technical Memoranda submitted to the City, February 2006 and May 2007).

1. BASINS-HSPF: The HSPF was used in modeling overland flow and pollutant loading to the Lynnhaven River. BASINS was described previously in this chapter and HSPF was described in Chapter 2 "Watershed Models." The entire Lynnhaven River watershed was delineated into 1079 subwatershed or catchments, averaging 40 acres. Each catchment was modeled to simulate the following nine constituents and fecal coliform bacterial loadings: COD, BOD, TDS, NO_3, TKN, NH_3, TP, DP, and TSS. The HSPF model was calibrated by comparing model predictions with monitoring data collected at five sites within and/or nearby the Lynnhaven Basin. The results of the calibrated model (multiyear datasets of its hourly outputs)—freshwater discharge, nutrient, and sediment loads at high spatial and temporal resolutions—were used as input to the UnTRIM hydrodynamic model.

2. UnTRIM: As the HSPF modeling is not suitable for modeling the tidal sections of the river, a hydrodynamic model was developed for mass and volume transport, called UnTRIM (Unstructured Tidal, Residual, and Intertidal Mudflat), which is a semi-implicit finite-difference (volume) model based on the three-dimensional shallow water equations as well as on the three-dimensional transport equation for salt, heat, dissolved matter, and suspended sediments (VIMS 2009). UnTRIM uses unstructured orthogonal grids to better resolve complicated coastlines in shallow environments. Further, UnTRIM's independence from the Courant–Friedrich–Levy stability criterion allows for the use of comparatively long-time steps for calculations (several minutes) despite maintaining high spatial resolution on the order of 10 m. In other words, UnTRIM has unconditional stability. UnTRIM simulated the shallow tidal estuaries of the Lynnhaven River and provided hydrodynamic information that was needed by the water quality model, such as surface water elevation, three-dimensional velocity field, and vertical eddy diffusivity [*Development of Hydrodynamic and Water Quality Models for the Lynnhaven River System*, Special Report No. 408, submitted to the US. Army Corps of Engineers and the city of Virginia Beach, March 2009, prepared by the Virginia Institute of Marine Science (VIMS)].

3. CE-QUAL-ICM: CE-QUAL-ICM water quality model was used to compute concentrations, mass transport, kinetic transformations, and mass balances (Ref. VIMS Special Report No. 408, March 2009). The UnTRIM model was coupled with the CE-QUAL-ICM model through a special routine written for this purpose. The hydrodynamic simulation results (surface water elevation at each face and center of each polygon, 3D velocity field, and vertical diffusivity calculated at each time step) from the UnTRIM model were then read by CE-QUAL-ICM. The biggest advantage of coupling CE-QUAL-ICM with UnTRIM is that the model also employs an unstructured grid system, which is the same one used in building the UnTRIM model, which makes it highly compatible [*Development of Hydrodynamic and Water Quality Models for the Lynnhaven River System*, Special Report No. 408, submitted to the U.S. Army Corps of Engineers and the city of Virginia Beach, March 2009, prepared by the Virginia Institute of Marine Science (VIMS 2009)].

Hydrologic calibration of the HSPF model was more of an iterative process because the model was used only for the land-based process of runoff and nutrients. During HSPF hydrologic model simulation, the precipitation during any time period is balanced in the continuity equation in the model. The land segments for the HSPF model of the Lynnhaven Basin were developed based on the best available data and information. The primary input data and parameters and their sources for the hydrologic model, which were used in its calibration, and the calibration process are briefly described as follows:

(a) Precipitation data: The hourly data for Naval Air Station Oceana (NAS Oceana) were obtained from NOAA. The NAS Oceana meteorological station is situated in the southwest quadrant of the Lynnhaven River watershed. It was assumed that point observations of rainfall at NAS Oceana represent the aerial average over the entire watershed. Therefore, no attempts were made to modify the precipitation data obtained from NAS Oceana for calibration purposes.

(b) Evaporation data: The daily evapotranspiration data were also obtained from NOAA for NAS Oceana. Therefore, no attempts were made in modifying NAS Oceana data for calibration purposes.

(c) Change in storage in the upper, lower, and groundwater storage zones: Calibration of an HSPF model involves adjustment of infiltration capacities and groundwater recession rates. As the watershed is large and no field measurement was made to determine actual or realistic values, initial values input to the model were based on known watershed characteristics. Therefore, these were not considered for modification or fine-tuning during the calibration process.

(d) Runoff: Land-based runoff, peak and volume, data for the period January 2000 through February 2006 were provided. Runoff in a watershed is simulated by diverting a constant percentage, equal to the percentage of the impervious area directly connected to the storm drain network, of precipitation each hour to the stream as "impervious-area runoff." Waterbodies in the basin are considered 100% impervious areas. Changes in the perviousness of the land segment result in changes in the overland flow component of the stream flow. In the Lynnhaven Basin model, the imperviousness of each land use is an estimate from GIS and can be modified within acceptable tolerances to achieve hydrologic calibration.

(e) Initial calibration process: Initial calibration was performed by coupling land-based runoff peak and volume with the UnTRIM hydrodynamic model for several time periods in the year 2005, in which no precipitation occurred. Each period of the simulation was for a 2-week period and covered spring, summer, and winter seasons. The resulting modeled water surface elevation obtained from the UnTRIM hydrodynamic model was compared with observed water surface elevation data collected at five monitoring sites within and/or nearby the Lynnhaven Basin. If and when not in agreement with observed values, parameters representing HSPF's IMPLND module were fine-tuned within reasonable limits to obtain satisfactory comparison. This was an iterative process. Storm-event calibration was taken up separately for three storm types, discussed subsequently.

(f) Storm calibration: Runoff volumes for three types of storm events in the year 2005 were inputs to the hydrodynamic model and are based on rainfall duration, intensity, and interevent duration. The three storm types are as follows:

- Brief, high intensity, 72 h antecedent dry period;
- Long duration, low intensity, 72 h antecedent dry period; and
- Long duration, high intensity, 72 h antecedent dry period.

These storm types are expected to contribute significant runoff to the Lynnhaven River. An accurate simulation of runoff from the aforementioned storms aid in pollutant loading calibration. The hydrodynamic model dictated any calibration adjustments deemed necessary based on the observed data. An iterative process of adjusting the imperviousness of various land uses (within reason) was made until agreement was obtained between modeled and observed data.

Following the initial and storm calibration, the HSPF model was subjected to runoff verification (confirmation) period. The year 2003, January through December, was used for model verification. The observed and modeled water surface elevation for 2003 was found to be satisfactory and the model was considered hydrologically calibrated. The calibrated model was then used to provide multiyear datasets of its outputs of hourly nutrient loadings and freshwater discharge to the UnTRIM hydrodynamic model. It is worth noting that the iterative process was challenging as it involved two sets of models (HSPF and UnTRIM) and two different modeling teams and organizations.

Calibration of the UnTRIM hydrodynamic model for tides was performed by comparing the model results with synoptic measurements at five locations spanning from Long Creek to Broad Bay to Linkhorn Bay, as well as by comparing the NOAA predicted tide ranges and phases to model the results at two Western Branch stations (Bayville Creek and Buchanan Creek) and one Eastern Branch location (Brown Cove). The dampening of the tidal amplitude was from approximately 0.35 m at the Inlet to approximately 0.18 m at the head of Linkhorn Bay. The model prediction versus measured comparison of amplitude was within 2 cm at all five stations.

Calibration of the CE-QUAL-ICM water quality model was performed for 2006 by comparing model predictions with measurements taken every other month at the 16 Lynnhaven VDEQ (Virginia Department of Environmental Quality) monitoring stations for the parameters of DO, chlorophyll-a (Chl-a), total Kjeldahl nitrogen (TKN), total phosphorus (TP), ammonium (NH_4), nitrate–nitrite (NO_3), and orthophosphate (PO_4). A qualitative comparison between model results and observed values, the model predictions were represented as a gray band bounded by daily minimum and maximum predictions indicate that the CE-QUAL-ICM water quality model can reproduce the physical, chemical, and biological processes that affect the eutrophication process in the Lynnhaven River of high quality. To provide a more quantifiable measure of the performance of the water quality model, statistical analysis was employed to the predicted and observed data of the water-quality calibration results obtained for the year 2006. For the sake of brevity of this section, only relative errors in the measurement value and correlation coefficient are provided in Table 4-4. The relative error statistic normalizes the absolute mean error by the magnitude of observation. It is worthwhile to note that the error statistic of the computed water quality parameters shown in Table 4-4 is in good agreement with the observed values.

4.4 PERFORMANCE EVALUATIONS OF INTEGRATED MODELING SYSTEMS AND LINKED MODELS

In general, model uncertainty increases with an increase in the number of linked components or models (Dubois et al. 2013, Geller and Turner 2007). The key challenges of linked models include issues related to time

Table 4-4. Water Surface Comparison of Predicted Versus Observed Water-Quality Parameters at the 16 Lynnhaven Monitoring Stations by Virginia DEQ.

Water quality parameter	Sample size	Relative error	Correlation coefficient (r)
Dissolved oxygen (DO)	90	0.13	0.90
Chlorophyll-a (Chl-a)	86	0.40	0.66
Total Kjeldahl nitrogen (TKN)	90	0.18	0.79
Total phosphorus (TP)	90	0.52	0.60
Ammonium (NH_4)	90	0.73	0.74
Nitrate-nitrite (NO_x)	90	0.57	0.76
Orthophosphate (PO_4) or dissolved inorganic phosphorus (DIP)	90	0.79	0.42

Notes: Calculated based on information from VIMS (2009).

The approach discussed here brings out, as an example, how the various modeling components were integrated in the desired outcome in support of TMDL and water quality management decisions.

steps (Argent 2004), model calibration and uncertainty analysis (Voinov and Cerco 2010), and issues related to the interdependence between scale and model processes (van Delden et al. 2011). Voinov and Cerco (2010) reported that linked models need adjustment and recalibration, which may eliminate the advantages of linked models. For nonlinked complex models such as Hydrological Simulation Program-FORTRAN (HSPF), TMDL developers need to establish a reasonable level of confidence with the model prediction results. Typically, watershed loading models such as HSPF are calibrated in a sequential manner whereby flow is calibrated first, followed by sediment, and then sediment-dependent stressors (Mohamoud et al. 2009). At each stage, the model loses its predictive power because of poor data quality (Mohamoud and Prieto 2011) or inadequate representation of key hydrologic or hydraulic processes, and inadequate system representation (Mohamoud 2007).

Meeting the modeling objectives of a TMDL study requires an acceptable model performance criterion. Running a stand-alone model or linked models just to generate model outputs is not the ultimate goal of a TMDL study. Shirmohammadi et al. (2006) reported that uncertainty of model results is a major concern in TMDL development and proposed that explicit quantification of uncertainty be made as an integral part of the TMDL process. Shoemaker et al. (2005) stated a need for model performance criterion for flow and water-quality simulations. They stated that stakeholders suggested the use of standardized statistical tests that provide a common context for model performance and compilation of model Performance Evaluation Criteria (PEC) for TMDL studies. They also noted that performance measures provide confidence in model predictions. Ritter and Muñoz-Carpena (2013) and Moriasi et al. (2015) reported that a Nash–Sutcliffe efficiency (NSE) of 0.65 represents an acceptable performance criterion (e.g., for hydrologic calibration such as flows, at daily, monthly, and annual scales). Nash–Sutcliffe efficiency ranges from $-\infty$ to 1. An NSE value of 1 corresponds to a perfect fit. Lower than zero efficiency values indicate that the mean value of the observed time series would have been a better predictor than the model (Krause et al. 2005). Please also refer to Chapter 8 on "Model Calibration and Validation" and Chapter 9 on "Model Uncertainty Analysis and Margin of Safety."

4.5 SUMMARY

The choice of a model for TMDL development for impaired waterbodies depends mainly on the modeling objectives (e.g., applicable water-quality criterion and TMDL endpoints) and the system complexity of watershed and receiving waters. The model complexity needed for specific TMDL development should be identified by the relationship between system attributes, pollutant and source relationship, and key forcing functions. The needed sophistication or explicit model simulation need is related back to the question, "What is needed to solve the problem?". Sometimes, the use of linked models evolves from an earlier simpler application, which has identified a key factor for more sophisticated analysis (e.g., a need for enhanced accuracy for management decision marking).

Integrated modeling systems demonstrate a high level of support for TMDL needs, based on the model application criteria established by USEPA (2005) and van Evert et al. (2005), for example, TMDL endpoints, watershed and land processes, receiving water processes, and model application considerations (e.g., experience required, the time needed for application and data needs).

Furthermore, stand-alone complex models or linked models are, in general, selected for systems of large watersheds with urban and rural areas and/or where a network of flow-controlled water impoundments (e.g., lakes and reservoirs) influence watershed behavior, or where estuaries and related tidal processes are the key considerations where TMDL impairments need to be evaluated and addressed through comprehensive modeling.

Recommended quantitative methods that are more commonly used by TMDL practitioners include the Nash–Sutcliffe model efficiency (NSE) and the root-mean-squared error (RMSE) to capture the interactions between magnitude bias and time-offset errors and the coefficient of determination (R^2) to capture time-offset errors. Recommended qualitative methods include comparisons of observed and simulated time-series plots and scatter plots with correlation coefficients and p-values. Model uncertainty assessment should be an integral part of TMDL modeling studies, including for integrated modeling systems and linked models. Please also refer to Chapter 8 "Model Calibration and Validation" and Chapter 9 "Uncertainty Analysis and Margin of Safety."

As one of the most comprehensive integrated modeling systems to date, the BASINS modeling system was developed by USEPA for better streamlining multiple needed steps in TMDL studies. It supports model linkage, data management, model setup, postprocessing, and web-based data downloads. Complex TMDL modeling options available in BASINS include the HSPF model, which simulates flow and various water-quality constituents at the landscape and receiving waterbodies.

For linked models, one well-tested practice is to connect watershed loading models such as HSPF and LSPC with hydrodynamic models such as EFDC and instream models such as WASP for evaluation of complex TMDL development.

Integrated modeling systems can satisfy multiple model application criteria because they include the capabilities of multiple models, provide various software tools, and include data and analysis support. Much of the recent development of integrated systems for TMDL applications has focused on improving the efficiency and consistency of modeling applications. Integrated systems typically provide linkages between data and models and include a set of tools to efficiently build, test, and apply models to support environmental decision-making (USEPA 2005, van Evert et al. 2005).

4.6 STATE-OF-THE-ART AND STATE-OF-THE-PRACTICE

In the context of TMDL development, the need for integrated modeling systems (e.g., BASINS and WMS) and linked models is typically driven by factors such as the need to adequately capture system complexity (e.g., large watersheds with large areas of urban centers and rural areas, a network of flow-regulated rivers and reservoirs, and estuaries) and the need to model complex management goals (e.g., multiple stressors for TMDL impairments). For example, one main objective for using linked models could be to represent complex natural systems such as watersheds and their estuaries when such systems cannot be represented by a single model to meet the required level of modeling prediction accuracy.

As the state-of-the-practice, the BASINS modeling system supports model linkage, data management, model setup, postprocessing, and web-based data downloads. Complex TMDL modeling options available in BASINS include the HSPF model, which simulates flow and various water-quality constituents of the landscape and nontidal receiving waterbodies. In addition, WMS is a comprehensive graphical modeling environment for all phases of watershed hydrology and hydraulics, which was used to support TMDL development.

Linked models were used in support of various complex TMDLs. One example of a linked model system was to connect loading models such as HSPF or LSPC with a hydrodynamic model such as the EFDC and an in-stream water quality model such as WASP. It is worth noting that the use of linked complex models is not a guarantee of a good modeling practice by itself unless the models are supported by performance metrics, such as Nash–Sutcliffe efficiency (NSE) values that are greater than a prespecified threshold (Mohamoud and Zhang 2019), although these models could provide a more refined representation of a real-world system.

From the perspective of model uncertainty, in general, this uncertainty increases with an increase in the number of linked components or models (Dubois et al. 2013, Geller and Turner 2007). The key challenges of integrated modeling systems and linked models include issues related to the time-step used (Argent 2004), model calibration and uncertainty analysis (Voinov and Cerco 2010), and issues related to the interdependence between scale and model processes (van Delden et al. 2011). Please also refer to Chapter 9 "Model Uncertainty Analysis and Margin of Safety."

In summary, integrated modeling systems and linked models can satisfy multiple model application criteria because they include the capabilities of multiple models, provide various software tools, and include data and analysis support. Much of the state-of-the-art development of integrated systems for TMDL applications has focused on improving the efficiency and consistency of complex modeling applications.

ACKNOWLEDGMENTS

Reviews, edits, and comments provided by Deva K. Borah in this chapter are greatly appreciated.

REFERENCES

ADEM (Alabama Department of Environmental Management). 2008. *Final total maximum daily load nutrients & OE/DO.* Pepperell Branch (AL03150110-0201-700; Nutrients) and Sougahatchee Creek Embayment (Yates Reservoir) (AL03150110-0204-101; Nutrients & OE/DO). Montgomery, AL: ADEM.

Ames, D. P., C. Michaelis, A. Anselmo, L. Chen, and H. Dunsford. 2008. "MapWindow GIS." In *Encyclopedia of GIS*, (Eds.) Shekhar S. and Xiong, H. 633–634. New York, New York: Springer.

Aquaveo, Inc. 2020. "Watershed modeling system v11.0." https://www.aquaveo.com/software/wms-watershed-modeling-system-introduction.

Argent, R. M. 2004. "An overview of model integration for environmental applications—Components, frameworks and semantics." *Environ. Modell. Software* 19 (3): 219–234.

Battin, A. T., R. Kinerson, and M. Lahlou. 1998. "EPA's better assessment science integrating point and non-point sources (BASINS)- A powerful tool for managing watersheds." In *Proc., GISHydro98, 1998 ESRI User Conf.* Washington, DC: EPA, Office of Water-Office of Science and Technology.

Bharati, L., C. Rodgers, T. Erdenberger, M. Plotnikova, S. Shumilov, P. L. G. Vlek, et al. 2008. "Integration of economic and hydrologic models: Exploring conjunctive irrigation water use strategies in the Volta Basin." *Agric. Water Manage.* 95 (8): 925–936.

Bicknell, B. R., J. C. Imhoff, J. L. Kittle, A. S. Donigian, and R. C. Johanson. 2011. *Hydrologic simulation program—FORTRAN, HSPF version 12 user's manual.* Reston, VA: U.S. Environmental Protection Agency and Water Resources Discipline, US Geological Survey.

Cerco, C. F., and T. Cole. 1993. "Three-dimensional eutrophication model of Chesapeake Bay." *J. Environ. Eng.* 119 (6): 1006–1025.

Costanza, R., A. Voinov, R. Boumans, T. Maxwell, F. Villa, L. Wainger, and H. Voinov. 2002. "Integrated ecological economic modeling of the Patuxent River watershed, Maryland." *Ecol. Monogr.* 72 (2): 203–231.

Dellman, P. N., C. E. Ruiz, C. T. Manwaring, and E. J. Nelson. 2002. *Watershed modeling system hydrological simulation program; watershed model user documentation and tutorial.* Vicksburg, MS: Engineer Research and Development Center, Environmental Lab.

DiToro, D. 2001. *Sediment flux modeling.* New York: Wiley.

Downer, C. W., E. J. Nelson, and A. Byrd. 2003. *Primer: Using watershed modeling system (WMS) for gridded surface subsurface hydrologic analysis (GSSHA) data development—WMS 6.1 and GSSHA 1. 43C.* Vicksburg, MS: Engineer Research and Development Center, Coastal and Hydraulics Lab.

Dubois, G., M. Schulz, J. Skøien, L. Bastin, and S. Peedell. 2013. "eHabitat, a multi-purpose Web Processing Service for ecological modeling." *Environ. Modell. Software* 41: 123–133.

Elewa, H. H., and A. A. Qaddah. 2011. "Groundwater potentiality mapping in the Sinai Peninsula, Egypt, using remote sensing and GIS-watershed-based modeling." *Hydrogeol. J.* 19: 613–628.

Erturk, A., M. Gurel, M. A. Baloch, T. Dikerler, E. Varol, N. Akbulut, et al. 2006. "Application of watershed modeling system (WMS) for integrated management of a watershed in Turkey." *J. Environ. Sci. Health, Part A Toxic/Hazard Subst. Environ. Eng.* 41 (19): 2045–2056.

Geller, G. N., and W. Turner. 2007. "The model Web: a concept for ecological forecasting." In *Proc., 2007 IEEE Int. Geoscience and Remote Sensing Symp.*, 2469–2472. New York: IEEE.

Haith, D. A., and L. L. Shoemaker. 1987. "Generalized watershed loading functions for stream-flow nutrients." *Water Resour. Bull.* 23: 471–478.

Johnson, B. H., K. W. Kim, R. E. Heath, B. B. Hsieh, and H. L. Butler. 1993. "Validation of three-dimensional hydrodynamic model of Chesapeake Bay." *J. Hydraul. Eng.* 119 (1): 2–20.

Krause, P., D. P. Boyle, and F. Bäse. 2005. "Comparison of different efficiency criteria for hydrological model assessment." *Adv. Geosci.* 5: 89–97.

Linker, L. C., G. W. Shenk, R. L. Dennis, and J. S. Sweeney. 2000. "Cross-media models of the Chesapeake Bay watershed and airshed." *Water Qual. Ecosyst. Model.* 1 (1–4): 91–122.

Mohamoud, Y. M. 2007. "Enhancing hydrological simulation program–FORTRAN model channel hydraulic representation." *J. Am. Water Resour. Assoc.* 43 (5): 1280–1292.

Mohamoud, Y. M., and L. M. Prieto. 2011. "Effect of temporal and spatial rainfall resolution on HSPF predictive performance and parameter estimation." *J. Hydrol. Eng.* 17 (3): 377–388.

Mohamoud, Y. M., A. C. Sigleo, and R. S. Parmar. 2009. *Modeling the impacts of hydromodification on water quantity and quality.* EPA/600/R-09/116 (NTIS PB2010-104718). Washington, DC: Environmental Protection Agency.

Mohamoud, Y., and H. X. Zhang. 2019. "Applications of linked and nonlinked complex models for TMDL development: Approaches and challenges." *J. Hydrol. Eng.* 24 (1): 04018055.

Moriasi, D., M. W. Gitau, N. Pai, and P. Daggupati. 2015. "Hydrologic and water quality models: Performance measures and evaluation criteria." *Trans. ASABE* 58 (6): 1763–1785.

Ritter, A., and R. Muñoz-Carpena. 2013. "Performance evaluation of hydrological models: Statistical significance for reducing subjectivity in goodness-of-fit assessments." *J. Hydrol.* 480: 33–45.

Rosegrant, M. W., C. Ringler, D. C. McKinney, X. Cai, A. Keller, and G. Donoso. 2000. "Integrated economic-hydrologic water modeling at the basin scale: The Maipo River basin." *Agric. Econ.* 24 (1): 33–46.

Ross, M., J. Geurink, A. Aly, P. Tara, K. Trout, and T. Jobes. 2004. *Integrated hydrologic model (IHM) Vol. 1: Theory manual.* Tampa, FL: Water Resource Group, Dept. of Civil and Environmental Engineering, University of South Florida.

Rossman, L. A. 2010. *Storm water management model, user's manual, version 5.* EPA/600/R-05/040. Cincinnati, OH: Water Supply and Water Resources Division National Risk Management Research Laboratory, Environmental Protection Agency.

Shirmohammadi, A., I. Chaubey, R. D. Harmel, D. D. Bosch, R. Munoz-Carpena, C. Dharmasri, et al. 2006. "Uncertainty in TMDL models." *Trans. ASABE* 49 (4): 1033–1049.

Shoemaker, L., T. Dai, J. Koenig, and M. Hantush. 2005. *TMDL model evaluation and research needs.* EPA/600/R-05/149. Cincinnati, OH: USEPA National Risk Management Research Laboratory.

USEPA (US Environmental Protection Agency). 2000. *Ambient water quality criteria recommendations, information supporting the development of state and tribal nutrient criteria, rivers and streams in nutrient ecoregion XI.* EPA 822-B-00-020. Washington, DC: EPA.

USEPA. 2001. *Better assessment science integrating point and nonpoint sources BASINS version 3.0 user's manual.* EPA-823-B-01-001. Washington, DC: Office of Water.

USEPA. 2005. *TMDL model evaluation and research needs.* EPA/600/R-05/149. Prepared by L. Shoemaker, T. Dai, and J. Koenig. Washington, DC: EPA.

USEPA. 2009. *BASINs 4.0 climate assessment tool (CAT).* Supporting Documentation and User's Manual (Final Rep.). EPA/600/R-08/088. Washington, DC: EPA.

USEPA. 2010a. *Chesapeake Bay total maximum daily load for nitrogen, phosphorus and sediment.* Washington, DC: USEPA.

USEPA. 2010b. *Chesapeake Bay phase 5 community watershed model.* Section 11: Riverine simulation EPA 903S10002—CBP/TRS-303-10. Annapolis, MD: Chesapeake Bay Program Office, EPA.

USEPA. 2012. *Better assessment science integrating point and nonpoint sources (BASINS Version 4.1).* EPA-823-C-07-001. Washington, DC: Office Water.

USEPA. 2015. *TMDL modeling toolbox.* Washington, DC: EPA.

USEPA. 2019. *Better assessment science integrating point and nonpoint sources (BASINS version 4.5).* Washington, DC: USEPA. https://www.epa.gov/ceam/basins-download-and-installation. Accessed November 11, 2021.

USEPA Region 2 and New York State Department of Environmental Conservation (NYSDEC). 2019. "Total maximum daily load (TMDL) for Phosphorus in Conesus Lake Livingston County, New York." https://www.dec.ny.gov/docs/water_pdf/conesuspres.final.pdf.

van Delden, H., J. van Vliet, D. T. Rutledge, and M. J. Kirkby. 2011. "Comparison of scale and scaling issues in integrated land-use models for policy support." *Agric. Ecosyst. Environ.* 142 (1): 18–28.

van Evert, F. V., D. Holzworth, R. M. Muetzelfeldt, A. E. Rizzoli, and F. Villa. 2005. "Convergence in integrated modeling frameworks." In *Proc., MODSIM 2005 Int. Congress on Modelling and Simulation*, 745–750.

VIMS (Virginia Institute of Marine Science). 2009. *Development of hydrodynamic and water quality models for the Lynnhaven River System*. Special Rep. No. 408, Washington, DC: US Army Corps of Engineers and the City of Virginia Beach.

Voinov, A., and C. Cerco. 2010. "Model integration and the role of data." *Environ. Modell. Software* 25 (8): 965–969.

Whittemore, R. C., and J. Beebe. 2000. "EPA's BASINS model: Good science or serendipitous modeling." *J. Am. Water Resour. Assoc.* 36: 493–499.

Wool, T. A., R. B. Ambrose, J. L. Martin, E. A. Comer, and T. Tech. 2006. *Water quality analysis simulation program (WASP). User's manual, Version 6.* Washington, DC: EPA.

CHAPTER 5
SIMPLE MODELS AND METHODS

Harry X. Zhang, Nigel W. T. Quinn

5.1 INTRODUCTION

The determination of a total maximum daily load (TMDL) requires methods or models that can range from simple empirical (statistical) relationships, usually based on regional or site-specific data (land-use and other watershed characteristics) from impaired or similar receiving waterbodies, to detailed process-based models that might need months or even years to apply (USEPA 1999, Chesapeake Bay Program 2019). The selection of one or more model(s) to simulate an impaired waterbody involves complex trade-offs among model complexity, degree of model generalization and development, required reliability, modeling expertise available, project cost, and time available among other factors (Chapra 2003, McCutcheon 1983, 1989, Martin and McCutcheon 1999, Mysiak et al. 2005; also refer to Chapter 11). Simple models or methods are often used when data limitations and budget and time constraints preclude using more detailed process-based models. These tools can provide a rapid means of assessing pollutant loads with minimal effort and data, noting the limitations of the models in comparison with the detailed models and uncertainties of the assessments derived from those simple models or methods. Simple models and methods are easier to understand than more detailed modeling analysis (USEPA 1999) to certain stakeholders, which encourages their longer-term engagements throughout the TMDL process helping in compliance with regional water quality objectives (Voinov 2008, Parrott and Quinn 2016).

This chapter reviews simple models and methods found in the literature, some used in TMDL developments and implementation planning and others having potential, and notes the strengths and weaknesses of all reviewed, expanding from Zhang and Quinn (2019). Most of the simple models and methods are based on empirical relationships that can be used to estimate pollutant loads, export, or yields based on land-use or other annual averaged watershed characteristics (e.g., area, slope, shape, drainage, land use, and soil characteristics). These models and methods typically rely on a large-scale, regional aggregation of watershed characteristics and should be applied with caution when used to represent a single watershed and impaired waterbody, given that empirical regional relationships rarely undergo the rigorous performance testing that is needed to be considered reliable to determine a TMDL. Where possible, the use of regional statistical equations should be accompanied by extensive data collection and hypothesis testing to quantify the mean differences between observed and estimated measures of pollution.

Some of the simple models or methods are limited to providing preliminary estimates of sediment and pollutant loadings without predictive capabilities (Zhang 2005). Some are adequate to address the dominant or driving considerations for a specific TMDL. For example, if annual phosphorus loading is the dominant driver for impairment from lake eutrophication, it may be enough to use a simple annual loading model. The model can be used to support an assessment of the relative significance of different pollutant sources, guide decisions for management plans, and focus continuing monitoring. The monitored data and further analysis might suggest the need and development of a more detailed modeling approach in the future. When and where appropriate, simple models can provide fast, reliable, and practical analysis that can support decision-making. The review in this chapter provides an analysis of the characteristics of currently available simple models and methods for use in the TMDL development and implementation process.

5.2 REVIEW OF SIMPLE MODELS AND METHODS

The simple models and methods described in this chapter may be used to (1) determine a TMDL for uncomplicated,impaired waterbodies and when the important water quality processes are unknown, (2) be deployed in a phased determination of a TMDL, or (3) be employed to check TMDL determinations by other methods (Mysiak et al. 2005, Voinov 2008). Some auxiliary methods such as the Revised Universal Soil Loss Equation 2 (RUSLE2) that utilize the curve number (CN) method can be used to estimate sediment yields from different catchments to prioritize TMDL allocation and implementation planning. Spreadsheets are typically used to list and track implementation actions as well as perform simple mass balances for checking TMDL determinations and for other tasks. Occasionally, when used by an expert, methods like a simple mass balance spreadsheet can assist in ruling out certain pollutant allocations and can be used to enhance implementation options.

Several simple methods for receiving water quality analysis use an annual or seasonal steady-state mass balance. These methods also ignore short-term fluctuations in pollutant loading (i.e., sporadic violations of water quality standards) in developing an allocation schema for achieving annual pollutant load reductions (USEPA 1999). In limited circumstances, a reasonable estimate of the average watershed runoff and constituent concentrations can be sufficient to determine and allocate a TMDL.

The following sections provide brief descriptions of the simple models and methods reviewed to help understand their usefulness and limitations in TMDL developments and Table 5-1 provides a summary overview of these models and methods. These simple models and methods were divided into two subsections: (1) simple watershed models and methods, and (2) simple receiving water models and methods.

5.2.1 Simple Watershed Models and Methods

The following subsections describe 10 simple watershed models and methods or types of models and methods. The underlying fundamental concepts behind them are mass balance, derivation of pollutant load by multiplying the flow and concentration, or regression. In addition, simple transient mass balance models and GIS-based workflow for simple models are presented with a connection to Chapter 2 "Watershed Models."

5.2.1.1 Simple Mass Balance. Simplified mass balances are typically performed in spreadsheet models that consider discrete water volumes containing a uniform concentration (or reliably represented by an average or median concentration) of a nonreactive material or pollutant. The concentration C and load W are easily related via flow Q as in Equation (5-1) (McCutcheon 1989, Chapra 1997):

$$C = \frac{1}{Q}W; \quad W = QC \qquad (5-1)$$

The pollutant assimilative capacity or TMDL for any discrete volume of water containing a conservative substance is the numerical criterion of the water quality objective or standard expressed as the concentration of the substance multiplied by the flow rate to obtain a pollutant load. The derived pollutant load or TMDL is also a flux measured at any waterbody reach cross section as well as for any tributary or other pollutant source entering the impaired waterbody.

Whereas a simple mass balance is useful to determine and allocate TMDLs achieved by dilution with sources of better quality water in

Table 5-1. Comparison of Simple Models and Methods for TMDL Determination.

	Method	Advantage and benefit	Disadvantage or shortcoming	Key references/brief descriptions
	Simple Watershed Models and Methods			
1	Simple mass balance	1. Most easily and clearly understood by stakeholders 2. Most useful for confirming more elaborate determinations of TMDLs and quality assurance of existing water quality records 3. Simplicity with fundamental governing equations used, such as conservation of water and dissolved solids, to quantify dilution-based waste assimilative capacity	1. Usually oversimplified and inaccurate for most waterbodies and for nonconservative pollutants 2. Primarily limited to freshwater total dissolved solids and estuarine salinity to determine dilution in inland and coastal waters	Ketchum (1951a, b), Pritchard (1969), Mills et al. (1985), McCutcheon (1989), Chapra (1997), Martin and McCutcheon (1999)
2	Simple Method to estimate urban stormwater loads	1. Simplicity based on the fundamental definition of flux: loading = runoff or instream flow × pollutant concentration 2. Applicable to a broad range of durations: annual to critical events 3. Statistically proven that annual, flow-weighted, event-mean concentration of nutrients and lead from the EPA National Urban Runoff program observations can be used in Washington, DC, metro area with runoff estimates for ungauged catchments; with proper testing with a complete National Urban Runoff Program database, expected to expand to ungauged catchments nationally 4. Evaluated for use in portions of the Chesapeake Bay Watershed	1. Ignores loads from groundwater recharge catchments <2.6 km² (1 mi²) 2. Less reliable for ungauged catchments; requires extensive calibration and testing outside the Washington, DC, area 3. Uses dated approximation of runoff as a catchment constant ratio of rainfall based on imperviousness and corrected for rainfall that does not result in runoff	USEPA (1983), Schueler (1987), Cappiella and Brown (2001)

3	Watershed Treatment Model	1. Spreadsheet that expands upon the Simple Method by using rural export coefficients for efficient evaluation of all nonpoint sources simultaneously	1. Not rigorously evaluated for reliability except for simple method use in Washington, DC, area 2. Lacks rigorous scientific basis for ungauged catchments 3. Documentation says that the original purpose was for watershed restoration, planning, and management and does not mention uses for TMDL determination or provide TMDL case studies	Caraco (2013)
4	Spreadsheet Tool for Estimating Pollutant Loads (STEPL)	1. Customized spreadsheet-based model with a user-friendly Visual Basic interface 2. Input data server uses the ArcGIS Viewer for additional map layers	Only provides annual pollutant loading estimation	USEPA (2018)
5	Revised Universal Soil Loss Equation 2	1. Tested and applied by many users for decades to estimate annual erosion or critical event–based loads 2. Extensive database of soils, climate, and crop management for every county in the United States 3. Long-term support and enhancement by the United States Department of Agriculture Agricultural Research Service and Natural Resources Conservation Service 4. May avoid use of more elaborate auxiliary watershed models of runoff and erosion to define and allocate load reductions	1. Not rigorously tested for specific watersheds, reliable TMDL determination but has been used to support many TMDL analyses 2. The NRCS requires all staff agronomist and engineers in conservation planning receive training and follow-up guidance before using RUSLE2; outside consultants and state water-quality managers may not have access to comparable training	Wischmeier and Smith (1978), Renard et al. (1997), USDA (2003). Web link: (accessed 6/26/2020) https://www.ars.usda.gov/southeast-area/oxford-ms/national-sedimentation-laboratory/watershed-physical-processes-research/research/rusle2/

(Continued)

Table 5-1. (*Continued*)

Method	Advantage and benefit	Disadvantage or shortcoming	Key references/brief descriptions
6 Load Estimator (LOADEST)	1. Simple regression-based model for the estimation of water-quality constituent load through calibration 2. Output includes diagnostic tests to assist the user in interpreting the estimated loads	1. Has certain potential for producing biased load estimates when the selected regression model is a poor representation of the relationship between load and the explanatory variables	Runkel et al. (2004), Duan et al. (2012), Mullaney et al. (2016), USGS (2016)
7 Spatially Referenced Regression on Watershed Attributes (SPARROW)	1. The USGS describes the use of this software for TMDL development that involves nutrients and fecal coliforms 2. Used in implementation proposal for the Chesapeake Bay TMDLs 3. With years of monitoring, there is a limited chance of determining a TMDL by black-box regression 4. USGS experts are able to infer very limited process knowledge 5. Uses mass conservation at junctions with tributaries to overcome a major uncertainty caused by crude regression 6. Fair documentation and good support for USGS investigators	1. Lacks scientific evidence that any regional regression is reliable in determining a site-specific TMDL 2. Years or decades of data are necessary to confirm a regional regression, and failing confirmation, to develop a site-specific regression, compared with weeks or months of synoptic data collection for a process-based, mechanistic model	Tasker and Driver (1988), Driver and Troutman (1989), Smith et al. (1997), Preston and Brakebill (1999), Schwarz et al. (2006 and several references cited therein), Miller et al. (2020)
8 Long-Term Hydrologic Impact Analysis (L-THIA)	1. Quick accessible tool to assess the long-term impacts of land-use change 2. Does not require detailed data inputs for most planning settings	1. Only applies to areas where the curve number (CN) method is used 2. Only estimates average annual runoff	Purdue University (2013, 2015, 2016)

No.	Model	Advantages	Limitations	References/Remarks
9	Simple Transient Mass Balance Models (a) Wetland Management Simulator (WETMANSIM) (b) San Joaquin River Input-Output model (SJRIO)	1. Conceptually clear—addition/subtraction of mass 2. Model assumptions explicit and readily changed	1. Spreadsheet format can be cumbersome for simulations greater than one year. 2. Version control challenging because spreadsheet easily modified	1. WETMANSIM—spreadsheet-based monthly water and salt balance for managed wetlands 2. SJRIO—model performs daily flow and salt mass balance of inflow to the river and diversions from the river from surface and groundwater sources
10	GIS workflow model	1. Object-oriented approach, easy to implement 2. Visually appealing; takes advantage of GIS	1. Requires acquisition and knowledge of GIS 2. Data often lacking to fully exploit GIS applications	USDA (2003), Pennsylvania State University (2016)

Simple Receiving Water Models and Methods

No.	Model	Advantages	Limitations	References/Remarks
1	BATHTUB	1. Empirical simplistic model for eutrophication analysis for lakes and reservoirs typically with an auxiliary loading model 2. Reportedly used routinely in the lake TMDLs when the long-term average or steady-state TMDL determination but range of applicability not well defined	1. Not designed for sporadic or diurnal, dynamic impairments 2. Empirical water quality kinetics fundamentally limits projections to USACE reservoirs used to develop regression equations 3. Limitations in implementation planning	Walker (1985, 1986, 2014), Borah et al. (2006). Web link: (accessed June 26, 2020) http://www.wwwalker.net/bathtub/

(Continued)

Table 5-1. (*Continued*)

Method	Advantage and benefit	Disadvantage or shortcoming	Key references/brief descriptions
2 Stream Segment Temperature Model (SSTEMP)	1. Easy-to-use model that can simulate heat balance 2. Used to analyze the effects of changing riparian shade for temperature TMDL application	1. Lacks many of the detailed features of dynamic models needed for complex temperature TMDLs	Theurer et al. (1984), Bartholow (2010), Chen et al. (1993, 1998a, b). Web link: https://www.fort.usgs.gov/thesaurus-topic/stream-segment-temperature-model
3 Load Duration Curve	1. Has been applied in various types of TMDLs 2. TMDL load is expressed as a function of flow conditions	1. Does not mechanistically relate sources and receiving water-quality response 2. Does not allow simulation of scenarios evaluating the impact of various implementation options	USEPA (2007), Risley et al. (2008), SCDHEC (2010). Web link: https://www.epa.gov/tmdl/approach-using-load-duration-curves-development-tmdls

Source: Adapted from Zhang and Quinn (2019).

Note: GIS = geographic information systems; TMDL = total maximum daily load.

uncomplicated waterbodies, especially for total dissolved solids or salinity and occasionally total nitrogen, simple mass balances are more useful to check the continuity of numerical simulations of water and pollutant mass balances (McCutcheon 1989, Chapra 1997). These continuity checks are especially useful to (1) confirm the accuracy of point-source measurements of flow and concentration, (2) back-calculate background and other NPS loads, (3) confirm the reliability of questionable ambient water quality observations, and (4) gain an initial sense of what water quality processes may be important in TMDL model selection (McCutcheon 1989). Simple mass balances to determine estuarine dilution of loads with seawater may include the fraction of freshwater supplied as dilution (Ketchum 1951a, b). Simple mass balances have been referenced in Pritchard (1969), Mills et al. (1985), McCutcheon (1989), Lung et al. (1993), and Martin and McCutcheon (1999).

5.2.1.2 Simple Method to Estimate Urban Stormwater Loads. The simple method (Schueler 1987) makes use of the calculated flux of the discharged pollutant to estimate the annual pollutant load or yield from a small urban watershed (catchment). Modelers may consider a flow duration associated with the pollutant in a watershed as brief as the time for runoff to occur after a specific critical rainfall-runoff event and then specifying, approximating, or measuring mean pollutant concentration and the volume of runoff produced by the event. The catchment pollutant load or flux is the product of the catchment drainage area, depth of storm water runoff, and pollutant concentration (typically of carbon, nitrogen, and phosphorus) in the runoff. These loads can be calculated from annual runoff and flow-weighted, annual-average, event-mean pollutant concentrations (Schueler 1987, Huber 1993) or for a critical representative runoff event of a given probability using runoff volume and the critical event-mean concentration. After a thorough analysis of the data collected by the USEPA (1983) Nationwide Urban Runoff Program that included 22 catchments, Schueler (1987) determined that loads from less-polluted groundwater baseflow were not important for catchments of 2.6 km^2 (1 mi^2 or 640 acres) or less (USEPA 1999).

The method has occasionally been used to determine, allocate, and plan for the implementation of a TMDL at locations where a pollutant is diluted in swift-moving headwater streams. These streams rarely produce significant transformations of the pollutant during transport, and the flow-weighted, event-mean concentration and annual rainfall-runoff can be monitored for several years or during several critical events to complete the TMDL analysis. For example, in the Washington, DC, area, headwater impairments caused by excess carbon, nitrogen, and phosphorus could be assessed using annual-average, flow-weighted, event-mean concentrations of these nutrients (Schueler 1987). In this case, observations of eight local catchments were used by the USEPA (1983) Nationwide Urban Runoff Program to calculate annual-average concentrations for these constituents.

More often, the simple method is more useful when used as an adjunct to define tributary catchment loads in conjunction with receiving water quality modeling of more complex waterbody impairments involving eutrophication and resulting dissolved oxygen depletion, toxic cyanobacteria blooms, and fish kills. The chief advantage of the simple method is to avoid the more complex and expensive watershed modeling required to define catchment loads. However, in some cases, the use of the simple method to determine a nutrient TMDL in each catchment of a watershed can also be inefficient, overly conservative, and less reliable than simultaneously determining watershed-scale TMDLs using a eutrophication process model. For complex combinations of point and nonpoint source loads, the Center for Watershed Protection (Caraco 2013) developed a preliminary implementation spreadsheet that calculated runoff loads using the fundamental simple method definition of flux or yield.

The simple method calculates loads or fluxes (L in pounds) for chemical constituents as a product of the runoff volume (Q) (depth R in inches multiplied by the area A in acres) and the pollutant event-mean concentration (C in mg/L)—where 0.226 is a unit conversion factor to convert the concentration in mg/L to pounds/acre-inch (Schueler 1987, USEPA 1999). The equation follows:

$$L = 0.226 * R * C * A \approx 0.226 * P * f_Q * f_P * C \qquad (5\text{-}2)$$

The load (L) can also be approximated by multiplying P (rainfall in inches), f_Q is the dimensionless fraction of rainfall that actually produces runoff selected by Schueler (1987) usually as 0.9 (Lichter and Lindsey 1994, Schueler 2001a, b, Cappiella et al. 2005, Pitt et al. 2005), and $f_P = 0.05 + 0.9 * I$ is the empirical dimensionless ratio of runoff to rainfall (runoff coefficient) recommended by Schueler (1987), in which I is the fraction of the catchment that is impervious.

The approximate catchment yield or load calculation requires specifications of only three factors: precipitation, imperviousness, and event-mean pollutant concentration. Originally formulated for site development, Schueler (1987) tested the flux Equation (5-2) with measurements of polluted runoff from new suburban and existing central business district catchments in the District of Columbia, catchments with older suburban development in Baltimore, Maryland, and forested catchments in northern Virginia (representing undeveloped property) for the Metropolitan Washington Council of Governments. Schueler (1987) expanded the testing with national catchment data from the USEPA (1983)

Nationwide Urban Runoff Program observations collected in the contiguous 48 states and analyzed more than 300 storm events over 8 catchments in the Washington, DC, area from 1980 to 1981 (USEPA 1983). The method was evaluated using the entire database of 2,300 storms observed on 22 catchments nationally. The simple method was also applied to the Chesapeake Bay watershed (Cappiella and Brown 2001), which included urban, forestry, and agricultural land uses.

Schueler (1987) noted that the fundamental flux equation (5-2) is applicable for any catchment in the contiguous 48 states monitored for chemical pollutants (specifically, total nitrogen and phosphorus and the major species thereof, and chemical oxygen demand, but not suspended sediment). Thus, simple method urban load calculations should be as reliable as the measured or estimated runoff and flow-weighted event-mean concentrations of nitrogen, phosphorus, and organic carbon. The calculations should not be significantly affected by storage or transformation between the source areas and the impairments.

5.2.1.3 Watershed Treatment Model. The Watershed Treatment Model (WTM) was developed by the Center for Watershed Protection (Caraco 2013) and provides estimates of annual nitrogen, phosphorus, total suspended solids, and bacterial loads from urban and rural watersheds. This spreadsheet tool can also be used to determine the effects of stormwater best management practices, stream restoration, stormwater retrofits, septic system improvements, point-source reductions, and some nonstructural practices on reducing pollutant loads. All primary runoff pollutant loads that are quantifiable using land-use characteristics are lumped in WTM, as are all secondary pollutant sources that are not as easily related to watershed characteristics.

The spreadsheet is available in two versions (Caraco 2013): (1) off the shelf, and (2) customized. The off-the-shelf version, primarily used for preliminary assessments of all sources and treatment practice effectiveness, is more user-friendly and includes a graphical user interface and a parameter menu with default specifications. The customized version is less user-friendly but is more adaptable to the simulation of novel watershed management practices and the specification of pollutant control performance and data.

The spreadsheet calculates annual urban runoff loads from catchments for each land use using the simple method (Schueler 1987). Urban land use includes six general categories: residential, commercial, industrial, forest, rural, and open water. Residential land use is divided into four more detailed land-use categories: low, medium, high density, and multifamily. Rural runoff loads are calculated using the typical export coefficients of pollutant mass per unit land area. The default parameter specifications provided by the spreadsheet model are usually invoked when local catchment information is not available. Caraco (2013) compiled typical pollutant concentrations of total nitrogen and phosphorus, suspended sediment, and indicator bacteria for catchments in 22 cities in the United States but did not statistically confirm that these national average pollutant concentrations were different from independent catchment concentrations of the same pollutants.

The primary concern in using this spreadsheet model for TMDL determination is the lack of rigorous scientific testing nationally, especially in the use of rural rainfall-runoff yields. In addition, the documentation provided by Caraco (2013) and that available on the worldwide web does not mention any use of the model for TMDL determination. Nevertheless, this spreadsheet could be useful in guiding the early steps in TMDL development—in particular, the tasks of locating and quantifying all waterbody loads, especially for watershed-scale TMDLs. Use of this spreadsheet, when appropriately applied, could avoid the need for complex watershed modeling. WTM is discussed further in Chapter 12 "Modeling for TMDL Implementation".

5.2.1.4 Spreadsheet Tool for Estimating Pollutant Loads. The Spreadsheet Tool for the Estimation of Pollutant Load (STEPL) developed by Tetra Tech for USEPA (with the latest version as 4.4 in 2018) is an annual pollutant loading estimation tool. This tool is available through USEPA (2018). STEPL provides a user-friendly Visual Basic (VB) interface to create a customized spreadsheet-based model in Microsoft (MS) Excel.

STEPL calculates nutrient and sediment loads from six different land uses: urban, cropland, pastureland, forest, feedlot, and user defined. It also estimates reductions associated with various BMPs. Simple algorithms of STEPL calculate surface runoff, loading of nitrogen, phosphorus, and 5-day biological oxygen demand, as well as sediment delivery from different land uses and management practices. Pollutant sources include runoff from the six land uses, animal husbandry, and septic systems. Farm animals considered include beef cattle, dairy cattle, swine, horses, sheep, chickens, turkeys, and ducks.

The annual nutrient yield for a watershed is the runoff volume multiplied by the pollutant concentration, which reflects the land-use distribution and management practices. Calculations for urban areas are based on estimates of runoff derived from the NRCS method, derived specifically for each drainage area from soil and land cover data, and pollutant concentrations from wet weather sampling data. Pollutant concentrations are based on data available for nine detailed urban land uses: commercial, industrial, institutional, transportation, multifamily residential, single-family residential, urban-cultivated, vacant (developed), and open space. Sediment loads (from sheet and rill erosion only) generated in rural areas are calculated using the USLE and an applied sediment delivery ratio. Nutrient loads for these rural lands are calculated similarly to loads from urban areas using pollutant concentrations and annual runoff volume. BMPs and are represented using user-defined efficiencies in sediment and pollutant load reductions. Simulation results are summarized for untreated loads, pollutant reduction by BMPs, treated loads, and according to the percent reduction for each pollutant.

The Input Data Server for STEPL uses the ArcGIS Viewer for Flex (version 2.1) (USEPA 2018). The ArcGIS Viewer for Flex is a ready-to-deploy, configurable client application that relies upon the ArcGIS API for Flex. The Viewer application is designed to work with ArcGIS Server and ArcGIS Online Web services.

Key features of this data server include a more stable GIS platform using a simple and modern user interface (e.g., Web 2.0). Additional map layers include a street map, an aerial map, an elevation map, boundaries and places, state and county boundaries, a watershed boundary dataset (HUC12, HUC10, HUC8, HUC6, HUC4, and HUC2), NHDplus catchments, NHDplus flowlines, and waterbodies.

The STEPL software has been used throughout the United States to model nonpoint source pollution, particularly in grant applications (e.g., Section 319 grant projects) as a preliminary planning tool in estimating load reductions. The spreadsheet tool has been used for calculating baseline loads and reductions from proposed improvements from BMP implementations in both urban and agricultural land uses during watershed assessments and TMDL implementations (also refer to Chapter 12).

5.2.1.5 Revised Universal Soil Loss Equation 2. The Revised Universal Soil Loss Equation 2 (RUSLE2) (USDA 2003) is an updated, advanced erosion calculation procedure that estimates sediment loading to receiving waterbodies, primarily headwater streams. Thus, the RUSLE2 serves as an auxiliary TMDL model for simulating incipient sediment erosion from sources that must be linked to a receiving water sediment transport model to assess impacts on a receiving waterbody.

RUSLE2 is derived from the empirical USLE (Wischmeier and Smith 1978) where annual soil erosion, sediment delivery, and sediment yield are estimated as the product of the six annual factors from daily or event values of the factors. The six average annual factors are as follows: R, the average annual summation during a normal year of rainfall of the erosion expressed as the total kinetic energy times the maximum 30 min intensity for each rainfall in excess of 1.3 cm (0.5 in.); K, the empirical, base soil erodibility factor determined by a nomograph representing intrinsic soil properties, rainfall, and temperature; L, the slope length factor that compensates for increased erosion along the formative runoff channels called rills that eventually become gullies; S, the steepness topographic factor represents the effect of variation in erodibility owing to steepness (e.g., the effects of segments of concave and convex hillslopes); C, the land cover and management factor based on canopy and ground cover (Quinn and Laflen 1983), surface roughness, time since the last mechanical soil disturbance, amount and distribution of live and dead roots in the soil, organic material incorporated into the soil, ridge height, and antecedent soil moisture; and P, the support practice factor (the ratio of soil loss with contouring or strip cropping to that from straight row farming up-and-down slopes).

Although a segmented one-dimensional hillslope profile is the fundamental conceptual model with which RUSLE2 computes erosion and sediment delivery, RUSLE2 can also be used to estimate distributed hillslope runoff and sediment yields representing sediment transport and deposition on concave, convex, and complex segmented runoff pathways. RUSLE2 calculates transport capacity as a function of runoff rate, slope steepness, and hydraulic resistance using the 10-year, 24 h precipitation and the NRCS curve number method (Hawkins et al. 2009) to compute daily runoff as a function of cover and management conditions. The software estimates daily hydraulic roughness from the soil surface roughness, live ground cover, ground cover provided by crop residue and mulch, and vegetative retardance.

USLE and RUSLE2 were primarily developed for cropland conservation planning and estimation of rates of erosion and sediment production from agricultural watersheds, for primary applications by the USDA Natural Resources Conservation Service (NRCS) field offices. The USDA-NRCS supports applications of RUSLE2 with extensive soil, climate, and crop management databases for every county in the United States. The database is specifically tailored to quantify the six empirical factors defined by USLE and RUSLE2. This extensive database organizes land management approaches into 78 crop management zones. Each crop management approach represented using the RUSLE2 is created by combining farm field operations (e.g., grading, tillage, planting, applying materials, or harvest); vegetation growth over time; and decomposing residue biomass and cover. As of January 2011, the NRCS database had over 29,000 management scenarios composed of combinations of approximately 600 tillage and field operations, 1,400 vegetation records, and 140 crop residue records. At that time, the database also contained approximately 600 choices of support practices that include contour cultivation, runoff diversions, terraces, impoundments, and vegetative strips.

USLE, RUSLE, and other modifications of USLE (MUSLE) have been used in many of the detailed watershed simulation models (Chapter 2) to simulate soil erosion on the upland areas. In the original USLE procedure (Wischmeier and Smith 1978), an empirical sediment delivery ratio (a fraction of the eroded soil from raindrop impact as estimated by USLE) was used to compute sediment yield at the catchment outlet bypassing the runoff-induced erosion, deposition, and sediment transport processes. Some of the watershed models and RUSLE2 have replaced the delivery ratio by sediment transport capacity-based transport of the raindrop-impacted and runoff-induced eroded soil and sediment (refer to Chapter 2). Those still using the delivery ratio–based transport are not suitable for TMDL development and implementation and managing land and water resources (Boomer et al. 2008).

A computer interface makes RUSLE2 easy to use and adaptable to various conditions. This semiempirical model is robust, flexible, and computationally efficient and is best suited for estimating the effects of soil, climate, and land management on sheet (by overland runoff) and rill (concentrated flow) erosion and sediment delivery from hillslopes. One feature of the model is its ability to account for the size distribution and, thus, the clay enrichment of sediment delivered to the dendritic network of channels draining a watershed. RUSLE2 has been used in many TMDLs (also refer to Chapter 10 "USEPA TMDL Report Archive and Report Search Tool").

5.2.1.6 Load Estimator. LOAD ESTimator (LOADEST) is a software program for estimating constituent loads in streams and rivers, which can be used a tool in supporting TMDL development. Given a time series of streamflow, additional data variables, and constituent concentration, LOADEST assists the user in developing a regression model for the estimation of constituent load through calibration. Explanatory variables within the regression model include various functions of streamflow, time interval, and additional user-specified data variables. The formulated regression model is then used to estimate loads over a user-specified time interval (estimation). Mean load estimates, standard errors, and 95% confidence intervals are developed on a monthly and/or seasonal basis (USGS 2016).

The calibration and estimation procedures within LOADEST are based on three statistical estimation methods. The first two methods, adjusted maximum likelihood estimation and maximum likelihood estimation (MLE), are appropriate when the calibration model errors (residuals) are normally distributed. The third method, least absolute deviation, is an alternative to maximum likelihood estimation when the residuals are not normally distributed (Runkel et al. 2004).

In 2013, LOADEST was modified to include several features that facilitate residual analysis and bias identification by Stenback et al. (2011). These features are illustrated using the nitrate loading analysis for the Thompson Fork of the Grand River at Davis City, Iowa (Stenback et al. 2011).

LOADEST output includes diagnostic tests to assist the user in determining the appropriate estimation method and in interpreting the estimated loads. There are seven example applications that are distributed with the LOADEST software. In addition, LOADEST applications in various water quality studies (USGS 2016) across geographic regions have been published as USGS reports or as journal papers (e.g., Duan et al. 2012, Mullaney et al. 2016, USGS 2016). These applications can assist the pollutant load estimate in TMDL development.

5.2.1.7 Spatially Referenced Regressions on Watershed Attributes. The United States Geological Survey (USGS) has a long history of deriving regression equations for watershed yields of water (streamflow for ungauged watersheds) and pollutants based on land use, imperviousness, sewered area, drainage area and slope, mean annual rainfall, and mean minimum monthly temperature (Schwarz et al. 2006). This agency has developed an empirical approach to watershed characterization based on regional regression relationships for water quality and watershed characteristics (e.g., Tasker and Driver 1988, Driver and Troutman 1989, Hensel and Hirsch 1995). This approach evolved into the more flexible geographic information system–based USGS Spatially Referenced Regressions on Watershed Attributes (SPARROW) (Smith et al. 1997, Schwarz et al. 2006). Schwarz et al. (2006) notes that the USGS has few documented applications of the SPARROW software for TMDL determination and allocation. This black-box, empirical relation of point and nonpoint loads to watershed characteristics does not produce a definitive, reliable, cause-and-effect relationship that is more readily obtained using mechanistic, process models. As a result, SPARROW and any other regression equation are not endorsed for TMDL applications beyond the range of data used to develop the regression equations and the independent watershed-specific data necessary to test for reliability (Schueler 1987).

Applications and the uses of regional regressions to estimate a TMDL for a specific impaired water and contributing watershed are often unreliable because the National Water Portal developed by the US Geological Survey and USEPA has several known limitations (USGS and USEPA 2017). First, the data collection process does not uniformly cover the impaired waters of the United States. The data assimilated typically result from discontinuous USGS cooperative projects with state agencies and water quality management projects by USEPA and states. This has limited the ability of the United States to conduct long-term watershed flow and pollutant monitoring studies. Second, as climate change impacts become more serious and water resource infrastructure is developed in response (e.g., reservoirs), the long-term records for specific watersheds become nonstationary (risk and frequency of occurrence significantly change with time) and less reliable.

The application of software such as the USGS SPARROW model typically require long-term monitoring in specific watersheds that are used to develop annual steady-state, empirical relationships that may encounter change. Conversely, practical, numerical, process models, which have a limited scientific basis to extrapolate a TMDL beyond the range calibration and testing data, usually only require intensive, synoptic data collection for weeks or months to calibrate and independently test the model during critical conditions. Therefore, applications of SPARROW nonlinear regression models, even by USGS experts, occupy a limited niche for the development of TMDL. These niches include the following: (1) Applications to pollutants discharged from reliably constant sources that may take years or decades of accumulation to cause impairment of a waterbody, for example, nutrients. (2) Use for pollutants from ephemeral, poorly defined sources for which transformation and transport processes are not well understood, for example, fecal coliform bacteria used as an indicator of water-borne pathogens.

Case studies of the regional regression approach include the pollutant loading assessment at 76 gauging stations draining land uses in 20 states using information from the extensive USEPA (1983) Nationwide Urban Runoff Program of 1979 to 1983. Moore et al. (2004) and Schwarz et al. (2006) note that the SPARROW model was used in the determining nitrogen and phosphorus TMDLs for New England streams.

For TMDL implementation planning, Preston and Brakebill (1999) and Miller et al. (2020) used SPARROW to identify the watersheds draining to Chesapeake Bay where reduction in fertilization would be more effective in achieving water quality standards than reductions in nitrogen point sources, atmospheric deposition, and agricultural manure applications. Nevertheless, none of these SPARROW applications reported reliability assessment through hypothesis testing.

Auxiliary SPARROW mappers are interactive tools that visualize streamflow and nutrient and sediment loads or yields in a specific watershed. The 2012 version of SPARROW mappers are available for five regions of the conterminous United States (USGS 2012). These mappers display long-term average streamflow and constituent loads for 1999 through 2014 and sources during or close to 2012.

5.2.1.8 Long-Term Hydrologic Impact Analysis. L-THIA was developed by Purdue University as a screening tool to use in assessing the long-term impacts of land-use changes. L-THIA results are intended to provide insight into the relative hydrologic impacts of different land-use scenarios. The results can be used to generate community awareness of potential long-term problems and to support physical planning aimed at minimizing disturbance of critical areas (Purdue University 2013, 2016).

L-THIA provides estimates of changes in runoff, recharge, and nonpoint source pollution resulting from past or proposed land-use changes. It gives long-term average annual runoff for a land-use configuration, based on actual long-term climate data for that area (e.g., 30 years of daily precipitation observations). L-THIA focuses on the average impact, rather than an extreme year or storm.

L-THIA is an ideal tool to assist in the evaluation of potential effects of land-use change and to identify the best location of a particular land use to reduce the impact on the natural environment of the area (e.g., land-use changes owing to urban sprawl).

In addition, L-THIA for the Great Lakes Watershed Management System (Purdue University 2016) focuses on Great Lakes regions. It helps delineate the area that flows to a pour point and allows users to send that soil and land-use data within that area and generate the outputs.

Long-Term Hydrologic Impact Analysis (L-THIA) Low-Impact Development (LID) Spreadsheet (L-THIA/LID) is an easy-to-use screening tool that evaluates the benefits of LID practices. The L-THIA/LID model consists of two screening levels for the LID approach. Basic screening allows the users to adjust the percent of imperviousness for particular land uses. Lot-level screening consists of a suite of LID practices such as bioretention (rain gardens), porous pavement, narrowing impervious surfaces (streets, sidewalks, and driveways), and vegetated rooftops (Purdue University 2015). L-THIA/LID can generate estimated runoff volumes, depths, and expected nonpoint source pollution loadings to waterbodies, based on the information provided by the user. L-THIA/LID can be used as a supporting tool during TMDL implementation.

5.2.1.9 Simple Transient Mass Balance Models. In some instances, standard models may not be suitable for TMDL development for certain pollutants. In these circumstances, customized model applications need to be developed. In most cases, these models rely on the concept of mass balance by first developing a hydrology budget for the three-dimensional volume that represents the domain of the system being analyzed. In some instances, this system or control volume can be further subdivided into smaller partitions, typically in the vertical plane where a number of vertical layers are used to improve representation of the interactions between above-surface, root zone, shallow, and deep groundwater aquifers. These partitions can also occur in the horizontal plane to represent subwatersheds with dissimilar soil and shallow aquifer characteristics. The configuration of the model depends on the most important characteristics of the system, available data, and the chemistry of the contaminant being regulated. Spreadsheets have been used to good effect to develop both simple steady-state and transient mass balance models.

1. Wetland Management Simulator
   The Wetland Management Simulator (WETMANSIM) (Quinn 2004) spreadsheet model is an example of a customized monthly mass

balance accounting tool that simulates the hydrology and salt loads generated by managed, brackish, seasonal wetlands. These seasonally managed wetlands are flooded in the fall and gravity drained in the spring to mimic natural wetland hydrology and hydroperiod, primarily in California and the arid west of the United States.

In California, canal deliveries from the brackish Sacramento–San Joaquin Delta provide overwintering habitat for migratory waterfowl and release the bulk of the ponded water, stored in shallow wetland impoundments, and considerable salt loading during spring wetland drawdown. Depending on water availability, the wetlands are flood-irrigated one or more times during the late spring, early summer months to encourage the growth of moist soil plants that provide food resources for the migratory waterfowl. The high clay content of wetland soils that desiccate and crack during the summer months, and which swell when wetted, required the use of a water infiltration algorithm that accounted for soil pore water displacement rather than the typical Richards equation used by most vadose zone models. Monthly time steps were sufficient to provide analysts and regulators with the necessary relationship between applied water salinity and the salinity of wetland drainage return flows to the receiving waterbody. Individual WETMANSIM models were developed for each of the seven major wetland complexes owned and managed by the state and federal wildlife agencies and the privately owned and managed Grasslands Resource Conservation District as an example of the spatial partitioning noted previously. The simple monthly steady-state spreadsheet formulation made it easy to adapt and update the individual submodels for state and federal wildlife refuges and privately owned wetland entities as more inflow and drainage monitoring was established—providing more reliable hydrology and salinity mass balances. These hydrology and salinity mass balances have allowed more local control of salt load discharge scheduling by these entities to the San Joaquin River—the receiving waterbody for these salt load exports. The WETMANSIM model has served wetland salinity TMDL planning activities and has provided the conceptual basis for salinity management decision support during Program implementation. The WETMANSIM model is typical of customized TMDL models used in TMDL development that are well matched to TMDL objectives and available data.

2. San Joaquin River Input–Output model

The San Joaquin River Input–Output (SJRIO) model (California Regional Water Quality Control Board—Central Valley Region, CVWB 2004) is another example of a customized mass balance model where neither a monthly nor an annual steady-state conceptual model was sufficient for analysis of the options being considered by the TMDL. SJRIO is an example of a data-driven model where synoptic data assimilated over several years provided the basis for a TMDL with monthly load allocations developed for prescribed hydrologic water-year categories ranging from wet to critically dry. Design flows and average drainage water quality ascribed to each water year hydrologic category were the primary factors that determined these monthly load allocations.

In this California application, the concept of real-time salinity management was being explored that involved improved coordination of saline drainage return flows produced on the west side of the San Joaquin River basin to coincide with reservoir releases of snowmelt runoff from the east side of the basin. This operational concept became the basis of regulatory policy and an amendment to the Basin Water Quality Control Plan. River hydrology and water quality are largely determined by releases from state and federally managed reservoirs on the east side of the river basin and agricultural and wetland drainage discharges from the west side of the river basin. A separate basin-scale water allocation model was needed to develop the logic for water deliveries to individual water districts in the basin by simulating the relationship between climate and reservoir water storage and agency water contract delivery policies. This auxiliary model was linked to the SJRIO model to develop an implementation strategy for the salinity TMDL, and the 30 year hydrologic time series it provided allowed the strategy to be tested for a historic sequence of water year types. This is an example of a simple data-driven mass balance model linked with a more complex decision model to produce realistic scenarios that formed the conceptual basis for a successful salinity TMDL. This linkage allowed the use of available monitoring time-series data of flow and salinity conditions to support the technical TMDL methodology.

5.2.1.10 Geographical Information System Workflow Models.   Increased use of geographic information systems (GISs) and high-resolution remote sensing analysis in support of TMDL modeling has led to the development of simple object-oriented modeling toolboxes where maps of land-use cover and other measurable geographic data are combined to yield estimates of pollutant loading and other pertinent decision variables. A common application of this methodology has been erosion estimation and sediment transport modeling. The RUSLE2 model, presented previously, has been implemented very effectively as a GIS workflow because many of the coverages essential to the model can be represented by map overlays.

Another GIS application was the development of a GIS-based graphical user interface use of the generalized watershed loading functions (GWLF) model using the ArcView platform by Pennsylvania State University

(2016) to create a software called AVGWLF. The AVGWLF helps the user determine generalized watershed pollutant loading, source assessment, and seasonal and interannual variability of pollutant impacts on a receiving waterbody. The AVGWLF tool has been used extensively for TMDL assessments in the northeast United States and in mid-Atlantic regions. The tool has been adopted statewide in Pennsylvania for TMDL development and for agricultural land management (USEPA 2005, Pennsylvania State University 2016).

To extend the utility of the software, a major revision was undertaken to make the software publicly available using an open-source, geographic information system platform MapWindows. The new software application in MapWindows has been named MapShed, which has helped to increase the user community among those who do not have the resources to purchase an ArcGIS license (Stroud Water Research Center 2019). In addition to the publicly available geographic information system upgrade, a number of additional GIS-based, analytical tools were developed to provide additional capabilities such as the estimation of pathogen loads, better simulation of pollutant transport in urban waters, and improved assessment of pollutant load reductions using best management practices.

The primary advantages of using a GIS include method transparency, the selection of a discretized model domain that allows for inclusion of greater spatial detail, and the ability to employ superior visualization of input data and model output. This use of a GIS works well with simple methods for which data such as land use can be readily assimilated and presented digitally in a map format. The technique is less effective as an aid for more complex, synergetic processes that are not easily discretized and that are not amenable to map-oriented visualization. Also refer to Chapter 2 "Watershed Models."

5.2.2 Simple Receiving Water Models and Methods

This subsection illustrates the utility of simple receiving water models and methods from three selected examples. It is worth noting that for dissolved oxygen and nutrient issues in streams and rivers, the Streeter–Phelps equation (Streeter and Phelps 1925) and its enhanced version (O'Connor 1960, Thomann 1963) are commonly used in many receiving water quality models. For a description of QUAL2E and QUAL2K models, refer to Chapter 3 "Receiving Water Quality Models."

5.2.2.1 BATHTUB. The simplified lake eutrophication model BATHTUB was developed for the US Army Corps of Engineers (USACE) in 1985 to evaluate and manage USACE reservoirs (Walker 1985, 1986) prior to the development of USEPA and state TMDL programs in the 1990s. This model uses empirical regression equations based on data from USACE reservoirs to approximate long-term, eutrophication kinetics. This approximation may limit the reliability of TMDL forecasts. The other major simplification is that BATHTUB is limited to simulations of steady-state or average eutrophication in lakes and reservoirs.

The program BATHTUB is based on steady-state water and nutrient mass balances in a spatially segmented reservoir network that accounts for advective and dispersive transport, and transport and sedimentation of particles with particle-bound nutrients. Eutrophication-related total phosphorus, total nitrogen, organic nitrogen, chlorophyll *a*, transparency (measured as Secchi depth), and hypolimnetic and metalimnetic dissolved oxygen depletion rates can be estimated using empirical relationships and tested for applicability in reservoirs (Walker 1986, 2014).

This model can be used to assess the impacts of water inflows and nutrient loads and the impacts of mean pool elevation during the growing season and determine maximum nutrient loadings allowable while achieving water quality objectives for the waterbody. To manage regional reservoir water quality, the BATHTUB model can be configured for simultaneous application to sets, sequences, or networks of reservoirs also involving multiple tributaries and point sources.

The BATHTUB model has been used routinely for determining TMDLs for nutrients to prevent eutrophication. These determinations include TMDLs for Beaver Creek and Grand Lake St. Marys watershed in Ohio (OEPA 2008). Borah et al. (2006) documented extensive use of the BATHTUB model to determine sediment and nutrient TMDLs with three TMDL determinations in Illinois. Borah et al. (2006) suggest that the BATHTUB model was selected for its simplicity after jurisdictions failed to budget resources to collect adequate, independent, synoptic calibration and confirmation data to develop reliable cause-and-effect relationships between loads and impairments for both sediment and nutrients. Borah et al. (2006) concluded that the BATHTUB model had limitations for TMDL implementation planning. Furthermore, the BATHTUB model has been used in recent nutrient TMDLs for lakes (e.g., IDNR 2020, MPCA 2020).

5.2.2.2 Stream Segment Temperature Model.   One of the important water quality parameters in receiving water streams is temperature. The Stream Segment Temperature (SSTEMP) model is a scaled-down version of the Stream Network Temperature (SNTEMP) model developed by Theurer et al. (1984). This USGS-supported model was based on the equilibrium temperature approximation of the fundamental, daily, steady-state heat balance. The model simulates steady-state daily stream temperatures in a specific stream or river segment for a specified period (1 day to usually 1 month or more) (Bartholow 2010).

SSTEMP is a mechanistic, one-dimensional, heat-transport model that simulates daily mean, minimum, and maximum water temperatures as a function of stream distance and ambient heat flux. Optionally this model simulates solar radiation penetration of the water column. The net heat flux is calculated as the sum of (1) direct short-wave solar radiation, (2) heat flux of long- wave atmospheric and water surface back radiation, (3) shading by streamside vegetation, (4) evaporation, (5) heat from groundwater recharge into the stream, (6) convection, (7) conduction, and (8) streambed fluid friction (Manning n coefficient). This heat transport model simulates the dynamic water temperature for steady flow equation. All specifications, including meteorological, hydrological, and shading data, are represented by 24-hour averages. SSTEMP requires specification of the average stream geometry.

Unlike the large network model, SNTEMP (Bartholow 2010), this program simulates single stream segments daily for a specific time period (e.g., a month, week, or day) for any given set of model specifications. Initially designed as a training tool, the SSTEMP program may be used satisfactorily for a variety of simple cases. The SSTEMP model is especially useful to perform sensitivity and uncertainty analysis. With good quality specifications, SSTEMP should adequately reproduce mean daily water temperatures throughout a stream reach. The users should not expect too much from SSTEMP if the input values are of poor quality or if the model assumptions are not met.

The SSTEMP model is one of the least complex representatives of one-dimensional, heat transport models (e.g., Beschta and Weatherred 1984, Jobson and Keefer 1979, Sinokrot and Stefan 1993, 1994, Deas and Lowney 2000, Boyd and Kasper 2003, Tetra Tech 2019). The Heat Source model version 7 (Boyd and Kasper 2003) was developed by a state pollution control agency for use by government and private TMDL modelers and provides a fully dynamic simulation of heat and hydrodynamics.

The SSTEMP model was not specifically designed for TMDL analysis and lacks many of the detailed features of the physics-based models adapted for the first temperature TMDL (Grande Ronde River in Oregon; Chen et al. 1993, 1998a, b). However, the SSTEMP model can be applied to problems such as analyzing the effects of changing riparian shade along rivers and streams or alterations that might affect the physical characteristics of a stream. The model can also be used to examine the effects of different stream withdrawals and returns on instream temperature for TMDL-related applications. Example applications of the model for TMDL development include Prickly Pear Creek near Helena, Montana, where it was applied for stream temperature management (MDEQ 2004), East and West Fork Bitterroot rivers in Montana (MDEQ 2011), Galisteo River in New Mexico (NMED 2017), and Upper Nine Mile Creek in Utah (UDEQ 2017).

5.2.2.3 Load–Duration Curve. The load–duration curve (LDC) approach allows the characterization of water quality concentrations for varied flow regimes. The pollutant load is expressed as a function of these diverse flow conditions, including critical flow condition (USEPA 2007). This statistics-based approach can rapidly estimate existing and allowable loads with limited information. Some practitioners value the insight that LDCs provide into the best-fit relationship between water quality impairment and the hydrologic regime (ASCE 2017).

The first step in TMDL development using LDCs is to generate a flow-duration curve. This is a cumulative frequency curve of daily mean flows without regard to chronology of occurrence (Leopold 1994). The flow-duration curve incorporates stream flow measured at staff gauge for the applicable period of record. These measured flows are usually sorted from the largest value to the smallest. For each flow in the sequence, the flow-duration curve provides the corresponding time interval that a certain flow rate is equaled or exceeded. This time interval expressed as a percentage is designated the flow–duration interval or flow–duration percentile (Risley et al. 2008). Once a flow–duration curve has been created, the LDC is calculated by multiplying the flow by the applicable water quality criterion or target. The independent variable (abscissa) depicts the flow–duration interval, and the dependent variable (ordinate) depicts the contaminant load at a designated flow monitoring station in the watershed where data are available. A specific curve derived from flow and water quality criterion represents the allowable load for each flow condition that the area above the curve represent exceedances of the water quality criterion, which represent excess pollutant loading as well. The area below the curve represents a condition of excess assimilative capacity and compliance with the water quality criterion and allowable pollutant loading.

A fecal coliform TMDL development for a river in South Carolina was prepared by the South Carolina Department of Health and Environmental Control (SCDHEC 2010) and is an example that follows the load duration curve approach. An appendix in the EPA's guide "An Approach for Using Load Duration Curves in the Development of TMDLs" (USEPA 2007) describes a case study in which load duration curves were used to support TMDL development.

LDCs can provide important information to support TMDL assessments. For example, the extent of an impairment can be visually assessed based on pollutant loading that exceeds or is lower than the data derived from the allowable loading curve. The temporal nature of an impairment can also be inferred based on the timing of pollutant loads to the waterbody (USEPA 2007). Pollutant loads that exceed those specified by the loading curve during low flow conditions are likely indicative of steady-state discharges from sources such as wastewater treatment plants. Loads that are greater than those specified by the curve for allowable pollutant loading during wet weather conditions may reflect contributions associated with sheet and rill erosion, washoff processes, and streambank erosion. Those loading rates that plot above the curve at the low and high extremes of the curve may reflect extreme hydrologic conditions of flood or drought. If sufficient data are available, the LDC method can accurately identify the allowable and existing loads in a stream reach where the data were collected and can be used to meet the basic regulatory requirement for TMDL development. Hence, LDCs have value to develop and offer insight into critical conditions.

Although it is possible to discriminate between low flow point sources and wet weather NPSs using an LDC, no specific information is typically provided regarding what types of point or NPSs that occur in the watershed. LDCs are not suitable for simulating alternate management scenarios and for evaluating the impact of various implementation options. These LDCs do not have underlying conceptual models or algorithms to relate source loading and water quality response. Therefore, the use of LDCs to forecast the impacts of pollutant load reduction strategies on impairments is very limited.

5.3 SUMMARY

In this chapter, a total of 13 simple models or methods, 10 for load estimations from watersheds and 3 for water quality analysis in receiving waterbodies that can be used in certain areas of TMDL development and implementation are presented. There may be more models or methods available in the literature. The Bacteria Loading Estimator Spreadsheet Tool (BLEST) is one of those, a customized tool similar to STEPL, presented previously. BLEST was designed as an easy-to-use indicator bacteria model that can overcome the shortcomings of many of the simpler TMDL modeling approaches by integrating spatial variation into load estimates. It was applied to an urban watershed in Houston, Texas (Petersen et al. 2009). The BLEST tool incorporates bacteria loading from point and nonpoint sources, such as wastewater treatment plants, sanitary sewer overflows, septic systems, storm sewer leaks, runoff, bed sediment resuspension, and direct deposition.

Simple methods can be used when poor data availability, budget constraints, and time limitations preclude the use of more comprehensive, physical-based models that often require significant input data. Simple models and methods still require more on expert judgment to interpret empirical relationships between watershed characteristics and pollutant loads to receiving waters. Many of these methods may use existing databases and can vary in complexity from a simple spreadsheet program or analytical solution to more detailed data-driven mass balance models. These may be custom applications or off-the shelf analytical tools.

Simple approaches are also, in general, easier to understand and are more transparent than more detailed analyses and can often help to elicit the input and review from stakeholders. The trade-offs associated with using simple approaches include a potential decrease in forecast accuracy and often an inability to make predictions at fine geographic and time scales (e.g., watershed-scale source predictions versus model detailed estimates, and annual versus seasonal estimates) (USEPA 1999). A major advantage of simple methods is their ability to provide a rapid assessment and screening tool for identifying critical pollutant loading areas or stream reaches with minimal effort and data requirements.

5.4 STATE-OF-THE-ART AND STATE-OF-THE-PRACTICE

In general, starting with simple analyses and iteratively expanding data collection and modeling as the need arises is acknowledged by many practitioners as the best approach (NRC 2001). The standard practice in modeling is to identify the dominant processes and the simplest models sufficient to meet the needs of the project (USEPA 2005). Models include suites of equations that represent most processes based on the understanding of real-world setting. For example, the Streeter–Phelps equation (Streeter and Phelps 1925) and its enhanced version (O'Connor 1960, Thomann 1963) are used in many receiving water quality models (e.g., QUAL2E and QUAL2K). Also refer to Chapter 3 "Receiving Water Quality Models."

Thomann and Mueller (1987) established that the simplest model sufficient to answer management questions with confidence should be applied. If data availability is limited and insufficient for calibration of more highly parameterized models, then a simpler model should be investigated and potentially The choice of a water quality model involves trade-offs among model complexity, required reliability, cost, and time.

Occasionally, situations arise where no off-the-shelf simple model or analytical procedure is available or applicable to the TMDL being undertaken. In these circumstances, new approaches or hybrid techniques may be employed that, if innovative and successful, might constitute the "state of the art". These instances are not well documented, and the methodologies developed are rarely published in peer-reviewed journals. In this case, the approach may require additional review or peer review to verify its applicability and appropriateness for TMDL development. Also refer to Chapter 11, which includes a section on "model review."

An adaptive approach to TMDL modeling could start with simpler models at the initial phases and then progress to more complex frameworks as additional data are collected and as more focused remedial measures for water quality impairment are assessed. However, as often occurs, analysts may initially embrace a comprehensive physically based modeling strategy only to find that constraints of time, financial resources, and available data force revisions to the initial TMDL development plan. In these circumstances, careful consideration of available simple modeling solutions may prove a more efficient and cost-effective solution.

ACKNOWLEDGMENTS

Reviews, edits, and comments provided by Deva K. Borah, G. Padmanabhan, and Steven C. McCutcheon in this chapter are greatly appreciated.

REFERENCES

ASCE. 2017. *Total maximum daily load analysis and modeling: Assessment of the practice*. Reston, VA: ASCE.

Bartholow, J. 2010. *Stream network and stream segment temperature models software*. Fort Collins, CO: USGS.

Beschta, R. L., and J. Weatherred. 1984. *A computer model for predicting stream temperatures resulting from the management of streamside vegetation*. USDA Forest Service Report WSDG-AD-00009. Washington, DC: US Forest Service, Watershed Systems Development Group.

Boomer, K. B., D. E. Weller, and T. E. Jordan. 2008. "Empirical models based on the Universal Soil Loss Equation fail to predict sediment discharges from Chesapeake Bay catchments." *J. Environ. Qual.* 37: 79–89.

Borah, D. K., G. Yagow, A. Saleh, P. L. Barnes, W. Rosenthal, E. C. Krug, et al. 2006. "Sediment and nutrient modeling for TMDL development and implementation." *Trans. ASABE* 49 (4): 967–986.

Boyd, M., and B. Kasper. 2003. Analytical Methods for Dynamic Open Channel Heat and Mass Transfer: Methodology for Heat Source Model Version 7.0.

Cappiella, K., and K. Brown. 2001. *Derivations of impervious cover for suburban land uses in the Chesapeake Bay watershed*. Prepared for the United States Environmental Protection Agency Chesapeake Bay Program Office. Ellicott City, MD: Center for Watershed Protection.

Cappiella, K., T. Schueler, and T. Wright. 2005. *Urban Watershed Forestry Manual. Part 2: Conserving and Planting Trees at Development Sites*. USDA Forest Service, Newtown Square, PA.

Caraco, D. 2013. *Watershed treatment model 2013 documentation*. Ellicott City, MD: Center for Watershed Protection.

Chapra, S. C. 1997. *Surface water-quality modeling*. New York: McGraw Hill.

Chapra, S. C. 2003. "Engineering water quality models and TMDLs." *J. Water Resour. Plann. Manage.* 129 (4): 247–255.

Chen, Y. D., R. F. Carsel, S. C. McCutcheon, and W. L. Nutter. 1998a. "Stream temperature simulation of forested riparian areas: I. watershed-scale model development." *J. Environ. Eng.* 124 (4): 304–315.

Chen, Y. D., S. C. McCutcheon, D. J. Norton, and W. L. Nutter. 1998b. "Stream temperature simulation of forested riparian areas: II. Model application." *J. Environ. Eng.* 124 (4): 316–328.

Chen, Y. D., S. C. McCutcheon, T. C. Rasmussen, W. L. Nutter, and R. F. Carsel. 1993. "Integrating water quality modeling with ecological risk assessment for nonpoint source pollution control: A conceptual framework." *Water Sci. Technol.* 28 (3–5): 431–440.

Chesapeake Bay Program. 2019. "Bay program history." Accessed July 18, 2020. https://www.chesapeakebay.net/who/bay_program_history.

CVWB (Central Valley Water Board). 2004. *Amendments to the water quality control plan for the Sacramento River and San Joaquin River Basins for the control of salt and boron discharges into the Lower San Joaquin River.* Final Staff Rep. Sacramento, CA: CVWB.

Deas, M. L., and C. L. Lowney. 2000. "Water temperature modeling review: Central Valley." Sponsored by the Bay-Delta Modeling Forum contract number 254-99 administered by the San Francisco Estuary Institute. Accessed September 17, 2020. http://www.cwemf.org/Pubs/BDMFTempReview.pdf.

Driver, N. E., and B. M. Troutman. 1989. "Regression models for estimating urban storm-runoff quality and quantity in the United States." *J. Hydrol.* 109: 221–236.

Duan, S., S. S. Kaushal, P. M. Groffman, L. E. Band, and K. T. Belt. 2012. "Phosphorus export across an urban to rural gradient in the Chesapeake Bay watershed." *J. Geophys. Res.* 117, doi:10.1029/2011JG001782.

Hawkins, R. H., T. J. Ward, D. E. Woodward, and J. A. Van Mullem. 2009. *Curve number hydrology: State of the practice.* Reston, VA: ASCE.

Hensel, D. R., and R. M. Hirsch. 1995. *Statistical methods in water resources.* Studies in Environmental Science 49. Amsterdam, Netherlands: Elsevier.

Huber, W. 1993. "Contaminant transport in surface water." In *Handbook of hydrology,* edited by D. R. Maidment, 14.7–14.10. New York: McGraw Hill.

IDNR (Iowa Department of Natural Resources). 2020. *Water quality improvement plan for Bob White Lake (Wayne County, Iowa) total maximum daily load for algae, turbidity, and dissolved oxygen.* Des Moines, IA: IDNR.

Jobson, H. E., and T. N. Keefer. 1979. *Modeling highly transient flow, mass and heat transfer in the Chattahoochee River near Atlanta, Georgia.* Geological Survey Professional Paper 1136. U.S. Government Printing Office, Washington D.C.

Ketchum, R. H. 1951a. "The flushing of tidal estuaries." *Sewage Ind. Wastes* 23 (2): 198–209.

Ketchum, R. H. 1951b. "The exchanges of fresh and salt waters in tidal estuaries." *J. Mar. Res* 10: 18–38.

Leopold, L. B. 1994. *A view of the river.* Cambridge, MA: Harvard University Press.

Lichter, J., and P. Lindsay. 1994. "Soil Compaction and Site Construction: Assessment and Case Studies." pp. 126–130 in The Landscape Below Ground. *Proceedings of International Workshop on Tree Root Development in Urban Soils.* International Society of Arboriculture. Champaign, Illinois.

Lung, W. S., J. L. Martin, and S. C. McCutcheon. 1993. "Analysis of eutrophication potential of Passage Cove and Snug Harbor, Prince William Sound, Alaska." *J. Environ. Eng.* 119 (5): 811–824.

Martin, J. L., and S. C. McCutcheon. 1999. *Hydrodynamics and transport for water quality modeling.* Boca Raton, FL: CRC Press.

McCutcheon, S. C. 1983. *The evaluation of selected one-dimensional stream water-quality models with field data.* Waterways Experiment Station Rep. No. E-11. Vicksburg, MS: US Army Corps of Engineers.

McCutcheon, S. C. 1989. *Water quality modeling: Vol. I, river transport and surface exchange.* Boca Raton, FL: CRC Press.

MDEQ (Montana Department of Environmental Quality). 2004. *SSTEMP Modeling—Lake Helena Watershed Planning Area.* Helena, MT: MDEQ.

MDEQ. 2011. *Bitterroot temperature and tributary sediment total maximum daily loads and framework water quality improvement plan.* Helena, MT: MDEQ.

Miller, M., P. D. Capel, A. M. Garcia, and S. Ator. 2020. "Response of nitrogen loading to the Chesapeake Bay to source reduction and land use change scenarios: A SPARROW-informed analysis." *J. Am. Water Resour. Assoc.* 56 (1): 100–112.

Mills, W. B., D. B. Porcella, M. J. Ungs, S. A. Gherini, K. V. Summers, M. Lingfung, et al. 1985. *Water quality assessment: A screening procedure for toxic and conventional pollutants.* EPA/600/6-85/002a, b. Athens, GA: EPA.

Moore, R. B., C. M. Johnston, K. W. Robinson, and J. R. Deacon. 2004. *Estimation of total nitrogen and phosphorus in New England streams using spatially referenced regression models.* Scientific Investigations Rep. 2004-5012. Denver: USGS.

MPCA (Minnesota Pollution Control Agency). 2020. *Winnebago river watershed total maximum daily load.* St Paul, MN: MPCA.

Mullaney, J. R. 2016. *Nitrogen loads from selected rivers in the Long Island Sound Basin, 2005–13, Connecticut and Massachusetts.* U.S. Geological Survey Open-File Report 2016–1007, https://pubs.er.usgs.gov/publication/ofr20161007

Mysiak, J., C. Giupponi, and P. Rosato. 2005. "Towards the development of a decision support system for water resource management." *Environ. Modell. Software* 20: 203–214.

NMED (New Mexico Environment Department). 2017. *Total maximum daily load for Galisteo River*. Santa Fe, NM: NMED.

NRC (National Research Council). 2001. *Assessing the TMDL approach to water quality management*. Washington, DC: National Academy Press.

O'Connor, D. J. 1960. "Oxygen balance of an estuary." *J. Sanitary Eng. Div.* 86 (SA3): 35–56.

OEPA (Ohio Environmental Protection Agency). 2008. *TMDL development for the Beaver Creek and Grand Lake St. Marys Watershed, Ohio*. Logan, OH: OEPA.

Parrott, L., and N. W. T. Quinn. 2016. "A complex systems approach for multi-objective water quality regulation on wetland landscapes." *Ecosphere* 7 (6): e01363.

Pennsylvania State University. 2016. *MapShed version 1.5. Users guide*. Prepared by B. M. Evans and K. J. Corradini. University Park, PA: Penn State Institutes of Energy and the Environment.

Petersen, C. M., H. S. Rifai, and R. Stein. 2009. "Bacteria load estimator spreadsheet tool for modeling spatial *Escherichia coli* loads to an urban Bayou." *J. Environ. Eng.* 135 (4): 203–217.

Pitt, R., A. Maestre, R. Morquecho, T. Brown, T. Schueler, K. Cappiella, and P. Sturm. 2005. *Evaluation of NPDES phase 1 municipal stormwater monitoring data*. Elliot City, MD: University of Alabama, Tuscaloosa and Center for Watershed Protection.

Preston, S. D., and J. W. Brakebill. 1999. *Application of spatially referenced regression modeling for the evaluation of total nitrogen loading in the Chesapeake Bay watershed*. Water Resources Investigations Rep. 99-4054. Reston, VA: USGS.

Pritchard, D. W. 1969. "Dispersion and flushing of pollutants in estuaries." *J. Hydraul. Eng. Div.* 95(HY1): 115–124.

Purdue University. 2013. *Long-Term Hydrological Impact Analysis (L-THIA)— Fact Sheet*. West Lafayette, IN: Purdue University.

Purdue University. 2015. *Long Term Hydrologic Impact Analysis (L-THIA)—Low Impact Development (LID) Spreadsheet*. West Lafayette, IN: Purdue Univ.

Purdue University. 2016. *Long Term Hydrologic Impact Analysis (L-THIA)*. West Lafayette, IN: Purdue University.

Quinn, N. W. T. 2004. *WETMANSIM v. 1.00: Wetland management simulator— Spreadsheet model of potential water quality impacts of level IV water supply on salt loading to the San Joaquin River*. Technical Memorandum. Washington, DC: United States Bureau of Reclamation.

Quinn, N. W. T., and J. M. Laflen. 1983. "Characteristics of raindrop throughfall under corn canopy." *Trans. ASAE* 26 (5): 1445–1450.

Renard, K. G., G. R. Foster, G. A. Weesies, D. K. McCool, and D. C. Yoder. 1997. *Predicting soil erosion by water: A guide to conservation planning with the revised soil loss equation (RUSLE)*. Agriculture Handbook No. 703. Washington, DC: US Dept. of Agriculture, Agricultural Research Service.

Risley, J., A. Stonewall, and T. Haluska. 2008. *Estimating flow-duration and low-flow frequency statistics for unregulated streams in Oregon.* Scientific Investigations Rep. 2008-5126. Revision 1.1. Washington, DC: USGS.

Runkel, R. L., C. G. Crawford, and T. A. Cohn. 2004. *Load estimator (LOADEST): A FORTRAN program for estimating constituent loads in streams and rivers.* USGS Techniques and Methods Book 4, Chapter A5. Washington, DC: USGS.

SCDHEC (South Carolina Department of Health and Environmental Control). 2010. "Total maximum daily load document RS-05590, Big Creek watershed: Fecal coliform bacteria." Accessed October 30. 2021. https://scdhec.gov/sites/default/files/docs/HomeAndEnvironment /Docs/tmdl_bigCreek.pdf.

Schueler, T. S. 1987. *The simple method in controlling urban runoff: A practical manual for planning and designing urban BMPs.* Prepared for Washington Metropolitan Water Resources Planning Board. Washington, DC: Metropolitan Washington Council of Governments.

Schueler, T. S. 2001a. "The compaction of urban soils." *Watershed Prot. Tech.* 3 (2): 661–665.

Schueler, T. S. 2001b. "Can urban soil compaction be reversed?" *Watershed Prot. Tech.* 3 (2): 666–669.

Schwarz, G. E., A. B. Hoos, R. B. Alexander, and R. A. Smith. 2006. *The SPARROW surface water-quality model: Theory, application and user documentation.* United States Geological Survey Techniques and Methods, Book 6, Section B, Chap. 3. Washington, DC: USGS.

Sinokrot, B. A., and H. G. Stefan. 1993. "Stream temperature dynamics: Measurements and modeling." *Water Resour. Res.* 29: 2299–2312.

Sinokrot, B. A., and H. G. Stefan. 1994. "Stream water-temperature sensitivity to weather and bed parameters." *J. Hydrol. Eng.* 120 (6): 722–735.

Smith, R. A., R. B. Alexander, and G. E. Schwarz. 1997. "Regional interpretation of water-quality monitoring data." *Water Resour. Res.* 33 (12): 2781–2798.

Stenback, G. A., W. G. Crumpton, K. E. Schilling, and M. J. Helmers. 2011. "Rating curve estimation of nutrient loads in Iowa rivers." *J. Hydrol.* 396: 158–169.

Streeter, H. W., and E. B. Phelps. 1925. *A Study of the pollution and natural purification of the Ohio river. III. Factors concerned in the phenomena of oxidation and reaeration.* Public Health Bulletin No. 146. Washington, DC: US Dept. of Health, Education, and Welfare.

Stroud Water Research Center. 2019. *MapShed GIS-Based Watershed Modeling Tool.* Accessed October 30, 2021. https://wikiwatershed.org/help/ model-help/mapshed/.

Tasker, G. D., and N. E. Driver. 1988. "Nationwide regression models for predicting urban runoff water quality at unmonitored sites." *Water Resour. Bull.* 24 (5): 1091–1101.

Tetra Tech. 2019. *Update of the RBM10 temperature model of the Columbia and Snake rivers.* Seattle: Prepared for the Environmental Protection Agency, Region 10.

Theurer, F. D., K. A. Voos, and W. J. Miller. 1984. *Instream water temperature model.* Instream Flow Inf. Pap. 16. FWS/OBS-84/15. Washington, DC: US Fish and Wildlife Service.

Thomann, R. V. 1963. "Mathematical model for dissolved oxygen." *J. Sanitary Eng. Div.* 89 (SA5): 1–30.

Thomann, R. V., and J. A. Mueller. 1987. *Principles of surface water quality modeling and control.* New York: Harper and Row.

UDEQ (Utah Department of Environmental Quality). 2017. *Temperature total maximum daily load (TMDL) for upper nine mile creek watershed.* Salt Lake City, UT: UDEQ.

USDA (US Department of Agriculture). 2003. *Revised universal soil loss equation 2.* Washington, DC: USDA.

USEPA (US Environmental Protection Agency). 1983. *Results of the nationwide urban runoff program.* Vol. I Final Rep. Washington, DC: Water Planning Division.

USEPA. 1999. *Protocol for developing nutrient TMDLs.* 1st ed. EPA 841-B-99-007. Washington, DC: USEPA.

USEPA. 2005. *TMDL model evaluation and research needs.* EPA/600/R-05/149. Washington, DC: USEPA.

USEPA. 2007. *An approach for using load duration curves in the development of TMDLs.* EPA 841-B-07-006. Washington, DC: USEPA.

USEPA. 2018. *Spreadsheet tool for estimating pollutant loads (STEPL) 4.4 user's guide.* Pasadena, CA: Tetra Tech.

USGS (US Geological Survey). 2012. *SPARROW mappers.* Reston, VA: USGS.

USGS. 2016. *Load estimator (LOADEST): A program for estimating constituent loads in streams and rivers.* Reston, VA: USGS. Accessed December 18, 2021. https://water.usgs.gov/software/loadest/.

USGS and USEPA. 2017. *Water Quality Portal.* Accessed October 30, 2021. https://www.waterqualitydata.us/portal_userguide/.

Voinov, A. A. 2008. "Conceptual diagrams and flow diagrams." In *Encyclopedia of ecology,* edited by S. E. Jørgensen and B. D. Fath, 731–737. Amsterdam, Netherlands: Elsevier.

Walker, W. W. 1985. *Empirical methods for predicting eutrophication in impoundments; Report 3, Phase III: Model refinements.* Tech. Rep. E-81-9. Vicksburg, MS: US Army Engineer Waterways Experiment Station.

Walker, W. W. 1986. *Empirical methods for predicting eutrophication in impoundments; Report 3, Phase III: Applications manual.* Tech. Rep. E-81-9. Vicksburg, MS: US Army Engineer Waterways Experiment Station.

Walker, W. W. 2014. "Software for eutrophication assessment and prediction: Description of diagnostic variables in bathtub model output." https://www.wwwalker.net/bathtub/help/table_diagnostics.htm.

Wingert, S., B. Holcomb, J. Bowcutt, and C. Adams. 2017. *Temperature total maximum daily load (TMDL) for Upper Nine Mile Creek watershed*. TMDL Document. Salt Lake City, UT: Utah Dept. of Environmental Quality.

Wischmeier, W. H., and D. D. Smith. 1978. *Predicting rainfall-erosion losses: A guide to conservation planning*. Agriculture Handbook No. 537. Washington, DC: US Dept. of Agriculture, Agricultural Research Service.

Zhang, H. X. 2005. "Water quality models for developing soil management practices." In *Water encyclopedia-Vol. 1: Water quality and resource development*, edited by J. H. Lehr, 248–255. Hoboken, NJ: Wiley.

Zhang, H. X., and N. W. T. Quinn. 2019. "Simple models and analytical procedures for total maximum daily load assessment." *J. Hydrol. Eng.* 24 (2): 02518002.

CHAPTER 6

CRITICAL CONDITION DETERMINATION FOR TOTAL MAXIMUM DAILY LOAD MODELING

Harry X. Zhang, G. Padmanabhan

6.1 INTRODUCTION

In any total maximum daily load (TMDL) modeling, one of the first steps would be to select a critical condition for streams transporting water quality constituents and the receiving waterbody to which the hydrologic and water quality models may be applied to track the evolution of water quality conditions of the waterbody. One of the key challenges in selecting a critical condition in the TMDL development process is to define it for waterbodies impacted by both point- and nonpoint-source pollutants. A knowledge of an appropriate critical condition could help determine the feasible TMDL allocation scenarios needed to be taken to meet water quality standards in the future. "Critical condition" is also one of the most important elements in determining the impairment status of a waterbody. In general, it implies instances in which the physical, chemical, and biological characteristics of the receiving waterbody interact with pollutant sources to produce the worst possible adverse impact on aquatic biota and existing or future characteristic water uses (USEPA 1991, 1999a, b, 2001).

The USEPA regulations for TMDL program development and implementation require that the TMDL modeling and process take into account the critical conditions for streamflow, loading, and water quality parameters to ensure that the water quality of an impaired waterbody is protected during times when it is most vulnerable [40 CFR 130.7(c) (1) (2011)]. Therefore, each TMDL is expected to meet water quality standards for defined critical conditions. A critical condition influences the factors that combine to cause water quality standard violations. Therefore, inadequately addressing the issue of critical condition may result in a less-than-satisfactory TMDL for restoring the affected watershed and ecosystem. A careful consideration of critical environmental conditions has the potential of reducing the uncertainty between the model estimation and the actual water quality environment, including those under worst-case scenarios.

Critical condition analysis needs to be conducted connecting it with water quality standards. USEPA's water quality criteria have three components: magnitude, duration, and frequency. Magnitude refers to the concentration of a pollutant and is represented by a numeric criterion. Duration refers to the time period in which receptors (e.g., aquatic organisms) would be exposed to the pollutant at the concentration of concern (e.g., daily average concentration). Concentrations exceeding criteria values beyond the designated duration are referred to as "excursions." An occurrence happening more often than the designated frequency is termed an "exceedance," which is the basis for listing that water as impaired by not meeting water quality standards. Each of the three components of water quality criteria (i.e., magnitude, frequency, and duration) is pollutant-specific and may vary with season. The frequency component should be expressed in terms of several allowed excursions in a specified period (return period) and not in terms of the low flow or an absolute "never to be exceeded" limit. The requirement of "no exceedances" for many water quality criteria is not achievable by using natural variability alone, much less with the variability associated with discharges from point and nonpoint sources (NRC 2001). Therefore, the selected critical condition should consider the aforementioned features of water quality criteria. The selected critical condition must represent potentially the most vulnerable combination of the aforementioned factors.

It is important that specific critical conditions such as persistent low flows, temperature, and so on be evaluated under various loading scenarios to determine whether they would cause water quality standard violations in the waterbody under consideration. Impairment of receiving waters may be caused by pollutant loads from either multiple point sources or nonpoint sources or both. Point sources are well-understood as a cause of impairment. In general, TMDLs addressing pollution in streams and rivers from point sources will use a low flow as a critical condition. An example is the low-flow condition defined by 7Q10 (the lowest 7-day average streamflow that occurs once on average every 10 years). Low flows are critical because as flows increase with constant point-source load, instream concentrations will decrease as the stream's waste assimilative capacity increases. However, critical conditions are rarely clear for flows originating from nonpoint sources dynamically generated across a watershed, particularly from storm runoff. As streamflow increases due to storm runoff, pollutant load into the streams from contributing areas will also increase, thereby the concentrations of pollutants in receiving waters will also increase. Therefore, in this case, the critical condition is the worst combination of pollutant influx and streamflow that produces violations in water quality standards. For example, the combination of low flows followed by the first flush of storm-related runoff can result in the highest pollutant concentrations observed in a watershed drainage network. Critical condition modeling and analysis are linked to water quality criteria used for the listed impairments and specific TMDL under consideration (e.g., duration and frequency that would be protective of aquatic health and the designated use of a waterbody).

This chapter on critical condition modeling and analysis methodologies in TMDL development and implementation is developed based on Zhang and Padmanabhan (2019). Four main methods are used for determining critical conditions. Brief descriptions of the situations to which these methods apply follow.

The first method is applicable for constant continuous flows from point-source discharge into a receiving waterbody, in which a statistically based low flow is used in combination with environmental factors such as temperature that would occur in a reasonable "worst-case" situation.

The second method is applicable for variable continuous flows from nonpoint sources and/or a combination of point and nonpoint sources. In these cases, continuous model simulation of the fate and transport of TMDL pollutants via watershed and their interaction with receiving waters is used to analyze various scenarios of impairment.

The third method is applicable when the long periods of flow records in receiving waterbody are available, but other data and/or resources needed for continuous model simulation are not available. The cumulative frequency distribution of daily flow conditions covering low, medium, and high flows is used as the basis for this method. Load–duration curves (LDCs) are developed by multiplying stream flows with the numeric water quality target and a conversion factor for the TMDL pollutant of concern.

The fourth and last method, titled "critical flow storm (CFS)," is in essence a risk-based approach. The risk here is defined as the joint probability of the occurrence of a selected set of rainfall and river-flow conditions. In the risk-based approach, for a defined percentage of risk and a known rainfall condition, the river-flow probability and corresponding return period are estimated. Compared with the other three methods, this method is more applicable for research-oriented TMDL modeling studies and is used only for those situations to date.

6.2 METHODOLOGY FOR CRITICAL CONDITION DETERMINATION FOR TOTAL MAXIMUM DAILY LOAD MODELING

The four major methods used for critical condition analysis in TMDL development and implementation are described in the following sections. They demonstrate critical condition determination in relation to water quality standards and TMDL requirements. A comparison of the methods is given in Table 6-1. Examples of TMDLs in which these methods have been used are also given in Table 6-1.

6.2.1 Steady-State Models for Analyzing Impairment under Constant Flow

When constant point sources are dominant in the impaired waters, a critical condition usually occurs when streams and rivers are at steady state, low flow, especially in late summer during the warmest temperatures of the year. Simpler, steady-state models are adequate and effective in relating impairments to specific loads in these situations (USEPA 1984, 1991).

A critical condition can be viewed as a combination of environmental factors (e.g., flow, temperature, etc.) with an acceptably low frequency of occurrence. Traditionally, a statistically based low-flow value is used as a critical condition in situations when point sources dominate. TMDLs for which critical conditions are readily determined usually involve the traditional scenario of a point source continuously discharging effluents with oxygen demand into a stream. A reasonable "worst-case" scenario is used for specifying a critical condition for a waterbody. For example, TMDL analysis of a stream often uses a low flow (the lowest 7-day average flow that occurs on average once every 10 years or 7Q10) for a critical condition because the ability of the waterbody to assimilate pollutants without exhibiting adverse impacts under this flow condition is expected to be minimum. In such cases, using the 7Q10 in tandem with a high water temperature represents a reasonable balance between the risk of water quality violations and the investment needed for wastewater treatment. Regulations in many states in the United States use a design flow statistic such as 7Q10 to define low flow for the purpose of setting permit discharge limits (USEPA 1986). For some year-round or continuous, chronic impairments that slowly react to pollutant accumulation, dynamic nonpoint- and point-source loads may be averaged annually as annual yields or average loads.

USEPA's DFLOW is a Windows-based tool to estimate design stream flows of user-selected frequency and averaging duration to perform low-flow analysis (i.e., 7Q10). Input to DFLOW consists of daily stream flows, such as those from the systematic data collection program maintained by the United States Geological Survey (USGS) to calculate user-specified design flows (USEPA 2006). In 2007, USGS published an overview of the National Streamflow Statistics Program that includes a computer program for estimating streamflow statistics for ungauged sites.

The low-flow condition of 7Q10, combined with a high temperature of water, is used for a critical condition only for TMDLs addressing impaired

Table 6-1. Comparison of Available Methods for Critical Condition Determination for TMDL Modeling.

Method	Advantage/benefit	Disadvantage/shortcoming	Example of TMDL case studies
1 Steady-state models (low-flow analysis)	1. Simple, well established 2. Approved approach by USEPA's guidance document on the WLA	1. Steady-state—technically sound for situations in which only point sources dominate 2. May reduce the level of protection depending on the assumptions regarding critical conditions used in the steady-state model approach	1. Blanchard River Watershed (Ohio) TMDL (OEPA 2009) and Ottawa River Watershed (Ohio) TMDL for total phosphorus (OEPA 2013) 2. Wyman Creek (Minnesota) TMDL for temperature and DO (MPCA 2018) 3. Wenatchee River Basin (Washington) TMDL for dissolved oxygen, pH, and phosphorus (WADOE 2006) 4. Nutrient TMDL analysis for Pocomoke River, Delaware (DNREC 2005) 5. Southampton Creek Nutrient TMDL, Pennsylvania (EPA 2008)

(*Continued*)

Table 6-1. (*Continued*).

Method	Advantage/benefit	Disadvantage/shortcoming	Example of TMDL case studies
2 Dynamic models (continuous simulation)	1. Widely used in the TMDL development for those impaired waterbodies affected by pollutants from both point and nonpoint sources 2. Allows for an analysis of long-term source loading and instream conditions if data are available 3. Generates multiple data points, which are essential for meeting certain water quality criteria (e.g., a 30-day geometric mean for a pathogen indicator pollutant)	1. There is no guarantee that the most critical condition or worst-case scenario during the selected hydrologic period will be accurately matched by the model, which could correspond to a short period of time when extensive data may not be available because of budget and resource constraints 2. Risk (exceedance probability and return period) associated with continuous simulation cannot be estimated 3. In general, data intensive	1. USEPA's Chesapeake Bay sediment and nutrient TMDLs (EPA 2010) 2. Beaver Creek (Virginia) bacteria and benthic TMDL revision (VADEQ 2016) 3. Bacteria TMDL Development for the Mattaponi River Watershed (Virginia) (VADEQ 2016a) 4. Lower Boise River (Idaho) TMDL (IDEQ 2015)

#	Approach	Advantages	Disadvantages	Examples
3	Statistics-based load–duration curves	1. Simple and a good screening tool for problem characterization 2. Accepted by USEPA as an alternate approach for TMDL development under certain circumstances 3. TMDL is expressed as a function of flow conditions (covering all flow conditions, including critical flow conditions)	1. Difficult to evaluate influencing factors on critical conditions and derive explicit percentage reduction of pollutant loads according to the listed source categories in TMDL allocation 2. Some watershed managers do not want to develop an average TMDL based on all flow conditions	1. Big Creek Watershed (South Carolina) TMDL for fecal coliform bacteria (SCDHEC 2010) 2. Salt Creek Watershed (Ohio) TMDL for bacteria (OEPA 2011) 3. Carson River (Nevada) TMDL for TSS and turbidity (NVDEP 2007) 4. Santa Maria (California) Watershed TMDL for fecal indicator bacteria (CEPA 2012)
4	Event-based critical flow-storm approach	1. Explicitly addresses a critical condition as a combination of streamflow, magnitude of storm event, and initial watershed condition 2. Offers the ability to estimate the risk and return period. Thus, the nonpoint-source management plan could be linked with its corresponding return period to determine the reasonable assurance of TMDL implementation 3. Event-based approach, less data intensive	1. Premodeling data analysis may be needed to determine the critical condition scenarios that include a site-specific combination of streamflow, storm size, and an antecedent condition 2. Further research and additional case studies are needed to demonstrate the application of this approach	1. Muddy Creek (Virginia) nitrate TMDL (VADEQ 2000) 2. Dy-yu Creek (Taiwan) Watershed modeling (Hsu et al. 2010) 3. Red River (North Dakota) fecal coliform TMDL (Gautam et al. 2006; Kasi et al. 2007)

Source: Adapted from Zhang and Padmanabhan (2019).

rivers and streams dominated by point sources. This approach is followed for nutrient and dissolved oxygen (DO) TMDLs because these conditions are, in general, favorable for nuisance plant growth. Low levels of DO are most likely to occur in streams during high temperatures because of lower saturation rates and higher decay rates, and low flow resulting in less reaeration. The assumption that concentrations of pollutants decrease as flows increase is likely true only for continuous discharges from a point source. This is not true for the cases with nonpoint-source contributions. In those cases, a dynamic continuous model simulation will be needed.

Table 6-1 lists several examples using this method, such as the Ottawa River Watershed (Ohio) TMDL for total phosphorus (OEPA 2013); Wenatchee River Basin (Washington) TMDL for DO, pH, and phosphorus (WADOE 2006); nutrient TMDL analysis for Pocomoke River in Delaware (DNREC 2005); and Southampton Creek Nutrient TMDL in Pennsylvania (USEPA 2008a).

The following TMDL development examples illustrate the use of steady-state models under critical low-flow conditions to support aquatic life and recreational use of receiving water.

The Blanchard River (Ohio) is a 166 km (103 mi) long stream in northwestern Ohio that drains a primarily rural farming area in the Lake Erie Watershed. A segment of the Blanchard River mainstem was not attaining aquatic life use because of a suite of causes defined as organic enrichment and DO, nutrients (particularly phosphorus), thermal modification, and habitat alteration. For the segment of the mainstem traversing through the urban corridor of a city, a steady-state water quality model QUAL2K was implemented to address the specific urban point-source-related causes and evaluate the management strategies for stream restoration. Critical stream conditions were defined as a critical low flow for the mainstem and tributaries, effluent flow at the design condition for a wastewater treatment plant, and an upstream boundary water quality at background concentrations. For developing the TMDL, the QUAL2K model was developed for critical stream conditions using a flow return interval of 10 years and 7-day averaged flow (7Q10). The 7Q10 flow was calculated at the USGS gauge location using DFLOW for the period 1982 to 2007. The allowable pollutant loading and corresponding effluent concentration for total phosphorus that can meet ambient water quality standard were simulated by the model (OEPA 2009). This TMDL was established by Ohio EPA and approved by USEPA in 2009.

As another example in Ohio, the Ottawa River (Lima area) watershed is a 365 mi^2 area, which is home to more than 130,000 people. Major causes of impairments include nutrients, flow alteration, and low DO. The QUAL2K model was used in the TMDL development for total phosphorus, such as simulating the projected impacts from pollutant loading reduction on ambient water quality improvement. The critical condition in the receiving water occurs at low streamflow. This is when continuously discharging point sources dominate during summer months when evapotranspiration and temperatures are the highest and daylight is the longest. The 7Q10 flow was used for modeling and waste load allocations (WLAs) according to the requirement stipulated by the Ohio Administrative Code. Point-source discharges were added to the system at design effluent flows with permit limits established as constituent concentrations (OEPA 2013). This TMDL was established by the Ohio EPA in 2013 and approved by the USEPA in 2014.

Furthermore, a TMDL study in Minnesota has provided a similar example of using a steady-state model under a low-flow condition (MPCA 2018). This TMDL addresses the stream and lake impairments in the St. Louis River Watershed in northeastern Minnesota, which is a tributary of the St. Louis River. The causes of impairment in the watershed include high levels of total suspended solids (TSS) and nutrients, in addition to high temperature and low DO, affecting aquatic life and aquatic recreation designated uses. For Wyman Creek, an 11 mi^2 area within the watershed, the water quality standard for DO must be met 50% of the time at which the flow of the stream is expected to be critically low based on 7Q10. A steady-state and diurnally variable water quality model that can simulate instream water temperatures and DO concentrations on an hourly time step, called QUAL2K, was used to support the development of temperature and DO TMDL modeling for the Wyman Creek. This TMDL was established by the Minnesota Pollution Control Agency and approved by USEPA in 2018.

6.2.2 Dynamic Continuous Simulation Models for Analyzing Impairment under Variable Flow

The worst-case scenario for impairment is not obviously known for TMDLs that need to consider point sources and nonpoint sources in combination. This is because the amount of pollutants generated and transported by nonpoint sources is usually dependent on the characteristics of the storms that generate runoff. The USEPA guidelines thus far do not specify how to define the critical conditions for TMDLs addressing impairments owing to the contributions from a combination of point and nonpoint sources.

As mentioned previously, USEPA's water quality criteria have three components: magnitude, duration, and frequency. Also, an occurrence happening more often than the designated frequency is termed an "exceedance" and a continuous modeling approach can analyze water quality impairments under variable flow conditions.

Continuous simulation using time-varying dynamic model offers another method for defining critical conditions. It is a method that can be used for evaluating or predicting pollutant behavior over a range of conditions. The critical condition is typically dictated by the standards. One might use a representative period to compare allocations, which would be a subset of the longer continuous simulation. This approach has been widely used in recent efforts to develop TMDLs, especially for an impaired waterbody affected by pollutants from point and nonpoint sources and where sediments or sorbed pollutants transported by sediments are of concern.

Varying pollutant loading with storm flows requires a dynamic modeling of loads and pollutant fate and transport in watersheds to relate loads to impairments. Two types of critical conditions can occur when loads vary with storm flow. First, when loads are quickly mobilized and transported to impaired receiving waters that quickly react to these storm loads, dynamic watershed models may be applicable to quantify the pollutant loads from nonpoint sources. For example, water quality impairments associated with immediate effects on designated use of receiving waterbody (e.g., for certain toxic substances and pathogen TMDLs) could fit into this category. Please refer to the protocol for developing pathogen TMDLs (USEPA 2001).

Second, when pollutant loads require more than one storm pulse to reach impaired waters and the resulting impairment requires years to accumulate, continuous, dynamic watershed modeling may be necessary as opposed to event models. Pollutants that sorb to sediments or move as solid particles (i.e., sediments) are particularly slow moving, sometimes by orders of magnitude, and deposit in impaired waters for years and decades. In TMDLs concerned with the cumulative loading of pollutants over a long period of time, continuous, dynamic watershed modeling may be necessary. For example, water quality impairments associated with cumulative effects on designated use of receiving waterbodies (e.g., for nutrient and contaminated sediment TMDLs or TMDLs owing to organic enrichment) could fit into this category. Please refer to the protocols for developing nutrient and sediment TMDLs (USEPA 1999b, c) and "PCB TMDL Handbook" (USEPA 2011).

When TMDLs consider point sources and nonpoint sources together, the worst-case scenario is not easily conceivable. Modelers may use a representative period of even several decades of climatic and hydrologic data, if available, to account for the varying climatic and hydrologic conditions occurring within a watershed. Other approaches use representative dry, wet, and average years of precipitation (USEPA 2010). In addition, a representative simulated period from a longer continuous simulation can be used to compare TMDL allocation scenarios.

The continuous simulation method using dynamic models is extensively used in TMDL development. However, it has disadvantages as well. The method often uses data from one specific representative hydrologic period.

Theoretically, if the period of modeling is sufficiently long, the critical conditions might be captured by the model. However, there is no guarantee that the most critical condition or worst-case scenario will be captured using the selected hydrologic period by the model, particularly in those cases where such selected periods may be short. Extensive data may not be available in some cases because of budget and resources constraints (Zhang and Yu 2005, 2008). In these situations, the return period (frequency of exceedance of water quality standard violations) and associated risks may not be able to be quantified rigorously using the selected "representative period." The quantification of risk of future water quality standard violations is an essential part of any water quality management plan. If the exceedance probability cannot be estimated, a plan for managing nonpoint-source pollutants would be unable to specify how often such a critical condition will likely occur in the future. This could be especially true when climate impact is considered in determining the most critical condition as the past may not be a good representation of a future climate.

In summary, continuous simulation is a valuable tool that can be used to evaluate a range of conditions using historic or forecasted meteorological conditions, when extensive data requirement can be met during the TMDL development. Techniques that have been used to evaluate the continuous simulation and assess the "critical condition" for the impairment of concern typically include statistical analysis of the period of record, selection of representative time periods, worse-case time periods, or reasonable worst-case time periods. In general, WQ Standards assume a specific frequency of violation, which could be especially important considering that some waterbodies experience extreme wet weather conditions.

Table 6-1 lists several examples using this method, such as USEPA's Chesapeake Bay sediment and nutrient TMDLs (USEPA 2010), Beaver Creek (Virginia) bacteria and benthic TMDL revision by Virginia Department of Environmental Quality (VADEQ) (VADEQ 2016a), Bacteria TMDL Development for the Mattaponi River watershed (Virginia) (VADEQ 2016b), and Lower Boise River (Idaho) TMDL (IDEQ 2015).

The Chesapeake Bay TMDL, the largest ever developed by the USEPA, encompassing a 64,000 mi^2 watershed, used a dynamic continuous simulation watershed model based on the hydrological simulation program-FORTRAN (HSPF) model. The HSPF is a comprehensive package for the simulation of watershed hydrology and water quality for both conventional and toxic organic pollutants. For more than two decades, the HSPF-based model has been used to simulate nutrient and sediment load delivery to the Chesapeake Bay and has become more complex in response to the watershed management challenges (Shenk et al. 2013). As a first step in developing the Chesapeake Bay TMDL, a critical period was established during which hydrologic, temperature, environmental, flow, and other such conditions could combine to produce an identified impairment. The 3-year period (1998 to 2000) coinciding with the Chesapeake Bay water quality criteria assessment period within the hydrologic period 1991 to 2000 was selected as the critical period (USEPA 2010). This 10-year period was considered adequate to represent long-term hydrology and included the model calibration period. The Chesapeake Bay Program required the critical period chosen to be representative of a 10-year return period event for a good balance between guarding against extreme events and ensuring at the same time the attainment of water quality goals during more-frequent critical events. This would require the determination of return periods of each of the 3-year time frames within the hydrologic period of 10 years selected (1991 to 2000). The selection of a 10-year return period was also based on its application for the 7Q10 low-flow conditions and on the need to be consistent with the critical periods selected for other TMDLs developed by the Chesapeake Bay watershed jurisdictions. The Chesapeake Bay TMDL identified the needed pollution reductions from major sources of nitrogen, phosphorus, and sediment across the bay jurisdictions and set pollution limits necessary to meet water quality standards.

Another example of using the dynamic continuous model is in the bacteria and benthic TMDL revision for the Beaver Creek watershed in Virginia (VADEQ 2016a). For this TMDL, VADEQ interpreted the bacteria standard as requiring compliance with both the geometric-mean and the single-sample maximum criteria. The inclusion of critical conditions during the TMDL analysis ensured that the water quality would be protected during times when ambient water quality is most vulnerable. Critical conditions were considered directly during model development. HSFP model was used in support of bacteria TMDL development for Beaver Creek. Hydrology calibration and validation modeling periods were selected to include critical conditions or combinations of environmental factors (e.g., rainfall, temperature) that yield high and low flows of an acceptably low frequency of occurrence. The period of rainfall selected for modeling was chosen as a multiyear period that was representative of typical weather conditions for the area and included "dry," "average," and "wet" years. In establishing the existing and allocation conditions, seasonal variations in hydrology, climatic conditions, and watershed activities were explicitly accounted for in the model. The use of a dynamic continuous model allowed consideration of seasonal aspects of precipitation patterns within the watershed as well. Throughout the modeling process, seasonal variations in hydrology, climatic conditions, and watershed activities were explicitly accounted for in the model. Modeling periods extended across high-flow and low-flow seasons over a period of several years.

6.2.3 Load–Duration Curves

Instead of focusing on only low flow or high flow, another statistics-based method involves a period that encompasses all possible flow conditions for developing a TMDL. Wet weather usually causes nonpoint-source pollution and low flow in dry weather controls point-source pollution. Therefore, the process of developing TMDLs and allocating loads should consider factors that ensure adequate water quality across a range of flow conditions. In keeping with this idea, the Kansas Department of Health and Environment devised a simple method for developing TMDLs based on the concept of a flow-based LDC, that is, the cumulative frequency distribution of daily flows for a stream's period of record (Stiles 2002). This flow-based method involves including all possible critical conditions using the cumulative frequency distribution of daily flows derived from a long-term, streamflow record of several years. Ideally, the streamflow data should cover low, medium, and high flows over a period of several years. This method also accounts for how streamflow patterns affect changes in water quality over the course of a year. This feature enables accounting for seasonal variations in TMDL development. The computer program developed by the USGS, "National Streamflow Statistics Program," can be used for estimating cumulative distributions of daily flows and other streamflow statistics (USGS 2007).

The approach avoids the constraints associated with steady-state modeling of a single flow condition and the complexity of a dynamic simulation of all flows. TMDL load is expressed as a function of flow conditions, which cover all flow conditions, including critical flow conditions. The TMDL may be expressed as an average allocation for all flow conditions, which may violate water quality standards during low and high flows (USEPA 2007a).

Flow-based LDC analysis identifies intervals that can be used as general indicators of hydrologic condition, for example, wet versus dry and to what degree. It may be difficult for LDC analysis to directly evaluate the factors most affecting critical conditions and reduce TMDL allocations accordingly. However, this indicator can help focus discussions on relevant watershed processes, important contributing areas, and key mechanisms delivering pollutants.

LDCs are developed by multiplying stream flows with the numeric water quality target (e.g., a water quality criterion) and a conversion factor for the pollutant of concern. Thus, no water quality modeling is performed. The LDC approach allows for characterizing water quality concentrations at different flow regimes. The method provides a visual display of the relationship between streamflow and loading capacity. LDCs are also relatively easy to develop and offer easy insight into critical conditions.

In a standard TMDL study, the high flow (i.e., less than 10th percentile flow exceedance) or low flow (i.e., greater than 90th percentile flow exceedance) may not be selected as critical conditions because these extreme flows are not representative of typical conditions.

LDCs provide only limited information on the magnitude of contributions from different contributing sources to the overall pollutant loads. LDCs also do not allow simulation of scenarios to evaluate the impact of various implementation options, because this method does not mechanistically relate pollutant sources and water quality response of the receiving waterbody. Although it is difficult to evaluate influencing factors on critical conditions to derive explicit percent reductions of source categories in TMDL allocation, the LDC remains a simple screening tool for problem characterization of TMDL development.

Table 6-1 lists several examples using this method, such as the Carson River (Nevada) TMDL for TSS and turbidity (NVDEP 2007), Santa Maria (California) watershed TMDL for fecal indicator bacteria (CEPA 2012), and Big Creek watershed (South Carolina) TMDL for fecal coliform bacteria (SCDHEC 2010). The following TMDL examples illustrate the use of the LDC approach.

An appendix in USEPA (2007a) describes a case study in which LDCs were used to support TMDL development in South Carolina. The case study refers to a fecal coliform TMDL prepared by the South Carolina Department of Health and Environmental Control. To calculate the fecal coliform load at the water quality standard, the instantaneous fecal coliform criterion (i.e., 400 cfu/100 mL) is multiplied by the measured or estimated flow rate at each flow exceedance percentile and a unit conversion factor. This calculation produces the maximum fecal coliform load in the stream without exceeding the instantaneous water quality standard over the range of flow conditions. The allowable fecal coliform loads at the water quality standard establish the TMDL and are plotted versus flow exceedance percentile as an LDC. To estimate existing loading, the loads associated with individual fecal coliform observations are paired with the flows estimated at the same site on the same date. In this TMDL study (SCDHEC 2010), the high flow (i.e., less than 10th percentile flow exceedance) or low flow (i.e., greater than 90th percentile flow exceedance) will not be selected as critical conditions because these extreme flows are not representative of typical conditions.

Another example is in the Salt Creek Watershed located in southeast Ohio that covers a 145 mi^2 watershed area and is home to more than 12,000 people. The watershed is primarily forest (52%) and pasture (30%), with nearly 8% being developed. A TMDL was developed for bacteria, which impaired recreation uses and precluded the attainment of applicable water quality standards. The LDC method was selected to assign instream bacteria loads at a given site to one or several potential bacteria sources

(OEPA 2011). LDCs plotted the concentration of a given pollutant according to the flow at which the sample was collected. The acceptable pollutant load varied according to flow. The LDC method assisted in distinguishing between point and nonpoint sources that contribute to *Escherichia coli* loading by highlighting the flow conditions under which impairment occurs. This TMDL was established by the Ohio EPA and approved by USEPA in 2011.

6.2.4 Critical Flow-Storm Approach

This storm-event approach has been developed to avoid one of the disadvantages of continuous simulation: The inability to guarantee that the critical condition is included during a particular hydrologic period. This storm-event approach explicitly addresses the critical condition caused by a combination of low streamflow, magnitude of the storm event, and initial watershed runoff condition. One example is choosing a low flow owing to a drought period subjected to a small volume storm for a critical condition.

One major advantage of the event-based, critical flow-storm (CFS) approach is the use of synthetic design storms to examine implementation options. The initial watershed condition (e.g., soil moisture content) can be established based on historical field data whenever available, literature review results in similar watersheds, and outputs from water quality modeling studies. Instead of basing an implementation plan completely on long-term, continuous simulations, the return period for a CFS defines the risk associated with a load-reduction scenario. Thus, nonpoint sources are controlled consistent with traditional approaches for managing point sources (Zhang and Yu 2005, 2008).

The event-based CFS approach can evaluate how the water quality of a particular waterbody is likely to respond to certain management practices during low-flow ambient stream conditions and storm events that have a return period that can be determined statistically using an intensity–duration–frequency curve, a plot of average rainfall intensity versus rainfall duration for various return periods.

The CFS approach was applied successfully in the TMDL development for the Muddy Creek in Virginia (VADEQ 2000). The technical approach was developed for the management of a combination of point- and nonpoint-source pollution through a research study in parallel with nitrate TMDL development for the Muddy Creek watershed, which was the first nutrient TMDL in Virginia. The objective of the CFS approach is to provide an alternate approach to continuous simulation of a multiyear period. The CFS approach demonstrated that for systems with significant nonpoint-source pollution, the hydrological critical conditions could be defined by a combination of initial instream flows and precipitation events. A "critical" scenario could look like the following: A river experiencing a low-flow condition is subjected to a small storm, and a combination of initial low flows, followed by storm-related runoff, results in the worst pollutant concentration levels ever recorded for that receiving waterbody. Small storms produce little runoff, whereas large precipitation events may act as a source of dilution. Thus, a small-to-medium-sized storm, coupled with an antecedent condition of low flow, may be the most problematic for nonpoint-source pollution (Zhang et al. 2001, Culver et al. 2002, Zhang and Yu 2005, Zhang and Padmanabhan 2019). This is consistent with an approach that emphasizes more on the removal of pollutants in urban runoff that has targeted control of high-frequency events (smaller than the 2-year storm) (Nehrke and Roesner 2004).

The event-based CFS approach explicitly addresses the critical condition as a combination of low streamflow and a small storm, both of which are likely to recur after certain intervals. One major advantage of the event-based CFS approach is its ability to examine the effects of management options under synthetic design storms. Instead of basing a management plan completely on the characteristics of the hydrologic period selected under the continuous simulation method, which may not have time-series data for a sufficiently long period, the CFS approach can assess the risk (e.g., in the form of a return period) associated with a certain load-reduction scenario (Zhang and Yu 2005, Zhang and Padmanabhan 2019). The implementation of this TMDL helped reduce the nitrogen load in the receiving water and was listed as one of the success stories under the USEPA's Section 319 Nonpoint Source Program (USEPA 2012).

In addition, a comparison study of the applicability of the CFS approach was conducted in the Dy-yu Creek watershed in Taiwan. Dy-yu Creek is a tributary of a reservoir, a major drinking water source for the metropolitan city of Taipei in Northern Taiwan. The Dy-yu Creek in Taiwan is similar in size to the Muddy Creek watershed in Virginia (e.g., approximately 31 mi²). However, it differs significantly from Muddy Creek in terms of climate, hydrology, terrain, and other characteristics. From a water quality perspective, a smaller storm is physically more important than a larger one. Therefore, the study considers 10 types of design storms combined with various duration and return periods as the rainfall control factor of critical storms in the Dy-yu Creek watershed. The study results echoed those obtained in a watershed in Virginia, in that there does exist a critical condition for smaller-size storms combined with a lower flow in another watershed in a different continent. It is worth noting that the watersheds in these two studies have relatively smaller areas. The small watershed is seen as more sensitive in response to hydrology and pollutant load (Zhang and Yu 2005, Hsu et al. 2010). In summary, the CFS approach was successfully applied in a comparison water quality modeling study in two different continents. The CFS approach can be considered an alternate method to a continuous simulation approach for TMDL development (Zhang and Yu 2005, Hsu et al. 2010, Zhang and Padmanabhan 2019).

Furthermore, another example was a risk-based critical condition analysis for Red River fecal coliform TMDL development in North Dakota (Chin 2009, Kasi et al. 2007). In this study, critical conditions were identified with the consideration of low river-flow conditions and rainfall intensity and duration combinations. Similar to the CFS approach, an event-based approach is considered with a limited number of rainfall events to simulate the impact of rainfall on river water quality. A statistical analysis was conducted to determine the risk associated with these events. The study results from this analysis identified the characteristics of rain events that caused high event mean concentrations in the storm runoff. The analysis results were then combined with river-flow conditions to determine the critical conditions that could cause the highest fecal coliform concentrations in the river (Gautam et al. 2006). The results from the risk-based analysis for critical river-flow and rainfall conditions were used to determine the river's assimilative capacity and TMDL load reduction. In this study, critical conditions were identified with the consideration of low river-flow conditions and rainfall intensity and duration combinations (Kasi et al. 2007).

The CFS concept should be more appropriate for urban rather than agricultural watersheds because of the difference in their runoff-producing characteristics. In watersheds such as agricultural watersheds with the relatively little impervious area, the critical condition defined by the CFS approach may be less distinct. Also, for larger watersheds, the CFS concept may be less suitable. The ambient water quality response may be relatively less sensitive because of factors such as heterogeneity of a watershed, uneven distribution of stormwater runoff, and induced nonpoint-source pollutant loading from upstream to downstream (Zhang and Yu 2005, 2008).

In summary, the size of a storm, as measured by intensity and duration, and temporal distribution directly affect a waterway's critical condition. Even storm events having the same total rainfall in them can affect the water quality of receiving waters differently if intensity patterns of rainfall within those storms are different. Furthermore, a watershed's antecedent condition, particularly the amount of time that has elapsed since the previous rainfall and the rate at which pollutants accumulate between storms, can significantly influence the extent to which a storm affects water quality (Zhang and Yu 2005).

Considering the probabilistic nature of the variables involved, it is reasonable to expect a probabilistic framework to be appropriate for determining the choice of critical condition. The decision-making authorities could substantially benefit from the knowledge of risks or probabilities associated with various combinations of rainfall and river-flow conditions, and the load generated from these combinations. The risk here is defined as the joint probability of the occurrence of a selected set of rainfall and river-flow conditions. In the risk-based approach, for a defined percentage of risk and a known rainfall condition, the river-flow probability (return period) is estimated. The associated river-flow rate is determined from flow–frequency curves. Then, for this combination of rainfall and river-flow conditions, the pollutant load in the river is determined using dynamic and/or steady-state models. A series of such critical conditions and the corresponding pollutant loads on the river for each percentage of risk can be developed as a matrix (Kasi et al. 2007). Using this matrix, decision makers will be able to evaluate and identify an appropriate critical condition along with consideration of key components of water quality standards such as the duration over which concentrations can be averaged.

Nonstationary hydrologic variables can be modeled stochastically to describe the temporal evolution of their probability distributions, with uncertainty estimates. For example, water management professionals could define plausible planning futures based on climate projection. However, such downscaled projections should be used in water quality management programs only when the planning horizon extends at least several decades into the future and the projections contain information reliable enough for planning purposes (Zhang 2010, 2012).

6.3 SUMMARY

This chapter presents a review of critical condition modeling and analysis approaches and illustrates the strengths and weaknesses of available methodologies to define critical conditions with a view to providing guidance for TMDL development and implementation. Properly defining a waterway's critical condition is one of the key challenges in developing a TMDL. However, many current TMDLs address this aspect only in a cursory manner. Careful consideration of critical conditions has the potential of reducing the uncertainty between the model estimation and the actual water quality under worst-case scenarios.

Four major approaches for defining a critical condition are typically employed in TMDL studies. They are low-flow analysis using steady-state models, continuous simulation using dynamic models, statistics-based LDCs, and an event-based critical flow-storm approach. TMDLs addressing pollution in streams and rivers from point sources will typically use a critical condition defined as a low-flow condition, such as 7Q10. For TMDLs from impaired waterbodies affected by pollutants from both point and nonpoint sources, a dynamic model is commonly used along with the selection of a representative period to account for the varying climatic and hydrologic conditions in the watershed (e.g., to cover dry, wet, and average years of precipitation). The LDC method is a simple screening tool for problem characterization of TMDL development. The event-based critical flow-storm method is essentially a risk-based approach, which explicitly addresses a critical condition as a combination of streamflow, magnitude of storm event, and initial watershed condition.

A consideration of the appropriate critical condition is required by the USEPA in all TMDLs. This requirement to account for critical conditions is intended to ensure that the water quality of a receiving waterbody is protected during its most vulnerable times. A knowledge of the critical conditions for the impairment situation for TMDL modeling can assist efforts to identify the remedial actions that would need to be taken to meet water quality standards. By understanding better how to define critical conditions, water quality professionals can develop more meaningful and improved estimates of TMDLs and formulate appropriate strategies to control pollution from point and nonpoint sources at a watershed level.

6.4 STATE-OF-THE-ART AND STATE-OF-THE-PRACTICE

The USEPA's TMDL program under the Clean Water Act requires consideration of the critical conditions for streamflow, loading, and water quality parameters for developing TMDLs. The intent of this requirement is to ensure that the water quality of an impaired waterbody is protected during times when it is most vulnerable. Obviously, because of the probabilistic nature of the variables involved, any method employed for choosing a critical condition must be in a probabilistic framework. However, defining a waterway's critical conditions is one of the difficult challenges in developing a TMDL. Consequently, many current TMDLs address this aspect only in a cursory manner.

The state-of-the-practice consists of four methods to address the choice of critical conditions. They are low-flow analysis using steady-state models, continuous simulation using dynamic models, statistics-based LDCs, and an event-based critical flow-storm approach. The decision-making authorities could benefit a great deal from the knowledge of risks or probabilities associated with various combinations of rainfall and river-flow conditions, and the load generated from these combinations. The risk here is defined as the joint probability of the occurrence of a selected set of rainfall and river-flow conditions. In the risk-based approach, for a defined percentage of risk and a known rainfall condition, the river-flow probability (return period) is estimated. The associated river-flow rate is determined from flow–frequency curves. Based on the combination of rainfall and river-flow conditions, the pollutant load in the river is determined using dynamic and/or steady-state models. A series of such critical conditions and the corresponding pollutant loads on the river for each percentage of risk can be developed as a matrix.

Water management professionals should adopt a more innovative approach for accepting the growing list of impaired waters that would require a TMDL because of climate impacts. For example, they should assess the TMDL, its implementation plan, and the effectiveness of both under projected climate scenarios and related management responses.

Current state-of-the-art thinking or research for advancement in critical condition identification is along the lines of risk-based approaches. Any advancement in risk estimation of the joint probability of river flows and rainfall parameters can improve the choice of critical conditions for TMDL modeling.

REFERENCES

ADEM (Alabama Department of Environmental Management). 2005. *Total maximum daily loads (TMDLs) for metals (zinc), pH and siltation in the village creek watershed, Alabama.* Montgomery, AL: ADEM.

ASCE. 2017. *Total maximum daily load analysis and modeling: Assessment of the practice.* Prepared by TMDL Analysis and Modeling Task Committee of the Environmental and Water Resources Institute of ASCE. Reston, VA: ASCE.

Bicknell, B. R., A. S. Donigian, and T. A. Barnwell. 1985. "Modeling water quality and the effects of agricultural best management practices in the Iowa River Basin." *Water Sci. Technol.* 17: 1141–1153.

Bicknell, B. R., J. C. Imhoff, J. L. Kittle Jr., and A. S. Donigian. 1996. *Hydrological simulation program - FORTRAN, user's manual for release 11.* Athens, GA: EPA Environmental Research Laboratory.

CEPA (California Environmental Protection Agency). 2012. *Santa Maria Watershed TMDL—Fecal indicator bacteria.* Sacramento, CA: CEPA.

Chin, D. 2009. "Risk-based TMDLs in pathogen-impaired waters." *J. Water Resour. Plann. Manage.* 135 (6): 521–527.

Culver, T. B., K. A. Neeley, S. L. Yu, H. X. Zhang, A. L. Potts, and T. R. Naperala. 2002. "Nitrate TMDL development: The muddy creek/dry river case study." *J. Contemp. Water Res. Educ.* 122 (1): 5–15.

DNREC (Delaware Department of Natural Resources and Environmental Control). 2005. *Total maximum daily loads (TMDLs) analysis for Pocomoke River, Delaware.* Dover, DE: DNREC.

Donigian, A. S., J. C. Imhoff, and B. R. Bicknell. 1983. "Predicting water quality resulting from agricultural nonpoint source pollution via simulation—HSPF." In *Agricultural management and water quality,* edited by F. W. Schaller and G. W. Bailey, 200–249. Ames, IA: Iowa State University Press.

DRBC (Delaware River Basin Commission). 1995. *Implementation policies and procedures: Phase I TMDLs for toxic pollutants in Delaware River Estuary.* Trenton, NJ: DRBC.

Gautam, B., M. Kasi, and W. Lin. 2006. "Determination of fecal coliform loading and its impact on river water quality for TMDL development." In *Proc., Water Environment Federation Annual Conf.*, Dallas, TX; Water Environment Federation; 3851–3874.

Hsu, T. H., J. Y. Lin, T. C. Lee, H. X. Zhang, and L. Y. Shaw. 2010. "A storm event-based approach to TMDL development." *Environ. Monit. Assess.* 163 (1–4): 81–94.

IDEQ (Idaho Department of Environmental Quality). 2015. *Lower Boise River TMDL—2015 Total phosphorus addendum.* Boise, ID: IDEQ.

Kasi, M., W. Lin, R. Magel, and B. Gautam. 2007. "Risk based critical condition analysis for Red river fecal coliform TMDL development." *Proc. Water Environ. Fed.* 2007 (11): 7014–7032.

Keller, A. A., Y. Zheng, and T. H. Robinson. 2004. "Determining critical water quality conditions for inorganic nitrogen in dry, semi-urbanized watersheds." *J. Am. Water Resour. Assoc.* 40 (3): 721–735.

Milly, P. C. D., J. Betancourt, M. Falkenmark, R. M. Hirsch, Z. W. Kundzewicz, D. P. Lettenmaier, et al. 2008. "Stationarity is dead: Whither water management?" *Science* 319 (5863): 573–574.

MPCA (Minnesota Pollution Control Agency). 2018. *St. Louis river watershed total maximum daily load report.* St. Paul, MN: MPCA.

Nehrke, S. M., and L. A. Roesner. 2004. "Effects of design practice for flood control and best management practices on the flow–frequency curve." *J. Water Resour. Plann. Manage.* 130 (2): 131–139.

NRC (National Research Council). 2001. *Assessing the TMDL approach to water quality management.* Washington, DC: National Academies Press.

NVDEP (Nevada Division of Environmental Protection). 2007. *Carson River: Total maximum daily loads for total suspended solids and turbidity.* Carson City, NV: NVDEP.

OEPA (Ohio Environmental Protection Agency). 2009. *Total maximum daily loads for the Blanchard River Watershed.* Logan, OH: OEPA.

OEPA. 2011. *Total maximum daily loads for the salt creek watershed (Muskingum River Basin).* Logan, OH: OEPA.

OEPA. 2013. *Total maximum daily loads for the Ottawa River (Lima Area) watershed.* Logan, OH: OEPA.

SCDHEC (South Carolina Department of Health and Environmental Control). 2010. *Total maximum daily load document RS-05590, Big Creek Watershed—Fecal coliform bacteria.* Columbia, SC: SCDHEC.

Shenk, G. W., J. Wu, and L. C. Linker. 2013. "Enhanced HSPF model structure for Chesapeake Bay watershed simulation." *J. Environ. Eng.* 138 (9): 949–957.

Stiles, T. C. 2002. "Incorporating hydrology in determining TMDL endpoints and allocations." In *Proc., National TMDL Science and Policy Conf.*, Phoenix, AZ; Water Environment Federation (WEF).

USEPA (US Environmental Protection Agency). 1984. *Technical guidance manual for performing wasteload allocations. Book II: Streams and rivers.* Rep. No. EPA-440/4-84-019. Washington, DC: USEPA.

USEPA. 1986. *Technical guidance manual for performing wasteload allocations, book VI: Design conditions—Chapter 1: Stream design flow for steady-state modeling.* Rep. No. EPA440/4/86-014. Washington, DC: USEPA.

USEPA. 1991. *Guidance for water quality-based decisions: The TMDL process.* Rep. No. EPA 440/4-91-001. Washington, DC: USEPA.

USEPA. 1999a. *Draft guidance for water quality-based decisions: The TMDL process.* 2nd ed. Rep. No. EPA 841-D-99-001. Washington, DC: USEPA.

USEPA. 1999b. *Protocol for developing nutrient TMDLs.* 1st ed. Rep. No. EPA 841-B-99-007. Washington, DC: USEPA.

USEPA. 1999c. *Protocol for developing sediment TMDLs.* 1st ed. Rep. No. EPA 841-B-99-004. Washington, DC: USEPA.

USEPA. 2001. *Protocol for developing pathogen TMDLs.* 1st ed. Rep. No. EPA 841-R-00-002. Washington, DC: USEPA.

USEPA. 2006. *DFLOW (a tool to estimate user selected design stream flows for low flow analysis).* Washington, DC: USEPA.

USEPA. 2007a. *An approach for using load–duration curves in the development of TMDLs.* Rep. No. EPA 841-B-07-006. Washington, DC: USEPA.

USEPA. 2007b. *Total maximum daily loads with stormwater sources: A summary of 17 TMDLs.* Rep. No. EPA 841-R-07-002. Washington, DC: USEPA.

USEPA. 2008a. *Nutrient and sediment TMDLs for the Southampton Creek Watershed, Pennsylvania: Modeling report.* Philadelphia: EPA Region 3.

USEPA. 2008b. *TMDLs to stormwater permits handbook.* Draft. Washington, DC: EPA.

USEPA. 2009. *TMDL program results analysis fact sheet.* Rep. No. EPA 841-F-09-004. Washington, DC: USEPA.

USEPA. 2010. *Chesapeake Bay TMDL document. Appendix G. Determination of critical conditions for the Chesapeake Bay TMDL.* Washington, DC: USEPA.

USEPA. 2011. *PCB TMDL handbook.* Rep. No. EPA 841-R-11-006. Washington, DC: USEPA.

USEPA. 2012. *Section 319 nonpoint source program success story - Implementing management practices reduces nitrate in Virginia's Muddy Creek.* Washington, DC: USEPA.

USGS (United States Geological Survey). 2007. "The national streamflow statistics program: A computer program for estimating streamflow statistics for ungaged sites." Chap. 6 of Book 4, *Hydrologic Analysis and Interpretation Section A, Statistical Analysis.* USGS Techniques and Methods 4-A6. Reston, VA: USGS.

VADEQ (Virginia Department of Environmental Quality). 2000. *Nitrate TMDL development for Muddy Creek/Dry River, Virginia.* Richmond, VA: VADEQ.

VADEQ. 2016a. *Bacteria and benthic total maximum daily load (TMDL) revision for the Beaver Creek Watershed located in Bristol City and Washington County, Virginia.* Richmond, VA: VADEQ.

VADEQ. 2016b. *Bacteria total maximum daily load (TMDL) development for the Mattaponi River Watershed Located in Orange, Spotsylvania, Caroline, King William, and King and Queen Counties, Virginia.* Richmond, VA: VADEQ.

WADOE (Washington State Department of Ecology). 2006. *Wenatchee river basin dissolved oxygen, pH, and phosphorus total maximum daily load study.* Lacey, WA: WADOE.

Zhang, H. X. 2010. "Changes ahead: Water management professionals should account for climate change when working with TMDLs." *Water Environ. Technol.* (February): 37–40.

Zhang, H. X. 2012. "Climate change and global water sustainability." In *Encyclopedia of sustainability science and technology,* edited by R. A. Meyers, 2061–2078. Berlin: Springer.

Zhang, H. X., and G. Padmanabhan. 2019. "Critical condition modeling and analysis in TMDL development and implementation." *J. Hydrol. Eng.* 24 (2): 04018061.

Zhang, H. X., and S. L. Yu. 2004. "Applying the first-order error analysis in determining the margin of safety for total maximum daily load computations." *J. Environ. Eng.* 130 (6): 664–673.

Zhang, H. X., and S. L. Yu. 2005. "Condition critical: Defining the "critical condition" for a total maximum daily load requires great care, especially when addressing nonpoint pollutants." *Water Environ. Technol.* 38–42.

Zhang, H. X., and S. L. Yu. 2008. "Critical flow-storm approach to total maximum daily load (TMDL) development: an analytical conceptual model." *Front. Environ. Sci. Eng. China* 2 (3): 267–273.

Zhang, H. X., S. L. Yu, and T. B. Culver. 2001. "The critical flow-storm approach for nitrate TMDL development in the Muddy Creek Watershed, Virginia." In *Proc., Water Environment Federation Annual Conf.*

CHAPTER 7

MODEL DATA, GEOGRAPHICAL INFORMATION SYSTEMS, AND REMOTE SENSING

Nigel W. T. Quinn, Saurav Kumar, Sanaz Imen, Vamsi K. Sridharan

7.1 MODEL DATA REQUIREMENTS

Three major types of data that are required to build a total maximum daily load (TMDL) model are as follows:

1. Data on model parameter values: These include either theoretical, measured, or fitted values for various physical mechanisms in the model such as reaction and decay rates of organic matter, settling velocities of sediment particles, release, adsorption and deposition rates, and fitting parameters in hydrological, chemical, and biophysical models.
2. Data on the system: These include data that are specifically required to develop the simulation model used to perform the TMDL analysis. Data requirements for calibration and validation of simulation models typically include information on topography, geography, land use/land cover (LULC), bathymetry, meteorological and hydrological data (e.g., air temperature, wind speed and direction, humidity, solar radiation, rainfall, streamflow, groundwater transport, and baseflow), water resource management data (e.g., withdrawal locations, well locations), soil characteristics, and estimates of the sources and loading rates of the water quality parameters simulated in the model. They also include information on current water management practices employed in watersheds. For example, salt loading from a watershed may be curtailed or stored for short periods of time in drainage ponds or impoundments when loads or salinity concentrations exceed TMDL-based load limits at designated compliance monitoring stations. Such information must be incorporated in the TMDL model.

3. Data on the TMDL: These include information on monitoring stations, the type of data that should be collected, and the duration and frequency of data collection that are incorporated in the TMDL program design and implementation strategy. These datasets are essential for model calibration and confirmation, as well as determining data needs and the efficacy of the TMDL program. The size and intensity of the monitoring program is related to the implementation strategy and the stakeholder and regulator tolerance of model uncertainty.

7.1.1 Model Parameter Values

Models essentially apply transformations to user inputs to produce outputs. The parameters in these transformations need to be specified. For simple models such as analytical models or models in which the whole water system is highly simplified, these parameter values are, in general, applicable and are not typically system-specific (Zhang and Quinn 2019). However, for more complex and sophisticated models representing detailed facsimiles of systems, parameters need to be adjusted during model calibration to represent the specific processes being simulated more closely to emulate the systems.

For example, the simple method to estimate watershed loading of pollutants owing to runoff requires the fraction of impervious cover in each land-use type within a watershed to estimate the runoff from the watershed (Zhang and Quinn 2019, Fu et al. 2020). In such a simple model, these values may be adopted directly from published tables (e.g., Cappiella and Brown 2001). For more complex models that resolve the functioning of the watershed with greater discretization, more sophisticated runoff models with coefficients that require calibration may be used.

An important aspect of parameterizing models is the physical realism of the parameters themselves (Whittemore and Beebe 2000). To the extent possible, data should be obtained that relate directly to physical measurement of the parameters rather than relying on proxy measurements and estimates. Occasionally, it may not be possible to provide a physically meaningful parameter description, such as an exponent in an allotropic equation, where the chemical constituent may exist in two or more different forms in the same physical state. In such cases, data are needed to provide plain-language explanation of the role of the parameter. If parameter values are nonphysical, but have been calibrated to fit the data, then both the range of parameter values and the range of applicability (i.e., over what flows, load levels, and system states, etc., that this submodel works) of this parameter should be identified. This is a crucial aspect for developing capability that supports valid model use. This practice can also enable stakeholder buy-in to the model-based TMDL development approach.

7.1.2 System Data

To accurately simulate the transport and fate of water quality variables, adequate information is required for point sources (PSs) and nonpoint sources (NPSs) of environmental pollutants (Borah et al. 2006). Discrete data are defined as data that are taken at discrete, but not necessarily equal, intervals of time for a predetermined period, whereas continuous data are data acquired at the same frequency, often with the aid of an electronic data acquisition system such as a datalogger coupled with water quality sondes and/or flow sensors. Although streamflow and water quality are apt to change on an hourly or a subhourly basis, and more rapidly during storm events, watershed LULC changes on much longer timescales—typically weeks to years.

The types of data that are prescribed for developing and running TMDL models are listed in Tables 7-1 and 7-2. In these tables, the actual data sources are not listed; such information are listed in Table 8-1 of this manual and may be also found in various reviews (e.g., Benham et al. 2006, Borah and Bera 2003, 2004, Borah et al. 2006, Quinn et al. 2019, Ahmadisharaf et al. 2019). For appropriate selection of a TMDL model,

1. Survey should be performed of the data sources available while censoring older datasets that are considered unreliable.
2. Ambient monitoring data in the watershed should be analyzed and interpreted.
3. Effort should be made to develop a systematic system-wide data collection endeavor in support of TMDL modeling and implementation in close collaboration with agencies and stakeholders who manage complementary data collection activities.

Typically, geographical, hydrological, pedological (soil characteristics), and meteorological data obtained by traditional gauging or remote sensing are available online nationally from federal agencies such as NOAA or the USGS or posted on local agency web portals. Agricultural water districts and other local agencies are making increasing use of the web to provide their customers and other watershed stakeholders with access to their data, not only for good public relations, but also to facilitate coordinated watershed activity.

Occasionally, TMDLs may have to be developed for ungauged streams or subbasins within a larger watershed where no data are available. In such cases, data from an adjacent or reference watershed or stream with similar conditions may be used to estimate model parameters and establish initial conditions for the model input data (Wallace et al. 2018). In such cases, the geographic and hydrologic properties of the target watershed need to be scaled and adjusted to emulate the characteristics of the reference watershed (Wallace et al. 2018).

Table 7-1. Data Requirements for a TMDL Model Setup.

Type	Data category	Discrete data	Continuous data	Sources
Geographical	Watershed topography	*		Terrestrial and aerial surveys
	Waterbody bathymetry	*		Terrestrial and aerial surveys
	Land cover		*	Satellite imagery
	Vegetation and soil type	*		Terrestrial surveys and satellite imagery
	Stream bottom and bank roughness	*		Surveys
	Land use		*	Surveys and satellite imagery
Pedologic	Soil permeability and infiltration capacity	*		Surveys and experimental data
Hydrological	Groundwater table depth		*	Surveys, models, and the NASA's Gravity Recovery and Climate Experiment (GRACE) satellite data
	Soil moisture		*	Surveys and satellite imagery
	Streamflow		*	Gauges, models, and satellite imagery
	Water stage		*	Gauges, rating curves, and models

Category	Parameter	*	Source
Meteorological	Air temperature	*	Measurements and models
	Rainfall	*	Gages, radars, satellite imagery, and models
	Wind speed and direction	*	Measurements and models
	Humidity	*	Measurements and models
	Heat budget terms such as incident shortwave and longwave radiation (can be obtained by remote sensing) and sensible and latent heat flux (can be obtained by in situ measurements and models)	*	Measurements, models, terrestrial and aerial surveys, and satellite imagery
	Ice cover and melt (low-spatial resolution remote sensing may be used for mesoscale analysis)	*	Measurements, models, and satellite imagery
	Soil heat budget	*	Measurements and models
Water resources	Hydraulic structures and operations	*	Surveys
	Water diversions	*	Surveys
	Recharge	*	Combination of groundwater table elevation data and consumptive-use data and modeling

*Data are discrete or continuous.

Table 7-2. Data Requirements for Running TMDL Models.

Type	Data	Discrete	Continuous	Sources
Water and wastewater resources	Locations	*		Maps, surveys, and local information
	Gate and pump operations	*		Local information
	Release schedules		*	Local information
Point source	Locations	*		Surveys and local information
	Operation schedule		*	Surveys and local information
	Flowrates		*	Local information
	Loading rates		*	Surveys and local information
Nonpoint source (including urban stormwater runoff)	Runoff rates		*	Models
	Sediment erosion rates		*	Gages, models, measurements, and aerial and satellite imagery
	Source locations (the areal coverage of pollution sources, such as the extent and proximity of farmlands to a stream, or the locations of unregulated discharges or unmetered diversions)	*		Maps, surveys and local information

Direct measurements	Source quantification (e.g., pesticide runoff rate, animal headcounts to estimate fecal contaminant loads, etc.)	*	Surveys, local information, and models
	Streamflow	*	Gages and models
	Water quality variables (such as DO, temperature, biochemical oxygen demand, chemical oxygen demand, salinity, pH, and dissolved sediments, pathogens, and chemical concentrations)	*	Gauges, models, and aerial and satellite imagery
	Total suspended solids, Total dissolved solids, and particulate matter	*	Gauges, models, and aerial and satellite imagery
Best management practices and stormwater control measures	Hydraulic operations	*	Maps, surveys, and local information
	Waste treatment operations	*	Local information
	Thresholds for interventions	*	Local information
	Flow and water quality outcomes of interventions	*	Local information, and models
	Structural and nonstructural BMPs, source control, and stormwater treatment	*	Local information

*Data are discrete or continuous.

When the TMDL model is developed with a time step or spatial scale that is more refined or discretized than the available data (e.g., an hourly time step with daily or monthly hydrological and meteorological data), one of the following two actions is suggested: (1) use constant values for the input variables over each window of time until the values change, and (2) disaggregate the available data to the temporal and spatial resolution required (e.g., Thomas and Henderson-Sellers 1991, Waichler and Wigmosta 2003).

More detailed information on local conditions, such as nutrient loading from farms and municipal waste discharge, may have to be collected directly with the assistance of local stakeholders or by conducting field research (Benham et al. 2006). When the TMDL model under development is used to forecast future water quality and analyze the impacts of selected management alternatives designed to limit nutrient loading, the data required to develop these alternate scenarios may be difficult to obtain. As a last resort, model parameter values and data obtained from other watershed simulation models relevant to a watershed may be used or, where models do not exist, data synthesized from multiple regional data sources may be used. This suggestion may be applicable to meteorological and some hydrological data.

7.1.3 Total Maximum Daily Load Data Resources

The TMDL limits should be set to meet or exceed the water quality standards in the region so that the designated use of a waterbody may be met. At the same time, adequate allocation of resources should be budgeted to establish a systematic system wide data collection workflow to collect the data necessary to resolve important physical/chemical/biological processes within the system and to implement the TMDL. Similarly, the model should be constructed, calibrated, and corroborated with the goal of being able to match available hydrology and water quality data available at watershed monitoring sites. When this testing of the model output is performed against independent observations, the model may be considered validated. Water samples may not be collected continuously and available discrete records may not be sufficient to calibrate certain models successfully. The LOAD ESTimator (LOADSET), developed by USGS, can be used to estimate water quality loads where streamflow and water quality data are limited (Gao et al. 2020).

Once TMDL model performance has been assessed to be acceptable, the model implementation workflow can proceed, which typically involves making production runs with the model simulating the effect of various best management practices (BMPs). The model can also be used to assess longer-term data requirements for more comprehensive TMDL compliance assessments while considering the available financial and personnel resources available to the TMDL program (Chapra 2003). To this end, data on environmental conditions are needed to compile time-series plots or phase-averaged scatter plots of the pollutant load and streamflow, together with flow–duration curves and load–duration curves. In addition, information is needed on the current and planned structural and nonstructural pollutant control management actions within the region that may impact pollutant loadings and receiving water quality.

As the TMDL includes both estimates of the actual loading and the margin of safety (MOS) (which is used to account for uncertainties in measurements of flow and water quality at sampling locations), it is important to apply a quantitative MOS. This can be accomplished if data are available on the uncertainty associated with the flow and water quality measurements (Shirmohammadi et al. 2006). For example, if a TMDL model for turbidity has hydrologic and sediment transport modules, then the errors that arise estimating the streamflow, sediment erosion rate, and suspended sediment concentration in the water column must all be considered in an error propagation model to quantify the overall uncertainty in estimates of the sediment load (Shirmohammadi et al. 2006). If, on the contrary, a TMDL model may be constructed for dissolved oxygen (DO) using a load–duration curve, the uncertainty in the sensor measurements of DO and flow should be incorporated into estimating the MOS, because this model is based on conditions affecting DO loading.

7.2 GEOGRAPHIC INFORMATION SYSTEM AND REMOTE SENSING

Geographic information system (GIS) and remote sensing have become indispensable tools for developing regional simulation models that form the backbone of many TMDL analyses (Quinn et al. 2019).

7.2.1 Geographic Information System

Spatially distributed, parametric TMDL models require soil, land-use information, as well as information on topography and hydrology as input data (Doherty and Hunt 2010). GIS and remote sensing tools have evolved in recent years with the capability of processing and synthesizing large quantities of spatial data to provide model input (Kang 2002, Kang and Park 2003) as part of the modeling process. Three of the best examples that demonstrate the use of a GIS as both a data preprocessor and an output postprocessor in TMDL model applications are the Better Assessment Science Integrating point and Nonpoint Sources (BASINS) model, the Automated Geospatial Watershed Assessment (AGWA) model, and the Watershed Analysis Risk Management Framework (WARMF) model. These models incorporate customized GIS workflows (ASCE 2017). In these TMDL modeling frameworks, the data preprocessor provides formatted input data from one or a number of GIS data layers, and the model output postprocessors are used to graphically display simulation results and help to visualize model output in a manner that aids communication with policy makers and stakeholders (Kang et al. 2006). In some cases, visualization can be used to customize model output such as using backdrops of satellite imagery to increase the relatability of model results to certain stakeholder and policy-making entities.

Most water quality models in current use for TMDL modeling rely on spatially referenced datasets as input (ASCE 2017). These datasets are available for download from multiple sources such as the NASA, USGS, the European Space Agency, and other private enterprises. The raw data downloads have different projections and spatial scales. Great strides have been made in recent years to provide accessible tools for routinely transforming these data to other common projections and handling the necessary computations that allow these data to be accurately represented at more useful spatial resolutions. This diversity of information formats makes GISs such as ArcGIS, QGIS, MapWindow GIS, and GRASS that are designed for handling spatially referenced data obvious choices for data management and graphics data processing. Specialized software developed for digital elevation processing includes topographic parameterization (TOPAZ) and terrain analysis using digital elevation models (TauDEM) (version 5). In addition, libraries and modules are included with most common GIS platforms such as *spatial analyst* in ArcGIS, *catchment area* in QGIS, and *watershed* in GRASS. These modules can be used to convert digital elevations to the model topology that aids in applications such as flow routing, which, in turn, helps in estimation of the constituent fluxes produced by water quality simulation models. In other cases, proprietary software modeling frameworks such as WMS (AQUAVEO 2017) have incorporated several widely used water resources models such as storm water management model (SWMM), gridded surface and subsurface hydrologic analysis, hydrological simulation program-Fortran, and CE-QUAL-W2 to give model users more flexibility in their choice of model, because these frameworks provide a common input data architecture accessible to all included models. This makes the task of running models easier and allows the outputs from multiple water quality models to be visualized and more readily compared using a common set of software tools (ASCE 2017). Direct comparison of the results of alternate TMDL models can be a difficult task and require an assessment of model data and the algorithms underpinning each model. The use of a common database for these models can reduce the degree of uncertainty in these comparisons. Proprietary extensions have also been developed to integrate GIS platforms such as ArcGIS with several other water quality models such as InfoSWMM (2017) for SWMM and ArcSWAT (2017) for the Soil and Water Assessment Tool (SWAT) that lack native GIS capabilities.

Spatial modeling of data, which may require the preparation of maps depicting water quality and other key geomorphological information, is a particular strength of GIS platforms. The use of GIS tools can help decision makers develop a comprehensive view of the features of the target watershed for TMDL development. Spatial overlays of available data can help the analyst organize and parse these data resources into the format required as input to the water quality models used in TMDL development. Examples of this data preprocessing capability are common in the published literature (Shafique et al. 2003, Ramirez et al. 2005, Viers et al. 2005). Other examples of GIS frameworks used for postprocessing of modeled results occur in the planning of remediation or abatement strategies, such as citing structural BMPs and targeting nonstructural BMPs in high-impacted areas.

7.2.2 Remote Sensing

Many water quality parameters have well-defined spectral properties that can yield unique spectral signatures (or amplitudes of reflectance of electromagnetic radiation of various wavelengths). These spectral signatures can be correlated with certain water quality parameters in a waterbody. Three spectral bands, Visible (VIS), microwave (MW), and infrared (IR), are the most utilized spectral bands for remote sensing of waterbodies (Richard 1986). Sensors housed on satellites and other platforms either measure the natural reflectance of the target (passive sensing) or emit radiation that is sensed by the target being investigated (active sensing). Sensors are also categorized into microwave radiometers (MWRs) and synthetic aperture radar (SAR). These sensors have broad applications in oceanographic remote sensing (Gholizadeh et al. 2016).

The following terms are defined:

1. Spectral: decomposition of some quantity (say the electromagnetic radiant energy emitted by an object) into various constituent frequencies and a description of the quantity in the frequency domain.
2. Band: collection of continuous frequencies within a specified range; each remote-sensed image contains multiple channels, each containing intensity information within one band.
3. Bandwidth: range of frequencies contained within a band.
4. Reflectance: coherent alteration of a path of an emitted wave after impinging on some surface.
5. Backscatter: random alteration of a path of an emitted wave after impinging on some surface.
6. Active scanning: scanning system in which an electromagnetic pulse is emitted and recovered after reflecting or backscattering from some surface.

7. Passive scanning: scanning system in which natural emittances from some surfaces are recovered.
8. Swath: spatial extent of a remote sensing scene.
9. Swath width: width along the swath of a remote sensing scene.
10. Range: number of levels of intensity of a signal recorded by a remote sensing platform.
11. Pixel: single unit of a remote-sensed image representing an area of the imaged scene.
12. Spatial resolution: smallest distance across which objects can be differentiated by a sensor in a scene; the size of one image pixel corresponds to the spatial resolution of the sensor. Typically, the swath width is equal to the spatial resolution.
13. Return period: time taken between successive images of a scene by a remote sensor.

Several government-sponsored and private satellites in orbit collect high-resolution imagery. For example, the Terra satellite, which includes the advanced spaceborne thermal emission and reflection radiometer, Clouds and Earth's radiant energy system (CERES), multiangle imaging spectroradiometer, moderate resolution imaging spectroradiometer (MODIS), and measurements of pollution in the troposphere (MOPITT) imagery, was launched to provide information on the spread of pollution around the globe. The Aqua Earth-observing satellite was launched in 2002 to collect information relevant to the Earth's water cycle. In addition, this satellite collects information on the vegetation cover, water temperature, and concentrations of phytoplankton and dissolved organic matter among other parameters in waterbodies. This satellite is a platform for six instruments, the Atmospheric InfraRed Sounder (AIRS), Advanced Microwave Sounding Unit (AMSU), CERES, MODIS, Advanced Microwave Scanning Radiometer for EOS (AMSR-E), and Humidity Sounder for Brazil (HSB). Another Earth observation satellite is ENVISAT launched in 2002, which is focused on providing constituent data for environmental studies. The satellite hosts have nine instruments, which are sensor arrays named the medium resolution imaging spectrometer (MERIS), advanced along track scanning radiometer (AATSR), Scanning Imaging Absorption SpectroMeter for Atmospheric CHartography (SCIAMACHY), *Red Alert 2* (RA-2), MWR, Doppler Orbitography and Radiopositioning Integrated by Satellite (DORIS), Michelson Interferometer for Passive Atmospheric Sounding (MIPAS), Global Ozone Monitoring by Occultation of Stars (GOMOS), and Advanced Synthetic Aperture Radar (ASAR).

Although the power and capability of satellite and airborne imagery and processing software has risen over the past decade, the cost of these remote sensing resources has declined significantly. Availability and access to simple graphical user interfaces for processing remote sensing imagery has increased during the past decade, in particular routines embedded in commercial software as ERDAS, ENVI, and ArcGIS Image Analyst. These remote sensing interpreted data resources are increasingly being used for basin-scale simulation modeling studies and TMDL development (ASCE 2017). However, in the relatively recent past, remote sensing analysis was conducted independently from model development—today, model input files can be created directly through the use of GIS as an intermediary interpretative step that can include basic data quality assurance. A number of model data preprocessors now allow the use of a suite of remote sensing data products.

Satellite and aerial imagery are captured at a distance from the rotating Earth's surface, which, because of its curvature, introduces a number of photogrammetric challenges. Although not as significant an issue for aerial imagery, for satellite imagery, electromagnetic energy passes through a substantial atmospheric path before it reaches satellite-based sensors. Atmospheric particles may absorb or scatter the radiation. This leads to external radiometric errors in the image. Moreover, sensor drift and other systematic malfunctions may also cause internal radiometric distortion. In addition, satellites follow orbits relative to the Earth while the satellite imagery is being processed, which results in geometric distortions in the image. The same is true of aerial imaging platforms such as unmanned drones and aircraft that follow flight paths while imaging a scene. Moreover, the curvature and relief of the Earth's surface also add to this geometric distortion (Humboldt State University 2016). Scan skew, earth rotation, platform velocity, mirror scan velocity, panoramic distortion, and perspective distortion all lead to systematic geometric errors. Finally, because of slight changes in the imaging swath with each orbital pass of a satellite, or minor alterations in an aerial platform's position along its flight path, successive images of a scene may be shifted from each other. This causes registration discrepancies (pixel shifts between images) between the images, which renders time-series analyses challenging. These factors are often overlooked in the decision to use satellite imagery in GIS model development and can add significantly to the cost of deploying this technology.

The techniques of processing and error-correcting satellite imagery can be divided into two major independent operations—radiometric correction and geometric correction. Radiometric correction is typically performed using calibration data that relates measured irradiance to the sensor output. This operation can be performed using a variety of methods, including image-based methods, radiative transfer models, and the empirical line method (Karpouzli and Malthus 2003). Radiometric calibration and correction procedures are particularly important when comparing datasets over multiple time periods and for improving the interpretability and integrity of remotely sensed data. Geometric corrections can be performed using the available information on the platform trajectory through space, control points with map coordinates on the Earth's surface, image-to-map rectification, and image-to-image rectification data. When surface relief is significant relative to the swath (an issue of relatively large significance for near-earth orbital platforms and aerial imagery), relative separations between objects within the image will be distorted and should be orthorectified. TMDL modelers are encouraged to verify that imagery used for analysis has undergone appropriate radiometric and geometric corrections prior to use or engage a professional remote sensing specialist to assist in this task. For example, USGS provides Level 1 and Level 2 images that have undergone geometric correction and orthorectification. In addition, USGS has also started providing Level 3 products that have been co-registered and have been labeled Analysis Ready Data (ARD).

The use of remotely sensed imagery for TMDL modeling can be significantly enhanced by improving the automation of the data quality assurance procedures relevant to the remotely sensed data. The urgent need for this innovation is related to the rapid increase in the number of new remote sensing platforms such as drones, which has driven down the cost of imagery acquisition and created a need for fast and uncomplicated data quality screening and imagery correction automation, especially for scientific research deployments. Other remote sensing technologies are being similarly advanced within the public domain and innovation continues at a rapid pace.

7.2.2.1 Light Detection and Ranging. Light detection and ranging (LiDAR) is categorized as active remote sensing that records laser pulses that strike an object to detect the object and determine the distance between the instrument and the object (range). The physical properties of an object can be determined based on the sensors that allow interpretation of data produced resulting from the effect of the object on reflected radiation (Diaz et al. 2013). LiDAR has applications in many different resource management fields, including agriculture, environmental assessment, forest planning and management, forest fire management, watershed and stream delineation, inundation modeling and flood assessment, ecological and land classification, river surveying, pollution modeling, management of coastlines, meteorology measurements, and estimation of glacier volume changes. As such, it has utility for data acquisition in support of TMDL modeling. LiDAR data analysis and interpretation has been incorporated into several GIS software platforms such as ArcGIS.

7.2.2.2 Multispectral Remote Sensing Imagery. Multispectral imagery is produced by sensors that capture the backscattered energy from multiple sections of the electromagnetic spectrum. Although multispectral sensors enable an analysis of extensive areas of the Earth's surface and produce cost-effective imagery with high spatial resolution, they are limited by cloud cover and spectral resolution.

Multispectral sensors such as MODIS, MERIS, Sea-viewing Wide Field-of-view Sensor (SeaWiFS), and Sentinel-3 Ocean and Land Color Instrument (OLCI) have a small number of relatively broad spectral bands within the visible to mid-infrared spectrum, which can complicate the retrieval of some water quality parameters (Topp et al. 2020). To capture the absorption features and backscatter peaks of these water quality parameters, hyperspectral sensors have been utilized, which provide many narrow bands covering the spectrum from visible to longwave infrared. In addition, lower spectral resolution of multispectral data could cover several spectral band subdivisions that cause issues with detecting clouds efficiently and accurately (Sun et al. 2017).

In recent years, multispectral imagery from platforms such as USGS Earth Explorer and NASA Earth data have been offered at no cost to the public. This has led to an explosion of applications, including real-time and near-real-time processing of satellite imagery around the world for different applications such as deforestation, reforestation, daily crop evapotranspiration estimates, and water quality monitoring. Procedures for cloud cover masking and image fusion need to be perfected to make the multispectral data more robust and reliable for TMDL model development.

7.2.2.3 Hyperspectral Remote Sensing Imagery.   Hyperspectral data are composed of many contiguous spectral bands with narrow bandwidths. Hyperspectral sensors such as the compact airborne spectrographic imager (CASI), the airborne prism experiment (APEX), airborne visible/infrared spectrometer (AVIRIS), airborne visible/infrared spectrometer-next generation (AVIRIS-NG), and portable remote imaging spectrometer (PRISM) produce complete spectral signatures without any wavelength omissions. The majority of hyperspectral sensors is airborne or is in the planning process for deployment on satellites in the future (Topp et al. 2020). Higher spectral resolution of hyperspectral data allows better identification, characterization, quantification, and subpixel detection. Hyperspectral imagery can be used to determine and map key water quality parameters by taking advantage of complex inherent optical properties (IOP) (Olmanson et al. 2013). These characteristics of hyperspectral imagery enable a myriad of applications in TMDL modeling for large and small watersheds.

The key challenges for acquiring and utilizing hyperspectral sensing data are the cost of acquisition, the high dimensionality and size of the hyperspectral data, the spectral mixing, and the degradation of received radiance at the sensor by atmospheric effects and instrumental noise

(Ramirez et al. 2005, Bioucas-Dias et al. 2013). To remove atmospheric effects, a large amount of hyperspectral data must be collected and processed to help eliminate compromising data (Gao et al. 2009, Zarco-Tejada and González-Dugo 2012). In addition, several screening methods have been developed to remove redundant and noisy data directly (Chang 2013).

Hyperspectral sensors are expensive and require specialized handling. These sensors also often have limited spatial swath and low resolution. The development of standardized workflows to deal with the large datasets generated by hyperspectral sensors would be a valuable accomplishment to support TMDL modeling.

7.2.2.4 Specialized Platforms. Apart from imaging platforms, several airborne and spaceborne platforms have been specifically designed to detect and track physical phenomena of interest. For example, the Ice, Cloud, and land Elevation Satellite 2 (ICESAT-2) has been designed to use the Advanced Topographic Laser Altimeter System (ATLAS) to measure the elevation of land and sea ice cover, canopies, and land with high precision. Another example is the Gravity Recovery and Climate Experiment (GRACE), which measures anomalies in the Earth's gravitational field to estimate changes in water storage within a region. Supplied with water-use data and a complementary hydrologic model, these data can provide useful information for use in regional water budget assessments. Such specialized technologies can be incorporated in TMDL modeling studies provided they can be included in the TMDL data acquisition and analysis workflow.

7.3 GEOGRAPHIC INFORMATION SYSTEM AND REMOTE SENSING APPLICATIONS IN TOTAL MAXIMUM DAILY LOAD MODELING

Modeling is a key requirement for TMDL development. As most of the data required for modeling (particularly complex models) are spatially distributed, GIS can be a cost- and time-saving tool. Remotely sensed data, as discussed previously, from aerial or satellite platforms, may also be valuable in learning more about the system under observation. Typically, the water quality data products from remote sensing are limited to those substances or conditions that can influence and change the optical (reflected) or thermal characteristics of the water surface. These characteristics include chlorophyll-*a*, suspended sediments, colored dissolved organic matter, water clarity, and temperature (see review by Topp et al. 2020).

The thermal band of the imagery supplied by satellite and certain aerial platforms can be used to estimate the surface temperature of waterbodies

(Caldwell et al. 2019) and evapotranspiration (ET) over land (Fisher et al. 2020, Hoffmann et al. 2015). Several validated ET data products for the continental United States exist that can be used to calibrate and validate detailed simulation models of moderate-size watersheds (Becker et al. 2019). Remote sensing–derived water surface data have also been used for this purpose (Domeneghetti et al. 2014). Some water quality parameters can be measured indirectly through surrogate indicators, such as chlorophyll-*a*, which is a characteristic of algal biomass that has a unique reflectance and can be a useful indicator of elevated nutrient levels and perhaps bacterial loads in certain situations. In these cases, data models can be developed between the surrogate indicators and these variables based on in situ measurements concurrent to the satellite overpass. Because the optical properties of the water column can change spatially and temporally, multitemporal satellite data and multipoint in-situ measurements are required for this purpose. Two classes of modeling, empirical and semianalytical learning models, have often been used (Topp et al. 2020). Empirical models are nongeneralizable, local models that use regression or other machine-learning techniques between observable spectral band or band combination and water quality parameters. Semianalytical models are more generalizable models that incorporate the inherent optical properties of water to assess the water quality parameters (e.g., suspended sediments). These methods are typically unique to a particular watershed and waterbody. Model developers will need to develop additional relationships to correlate spectral observations and water quality data that have potential to improve the fidelity of water quality modeling.

Within a watershed, remote sensing data can be useful for soil moisture estimation and LULC classification. For example, medium-spatial resolution LANDSAT satellite data are commonly used to classify land-use types in a scene. True color orthophotography produces images in which corrections have been applied to minimize the effects of topography on true distances between objects. Orthophotography, when made available at a higher resolution, can be useful for detecting impervious cover and forests and in small watersheds. New commercial satellite imagery is now available at a resolution as refined as 30 cm that may be beneficial for better LULC classification. Remote sensing and GISs can also be used together for formulating management plans with reliance on high-end, innovative visualizations and maps, which can lead to policy actions and interventions that lead to improvements in the quality of impaired waters. Effective TMDL implementation plans can be developed by enhancing land-use planning decision-making using remote sensing and GISs to demonstrate how BMPs might curtail pollutant movement to a waterbody (Zaidi 2012).

Because many datasets required for model calibration have spatial dimension, several water resources models have been updated with GIS-based user interfaces. Using the terminology defined by Martin et al.

(2005), GIS-water resource model interfaces may be categorized in three groupings: linked, combined, and integrated. Water resource modes that are linked with a GIS typically require manual or semiautomated data exchange between the model and the GIS. Models that have combined links may not need any additional programming for connecting the model with GISs. An example of a combined model is the QGIS Interface for SWAT (QSWAT) (Dile et al. 2016). Customized GIS processing may be needed, however, when applying such models, depending on the characteristic physiography of the local area. Integrated models require that all spatial data be projected to the same projected coordinate system. The utility of remote sensing imagery and the level of user control in a GIS workflow depend ultimately on the specific TMDL application.

7.4 STATE-OF-THE-ART AND STATE-OF-THE-PRACTICE

The use of GIS and remote sensing in TMDL modeling and analysis has evolved rapidly in the past decade to the point that both are available to practitioners using state-of-the-art TMDL modeling tools such as BASINS and other integrated modeling approaches. Popular watershed models such as SWAT have extensive user communities, which has led to continual updating of these models with new capabilities and easier use of remotely sensed data that can now be invoked from within the model user interface. Free access to powerful spatial analysis and assessment tools such as Google Earth Engine and the provision of free remotely sensed imagery have led to significant innovation in this field.

In addition, the proliferation of low-cost drones and the simultaneous development of low-cost and powerful image processing and quality control software have made use of these tools affordable for TMDL model applications. GIS and remote sensing are fast evolving into indispensable support tools for TMDL development and modeling with one of the most rapid transition rates between state-of-the-art and state-of-the-practice.

REFERENCES

Ahmadisharaf, E., R. A. Camacho, H. X. Zhang, M. Hantush, and M. M. Yusuf. 2019. "Calibration and validation of watershed models and advances in uncertainty analysis in TMDL studies." *J. Hydrol. Eng.* 24 (7): 03119001.

Aquaveo. 2017. Watershed Modeling System - The All-in-one Watershed Solution. AQUAVEO. Accessed November 13, 2021. http://www.aquaveo.com/software/wms-watershed-modeling-system-introduction.

ArcSWAT (ArcGIS-ArcView Extension of Soil and Water Assessment Tool). 2017. Texas A&M University and USDA-ARS. Accessed November 13, 2021. https://swat.tamu.edu/software/arcswat/.

ASCE. 2017. *Total maximum daily load analysis and modeling: Assessment of the practice.* Reston, VA: ASCE.

Becker, R., A. Koppa, S. Schulz, M. Usman, T. aus der Beek, and C. Schüth. 2019. "Spatially distributed model calibration of a highly managed hydrological system using remote sensing-derived ET data." *J. Hydrol.* 577: 123944.

Benham, B. L., C. Baffaut, R. W. Zeckoski, K. R. Mankin, Y. A. Pachepsky, A. M. Sadeghi, et al. 2006. "Modeling bacteria fate and transport in watersheds to support TMDLs." *Trans. ASABE* 49 (4): 987–1002.

Bioucas-Dias, J. M., A. Plaza, G. Camps-Valls, P. Scheunders, N. Nasrabadi, and J. Chanussot. 2013. "Hyperspectral remote sensing data analysis and future challenges." *IEEE Geosci. Remote Sens. Mag.* 1 (2): 6–36.

Borah, D., and M. Bera. 2003. "Watershed-scale hydrologic and nonpoint-source pollution models: Review of mathematical bases." *Trans. ASAE* 46 (6): 1553–1566.

Borah, D. K., and M. Bera. 2004. "Watershed-scale hydrologic and nonpoint-source pollution models: Review of applications." *Trans. ASAE* 47 (3): 789–803.

Borah, D. K., G. Yagow, A. Saleh, P. L. Barnes, W. Rosenthal, E. C. Krug, et al. 2006. "Sediment and nutrient modeling for TMDL development and implementation." *Trans. ASABE* 49 (4): 967–986.

Caldwell, S. H., C. Kelleher, E. A. Baker, and L. K. Lautz. 2019. "Relative information from thermal infrared imagery via unoccupied aerial vehicle informs simulations and spatially-distributed assessments of stream temperature." *Sci. Total Environ.* 661: 364–374.

Cappiella, K., and K. Brown. 2001. *Derivations of impervious cover for suburban land uses in the Chesapeake Bay Watershed.* Ellicott City, MD: EPA Chesapeake Bay Program Center for Watershed Protection.

Chang, C. 2013. *Hyperspectral data processing: Algorithm design and analysis.* Hoboken, NJ: Wiley.

Chapra S. C. 2003. "Engineering water quality models and TMDLs." *J. Water Res. Plan. Mgmt.* 129 (4): July 2003, doi: 10.1061/%28ASCE% 290733-9496%282003%29129%3A4%28247%29.

Diaz, J. C. F., W. E. Carter, R. L. Shrestha, and C. L. Glennie. 2013. "Lidar remote sensing." In *Handbook of satellite applications*, edited by J. N. Pelton, S. Madry, and S. Camacho-Lara, 757–808. New York: Springer.

Dile, Y. T., P. Daggupati, C. George, R. Srinivasan, and J. Arnold. 2016. "Introducing a new open source GIS user interface for the SWAT model." *Environ. Modell. Software* 85: 129–138.

Doherty, J. E., and R. J. Hunt. 2010. Approaches to highly parameterized inversion—A guide to using PEST for groundwater-model calibration.

Scientific Investigations Rep. No. 2010-5169. Reston, VA: United States Geological Survey.

Domeneghetti, A., A. Tarpanelli, L. Brocca, S. Barbetta, T. Moramarco, A. Castellarin, et al. 2014. "The use of remote sensing-derived water surface data for hydraulic model calibration." *Remote Sens. Environ.* 149: 130–141.

Fisher, J. B., B. Lee, A. J. Purdy, G. H. Halverson, M. B. Dohlen, K. Cawse-Nicholson, et al. 2020. "ECOSTRESS: NASA's next generation mission to measure evapotranspiration from the International Space Station." *Water Resour. Res.* 56 (4): e2019WR026058.

Fu, B., J. S. Horsburgh, A. J. Jakeman, C. Gualtieri, T. Arnold, L. Marshall, et al. 2020. Modeling water quality in watersheds: From here to the next generation." *Water Resour. Res.* 56: e2020WR027721.

Gao, B., M. Montes, C. Davis, and A. Goetz. 2009. "Atmospheric correction algorithms for hyperspectral remote sensing data of land and ocean." *Remote Sens. Environ.* 113 (1): S17–S24.

Gao, J., M. J. White, K. Bieger, and J. G. Arnold. 2020. "Design and development of a python-based interface for processing massive data with the LOAD ESTimator (LOADEST)." *Environ. Modell. Software* 135: 104897

Gholizadeh, M. H., A. M. Melesse, and L. A. Reddi. 2016. "Comprehensive review on water quality parameters estimation using remote sensing techniques." *Sensors* 16: 1298.

Hoffmann, H., H. Nieto, R. Jensen, R. Guzinski, P. J. Zarco-Tejada, and T. Friborg. 2015. "Estimating evapotranspiration with thermal UAV data and two source energy balance models." *Hydrol. Earth Syst. Sci. Discuss.* 12: 8.

Humboldt State University. 2016. "Introduction to remote sensing." Accessed October 16, 2021. https://extended.humboldt.edu/extended-education/online-geospatial-certificate-program/course/introduction-remote-sensing.

InfoSWMM. 2017. "Sophisticated geospatial urban drainage modeling." Accessed October 10, 2021. http://www.innovyze.com/products/infoswmm/.

Kang, M. S. 2002. "Development of total maximum daily loads simulation system using artificial neural networks for satellite data analysis and nonpoint source pollution models." [In Korean]. Ph.D. thesis, Seoul National University, Dept. of Civil and Environmental Engineering.

Kang, M. S., and S. W. Park. 2003. "Development and application of total maximum daily loads simulation system using nonpoint source pollution model." *J. Korea Water Resour. Assoc.* 36 (1): 117–128.

Kang, M. S., S. W. Park, J. J. Lee, and K. H. Yoo. 2006. "Applying SWAT for TMDL programs to a small watershed containing rice paddy fields." *Agric. Water Manage.* 79 (1): 72–92.

Karpouzli, E., and T. Malthus. 2003. "The empirical line method for the atmospheric correction of IKONOS imagery." *Int. J. Remote Sens.* 24 (5): 1143–1150.

Martin, P., E. LeBoeuf, J. Dobbins, E. Daniel, and M. Abkowitz. 2005. "Interfacing GIS with water resource models: A state-of-the-art review." *J. Am. Water Resour. Assoc.* 41 (6): 1471–1487.

Olmanson, L. G., P. L. Brezonik, and M. E. Bauer. 2013. "Airborne hyperspectral remote sensing to assess spatial distribution of water quality characteristics in large rivers: The Mississippi River and its tributaries in Minnesota." *Remote Sens. Environ.* 130: 254–265.

Quinn, N.W.T., S. Kumar, and S. Imen. 2019. "Overview of remote sensing and GIS uses in watershed and TMDL analyses." *J. Hydrol. Eng.* 24 (4): 1–9.

Ramirez, C. M., J. H. Viers, J. F. Quinn, M. L. Johnson, B. Kozlowicz, and J. Florsheim. 2005. "Mass wasting identification in the Navarro River watershed using hyperspectral imagery." In *California and the world ocean '02: Revisiting and revising California's ocean agenda,* edited by O. T. Magoon, H. Converse, B. Baird, B. Jines, and M. Miller-Henson, 1279–1288. Reston, VA: ASCE.

Richard, J. 1986. *Remote sensing digital image analysis: An introduction.* New York: Springer.

Shafique, N., F. Fulk, B. C. Autrey, and J. E. Flotemersch. 2003. "Hyperspectral remote sensing of water quality parameters for large rivers in the Ohio River basin." In *Proc., 1st Interagency Conf. on Research in the Watersheds.* Washington, DC: USEPA.

Shirmohammadi, A., I. Chaubey, R. D. Harmel, D. D. Bosch, R. Munoz-Carpena, C. Dharmasri, et al. 2006. "Uncertainty in TMDL models." *Trans. ASABE* 49 (4): 1033–1049.

Sun, L., M. Xueting, J. Wei, J. Wang, X. Tian, H. Yu, et al. 2017. "A cloud detection algorithm-generating method for remote sensing data at visible to short-wave infrared wavelengths." *ISPRS J. Photogramm. Remote Sens.* 124: 70–88.

Thomas, G., and A. Henderson-Sellers. 1991. "An evaluation of proposed representations of subgrid hydrologic processes in climate models." *J. Clim.* 4 (9): 898–910.

Topp, S. N., T. M. Pavelsky, D. Jensen, M. Simard, and M. R. V. Ross. 2020. "Research trends in the use of remote sensing for inland water quality science: Moving towards multidisciplinary applications." *Water* 12: 169.

Viers, J. H., C. M. Ramirez, J. F. Quinn, and M. L. Johnson. 2005. "The use of hyperspectral technologies to identify riparian habitats in coastal watersheds: An example from the Navarro River, California." In *California and the world ocean '02: Revisiting and revising California's ocean agenda,* edited by O. T. Magoon, H. Converse, B. Baird, B. Jines, and M. Miller-Henson, 1377–1391. Reston, VA: ASCE.

Waichler, S. R., and M. S. Wigmosta. 2003. "Development of hourly meteorological values from daily data and significance to hydrological modeling at HJ Andrews Experimental Forest." *J. Hydrometeorol.* 4 (2): 251–263.

Wallace, C. W., B. L. Benham, E. R. Yagow, and D. L. Gallagher. 2018. "Comparison of two alternative methods for developing TMDLs to address sediment impairments." *J. Hydrol. Eng.* 23 (12): 05018023.

Whittemore, R. C., and J. Beebe. 2000. "EPA'S BASINS model: good science or serendipitous modeling?" *JAWRA J. Am. Water Resour. Assoc.* 36 (3): 493–499.

Zaidi, A. 2012. "Water quality management using GIS and RS tools." In *Proc., World Environmental and Water Resources Cong. 2012*, edited by E. D. Loucks, 842–848. Reston, VA: ASCE.

Zarco-Tejada, P., and V. González-Dugo. 2012. "Fluorescence, temperature and narrow-band indices acquired from a UAV platform for water stress detection using a micro-hyperspectral imager and a thermal." *Remote Sens. Environ.* 117: 322–337.

Zhang, H. X., and N. W. T. Quinn. 2019. "Simple models and analytical procedures for total maximum daily load assessment." *J. Hydrol. Eng.* 24 (2): 02518002.

CHAPTER 8
MODEL CALIBRATION AND VALIDATION

Ebrahim Ahmadisharaf, Rene A. Camacho-Rincon, Harry X. Zhang,
Mohamed M. Hantush, Yusuf M. Mohamoud

8.1 INTRODUCTION

Model calibration and validation are necessary steps in modeling physical processes such as hydrologic and nonpoint-source pollutions in watersheds and pollutant assimilations in receiving waterbodies to demonstrate and ensure that the predictive capability of a model is acceptable to support decision making (Ahmadisharaf et al. 2019), including the development and implementation of total maximum daily loads (TMDLs). Model applications in TMDLs, calibration, and validation ensure reliable cause-and-effect relationships between pollutants at sources and assimilations in the receiving waterbodies to reliably determine the impacts of the sources on the receiving bodies (USEPA 1991). Also, as suggested in Martin and McCutcheon (1999) and Refsgaard and Henriksen (2004), an objective and informed calibration and validation protocol must be followed in applying models in the development and implementation of TMDLs. Model calibration involves running a model to simulate existing conditions and constraining the model outputs to the best available field data, whereas model validation involves running the model to represent conditions not evaluated during the calibration and to demonstrate that the predictive capability of the model is reliable and acceptable (Ahmadisharaf et al. 2019). Despite increasing uses of models in TMDL studies, guidelines for model calibration and validation remain limited. Guidance for measuring model performance and reliability also remains limited (refer to Chapter 11).

In this chapter, state-of-the-art in model calibration and validation approaches found in the literature (Ahmadisharaf et al. 2019) are presented as guidance for applications of models in TMDL studies. Although the focus is on watershed models, the same is applicable to receiving water models as well. In the following sections, data and sources of the data, including well-maintained databases as required in TMDL modeling, are presented, followed by data management resources, precalibration guidelines, calibration guidelines including manual and autocalibration, lists of hydrologic and water quality parameters needing calibration in the 14 watershed models presented in Chapter 2 [with the exception of the watershed assessment model (WAM)] and the Spreadsheet Tool for the Estimation of Pollutant Load (STEPL) presented in Chapter 5, various available goodness-of-fit equations to measure calibration, and five model performance testing criteria or protocols. Borah et al. (2019) did not include the WAM in their study, and, therefore, it was a new entry in Chapter 2.

8.2 MODEL DATA AND SOURCES OF THE DATA

As presented in Chapter 7, models require data to set up and run. Different models require different data defining the physical, biological, and chemical states of waterbodies such as watersheds, streams, rivers, lakes, estuaries, bays, and others to be modeled. The primary models used in TMDL studies are the watershed models (Chapter 2) simulating hydrologic, hydraulic, and water quality (pollutant) processes and receiving waterbody models (Chapter 3) simulating hydrodynamic and water quality (pollutant assimilation) processes. Both watershed models and receiving waterbody models require extensive datasets for model setup, calibration, validation, and decision making, including TMDL development and implementation. Modeling hydrologic processes requires characteristics of the watershed, including pedologic (soil physical characteristics), land use/land cover (LULC), and geomorphologic (topography, drainage area, and river network) data to set up the models; meteorological (e.g., precipitation and temperature) data to run the model; and hydrologic (e.g., streamflow) data to calibrate and validate the model (Chapter 2). Modeling hydrodynamic processes in a receiving waterbody typically requires geomorphologic (topography and bathymetry) and hydrologic (e.g., inflows, water surface elevations, or tide measurements in the case of tidal watersheds or waterways, and surface roughness properties of channels and hydraulic structures) information. Modeling water quality processes requires information on pollutant loads from watersheds and point sources as well as in-stream water quality observations [e.g., dissolved oxygen (DO), carbon, sediments, nutrients, and algae] for calibration and validation of the model. Studies of nonconventional toxic substances require more complex information such as loads of particulate refractory (low decay rate), particulate labile (moderate decay rate), and dissolved fractions of the substance, sediment diagenesis fluxes and speciation, among others (Chapter 3).

Given these extensive dataset requirements, the predictive capability of the TMDL models also depends on the availability and quality of the environmental records collected by the public, private sector, government agencies, and industry. Table 8-1 provides the major sources of publicly available data needed to set up, run, and calibrate–validate receiving water and watershed models.

Although the sources in Table 8-1 might satisfy the data requirements in most cases, for other cases, the required datasets (sometimes with a finer resolution) might be available through the state and local agencies as well as the private sector. For example, records of municipal and industrial water withdrawals and dischargers can be obtained from state environmental agencies. The Consortium of Universities for the Advancement of Hydrologic Science (CUAHSI) also provides hydrologic data across the globe. As such, modelers are advised to explore data availability based on the case under study.

Synoptic water quality data are usually less available than hydrodynamic data. The Water Quality Portal (WQP), established by USEPA and USGS and managed by the National Water Quality Monitoring Council, is the most extensive database to support TMDL model calibration and validation. The portal is a repository for data collected by more than 400 state, federal, tribal, and local agencies, including the third major contributor, the Agricultural Research Service of USDA. USEPA also compiles information from watershed groups, other volunteer groups, and universities [40 Code of Federal Regulations 130.7(b)(5)(iii)]. WQP provides links to other major repositories for groundwater, coastal and ocean monitoring as well as the California Water Quality Monitoring Council's My Water Quality, Washington Department of Ecology, Environmental Assessment Program database, and other state portals. This portal compiles mostly monitoring data collected by different agencies for a multitude of purposes using divergent quality assurance plans. Thus, finding coherent synoptic datasets for a specific impaired waterbody is often difficult. Like the hydrologic datasets, CUAHSI also archives water quality research data on various physical, chemical, and biological constituents. Water quality datasets are usually less available than those necessary for the development of hydrologic models. State and local agencies, as well as private industries, keep records of municipal and industrial water withdrawals, particularly in states that permit any withdrawal. CUAHSI archives hydrologic research data globally, and some of the data collected in the United States may not be archived in the national databases listed in Table 8-1.

The Permit Compliance System (PCS) and Integrated Compliance Information System (ICIS) databases provide information on all National Pollutant Discharge Elimination System permits to discharge wastewater, stormwater, combined sewer overflows, and other nonpoint sources (e.g.,

Table 8-1. Data Sources for Setup, Calibration, and Validation of Hydrologic, Hydrodynamic, and Water Quality Models in TMDL Studies.

Data type	Source	Link
Hydrologic Information		
Watershed boundary	United States Geological Survey (USGS) Watershed Boundary dataset	https://nhd.usgs.gov/wbd.html
Topography	USGS National Elevation dataset (NED)	http://ned.usgs.gov/
	National Aeronautics and Space Administration (NASA) Shuttle Radar Topography Mission (SRTM)	http://dds.cr.usgs.gov/srtm/
	Ministry of Economy, Trade, and Industry (METI)-NASA Advanced Spaceborne Thermal Emission and Reflection Radiometer (ASTER)	https://gdex.cr.usgs.gov/gdex/
Stream network	USGS National Hydrography dataset (NHD)	https://nhd.usgs.gov/
Soil	United States Department of Agriculture (USDA) Soil Survey Geographic (SSURGO) database	https://websoilsurvey.nrcs.usda.gov/
	USDA State Soil Geographic (STATSGO) dataset	
	National Ecological Observatory Network (NEON)	https://www.neonscience.org/
Land use/land cover	USGS National Land Cover dataset (NLCD)	https://www.mrlc.gov/about.php
	USDA National Agricultural Statistics Service's (NASS's) CropScape	https://nassgeodata.gmu.edu/

Hydrology	USGS National Water Information System (NWIS)	https://waterdata.usgs.gov/nwis
Meteorologic	National Oceanic and Atmospheric Administration (NOAA) National Climatic Data Center database (NCDC)	https://www.ncdc.noaa.gov/cdo-web/
	NOAA's Next Generation Weather Radar (NEXRAD)	https://www.ncdc.noaa.gov/data-access/radar-data/nexrad
	Parameter-elevation Regressions on Independent Slopes Model (PRISM)	http://www.prism.oregonstate.edu/
	NASA's Prediction of Worldwide Energy Resources (POWER)	https://power.larc.nasa.gov/
	NASA's North American Land Data Assimilation System (NLDAS)	https://ldas.gsfc.nasa.gov/nldas
Hydrodynamic Information		
Bathymetry	NOAA's Bathymetry and Global Relief database	https://www.ngdc.noaa.gov/mgg/bathymetry/relief.html
Hydrodynamic circulation	NOAA Tides and Currents database	https://tidesandcurrents.noaa.gov/

(Continued)

Table 8-1. (*Continued*)

Data type	Source	Link
Water Quality Information		
National Pollutant Discharge Elimination System (NPDES) permit monitoring of flow and water quality	US Environmental Protection Agency (USEPA) Permit Compliance System (PCS) and Integrated Compliance Information System (ICIS)	https://www.epa.gov/enviro/pcs-icis-search
Water quality observations	USGS–USEPA–National Water Quality Monitoring Council's Water Quality Portal	https://www.waterqualitydata.us/
Water quality observations	USEPA Storage and Retrieval and Water Quality Exchange (STORET) database	https://www.epa.gov/waterdata/storage-and-retrieval-and-water-quality-exchange
Water quality observations from selected estuaries	NOAA National Estuarine Research Reserves System (NERSS)	https://coast.noaa.gov/nerrs/
Demographics and population of animals for source assessment	USDA's NASS	https://www.nass.usda.gov/

Source: Adapted from Ahmadisharaf et al. (2019).

runoff from concentrated livestock pens) into US waters. However, these monitoring data rarely produce reliable synoptic loading data, unless the required monitoring by grab sampling or composite sampling is frequent enough to capture the diurnal, tidal, weekly, monthly, and seasonal dynamics of these permitted discharges. Permitted loads have been difficult to estimate from the permit-required sampling so much so that some waste load allocations have required more intensive synoptic sampling, particularly when Lagrangian sampling is used to guide synoptic data collection (McCutcheon 1989, Martin and McCutcheon 1999). Point sources legally require routine measurements of flow and various water quality constituents. These records are available to the public through the USEPA's PCS. In addition, water quality data are sometimes collected through local efforts, including community science groups and academic endeavors.

In almost all cases, conducting water quality assessments to define TMDL cannot be based solely on the monitoring data collected by public agencies, particularly if such data have important discontinuities or if they report only a few parameters of importance. This has become evident during the 1990s, when it was discovered that waterbodies were put on the Section 303(d) list of impaired waters with little information and sometimes with only one or two water quality measurements. In these circumstances, available data from all sources should be evaluated to determine whether they could be included in TMDL-related water quality assessments. To assess pollutant sources, the USDA National Agricultural Statistics Service (NASS) provides data regarding the population of animals (e.g., livestock and wildlife) and demographics at a county/city level.

8.3 DATA MANAGEMENT

Synoptic data collection for model calibration and validation, if not well planned, can be expensive and time-consuming. As such, adequate protocols to store, process, and distribute the available synoptic datasets must be an important part of approved quality assurance plans. Model evaluations against data collected during different hydrologic seasons typically result in a more robust evaluation of model performance than evaluations based on data collected sporadically or representative of only a particular hydrologic season (Ahmadisharaf et al. 2019).

Data management (e.g., downloading and processing large datasets from these web portals to be used as inputs) in watershed models has been performed in an ad hoc manner in the past and has led to substantial inefficiencies and errors (Ahmadisharaf et al. 2019). Because of these issues, there have been increasing efforts to develop automatic tools to download, store, and manipulate data for modeling purposes. Publicly available data management tools used in TMDL applications include the Water Resources Database (WRDB), the USEPA Better Assessment Science Integrating Point and Nonpoint Sources (BASINS) (USEPA 2013), and the US Army Corps of Engineers (USACE) Hydrologic Engineering Center Data Storage System (HEC-DSS) (USACE 2010). WRDB is a database system to store and process water resource datasets from multiple databases. It was initially designed in 1993 by the Georgia Environmental Protection Division motivated by challenges in the handling of vast amounts of data in multiple formats and for multiple variables during the Chattahoochee River Modeling Project. The WRDB has several utilities for the quality assurance (QA) of data. This tool can import output files from different models such as the Loading Simulation Program C (LSPC), EFDC, and WASP and has a GRAPH utility that can be used to compute the statistics of model performance. The other powerful multipurpose analysis system with capabilities to access national environmental data from multiple sources is BASINS. BASINS is integrated into a GIS allowing a spatial manipulation of data to generate maps, tables, and graphics. BASINS includes a preprocessing tool to allow the generation of inputs for multiple watershed models such as the Hydrologic Simulation Program-FORTRAN (HSPF) (Bicknell et al. 2005), Soil and Water Assessment Tool (SWAT) (Neitsch et al. 2011), Water Quality Analysis Simulation Program (WASP) (Ambrose et al. 1993), and AQUATOX (Clough 2018). USACE developed the HEC-DSS to efficiently store and retrieve scientific data that are used by most Hydrologic Engineering Center (HEC) modeling tools such as the HEC-River Analysis System (HEC-RAS) and the HEC-Hydrologic Modeling System (HEC-HMS).

In addition to WRDB, BASINS, and HEC-DSS, there are several other commercial web-scraping tools and data acquisition utilities that allow monitoring data to be downloaded from the internet and efficiently processed for model inputs while putting in each process strict data quality assurance protocols. Examples include the Water Information System by KISTERS (WISKI) and HYDSTRA (KISTERS 2013), the Aquatic Informatics AQUARIUS WebPortal (Aquatic Informatics 2017), and the MIKE-customized platform by the Danish Hydraulic Institute (DHI). These tools allow operations to be conducted on any time series and the actions to be annotated for later retrieval. Several statistical interpolation gap-filling and data-range functions are also available. The aforementioned tools are software products that have been increasingly adopted by water management agencies (ASCE 2017).

8.4 PRECALIBRATION

Prior to model evaluation, it is recommended that the modeler clearly understands the ultimate objective of the model application. Questions such as "what is the model application for?" and "at what spatiotemporal scale will the model be applied?" need to be thoroughly discussed among the modelers, stakeholders, and decision makers (i.e., fit-for-purpose). If the goal is to solely predict low flows (e.g., drought prediction), then low-flow observations should be given the highest priority and selected fit measures should focus more on low flows (Pushpalatha et al. 2012). If the goal is to predict design floods, the model should be calibrated to historical events, whereas prediction of long-term changes in a watershed (e.g., impact of climate change) requires that the calibration be done upon continuous simulations. Water quality calibration is more complex because, often, relatively few observations are available. A water quality sample is typically collected at a specific time of a day, whereas the constituent could have a substantial inter- and intradaily variability. The selected fit measure should account for such variabilities, and the water quality calibration should be done at a time step consistent with the applicable water quality criteria. We also recommend that the primary model inputs (e.g., precipitation) be visually compared with calibration data (streamflow or pollutant concentration). A correlation analysis between the inputs and calibration data could be helpful too. This could be simple assessments to investigate questions like the following: Is there a consistency between the rainfall and streamflow data? Is there a lag between rainfall and streamflow data? In addition, missing components (e.g., a waterbody or a point source of pollution) and physical processes (e.g., baseflow and pollutant buildup) in the model could result in wrongly forcing the selected calibration parameters and thereby misleading model calibration. For instance, if atmospheric deposition contributes to the pollution but is not considered in the modeling, the corresponding parameters of other processes (e.g., washoff) might be overestimated to reflect this missing process.

It is also important to clearly understand the available data. In the presence of multiple meteorologic stations, a geospatial interpolation (e.g., inverse distance weighted) is recommended to be performed to appropriately account for the spatial heterogeneity of the meteorologic variables (e.g., rainfall). This approach is often preferred to simple methods such as the nearest gaging if high-resolution meteorologic data are available. Data availability should also be considered in watershed delineation as this process should be based not only on the spatial resolution of input data (e.g., DEM, LULC, and soil) but also on the number of existing monitoring stations. If multiple stations are present in the watershed, a higher level of disaggregation is needed to test the model against all the available observations.

Changes in a watershed over time must be carefully investigated prior to selecting calibration and validation periods (KLEMEŠ 1986). For watersheds under major changes in the LULC (e.g., because of urbanization) or pollution sources (e.g., agricultural development), some historical periods might not necessarily represent the existing conditions, even if they are fairly recent. Using such time periods for model calibration and validation could result in model parameterization that reflects watershed conditions that differ from the existing conditions. An example is modeling existing conditions of a watershed that has been under substantial urban development (e.g., using predevelopment conditions for calibration and validation of postdevelopment conditions).

A warmup period is recommended to reduce the model dependence on initial conditions. This period is recommended by model developers to be longer for water quality simulations (e.g., sediment and nutrients) than hydrologic processes, although a comprehensive guideline cannot be provided for a warmup period, given the complexity of watershed-scale processes (Daggupati et al. 2015). If a model does not explicitly account for the initial conditions, the consideration of a warmup period becomes even more important. Additional precalibration checks, including verification of data completeness (e.g., input datasets as well as calibration and validation datasets) and accuracy of the model setup (i.e., all connections are appropriately modeled and all essential model elements are turned on), are recommended. During the model setup, basic mass and heat balance checks are recommended to ensure that models can conserve mass and energy throughout the modeled system as other precalibration checks (McCutcheon 1989, Martin and McCutcheon 1999, Chapra 2003). Mass balance checks in 1D transport models of rivers and streams are straightforward and can be performed by tracking the inflows, outflows, and channel volumes during a simulation period. Mass conservation checks in multidimensional transport models of lakes and estuaries can be performed using numerical dye studies or simulations of a conservative substance such as salt. This type of analysis is useful for identifying problems in the boundary conditions, model topography, and parameterization. In lake models, heat balances can also be used to ensure that solar energy is distributed vertically in the layers of the model and as first steps to calibrate transport and mixing coefficients. The amount and timing of fertilizer applications and management operations (e.g., tilling) are other important precalibration considerations in agricultural watersheds.

8.5 CALIBRATION

Model calibration or parameterization is an iterative process that consists of adjusting the parameters of a model until a satisfactory agreement between the simulations and observations is achieved. Manual calibration is the most common approach in practice, but automated calibration, typically used in research, seems to be on the cusp of widespread practicality. The calibration of a model is, in general, based on a combination of qualitative and quantitative assessments of relative model performance. Qualitative assessments of model performance include simple visual comparisons between time series of simulations and observations to identify how well the model captures the timing, trends, and magnitudes of the observations. An objective scientifically sound calibration should be based on quantitative assessments that evaluate the level of agreement between simulations and observations using statistics of goodness-of-fit measures that estimate model error, bias, and correlation. However, the sole use of these measures might not be sufficient to conclude that the model performance is satisfactory. In addition to the use of these measures, hypothesis testing of the residuals should be used to determine if the differences between observations and a calibrated simulation are not significantly different from zero for a probability of error (e.g., 0.05).

A TMDL determination, allocation, and implementation planning initially determines if a receiving water quality model or method can be configured to distinguish all substantial sources as manageable boundary conditions. If not, an auxiliary watershed model or method will be necessary. Occasionally, if the impaired waters are streams, several watershed models can also serve as the receiving water quality model. If synoptic data cannot be collected simultaneously to calibrate both models at the same time, then the watershed model should be first calibrated, followed by the receiving water model. A hydrologic calibration is the first step in watershed modeling to reliably simulate the streamflow, which, with the concentration of the water quality constituent of concern, defines the contaminant load anywhere on the watershed. In the absence of streamflow data on an ungauged watershed, the water yield from similar nearby watersheds can be regionalized (Linsley et al. 1975, Gitau and Chaubey 2010). The hydrologic calibration is followed by a water quality calibration through a comparative analysis between simulated and observed concentrations of the water quality constituent. We emphasize that in all these simulations (hydrologic and water quality calibration and validation) a warmup period should be used to reduce the model dependence of initial conditions. The warmup period, which helps avoiding the dependence of the simulation on uncertain initial conditions (e.g., antecedent soil moisture or ambient water quality), should be one to three times the watershed time of concentration (or time of travel for receiving waters).

In general, the following steps should be followed for model calibration:

1. Synoptic data that coherently connect all substantial sources of a pollutant to ambient receiving water quality data that define the dynamics and varying extent of impaired waters or the critical conditions when the impairment is at the maximum intensity are

collected and compiled. Coherency is achieved when the hydrologic and water quality data collection defining the impairment is lagged by the travel time from each source because of any overland, interflow or quick flow, and groundwater recharge plus tributary, and waterbody travel times. The watershed time of concentration can be a conservative initial estimate of travel time (see Perdikaris et al. 2018 for a comprehensive list of equations) at which flow water quality is typically measured. USGS has determined the travel time for many nationwide streams. Sampling coherency between direct discharges or contaminated tributaries and impaired waters could also be achieved by Lagrangian sampling of dyed parcels of water used by USGS to determine the travel time.

2. Sensitive parameters and other specifications should be identified initially to guide efficient model calibration. This can be done through a simple sensitivity analysis. Including too many parameters in a poorly developed model can result in nonunique parameterization that prevents convergence to a global optimal parameter set and puts the model process integrity into question. Including too few calibration parameters because of process lumping or ignoring important processes is also not desirable. Tables 8-2 and 8-3 list principal parameters for hydrologic and water quality calibration in the 14 commonly used watershed models in TMDL development, as identified in Chapter 2. We first performed a literature review to obtain these parameters and contacted the model developers and other experts to confirm them. Tables 8-2 and 8-3 provide TMDL modelers with a suite of potential sensitive parameters, but the authors recommend that a sensitivity analysis be done because calibration parameters vary on a case-by-case basis and depend on watershed characteristics, available data, and project goals. It should also be noted that the selected underlying processes are important for the selection of the calibration parameters, and not all the parameters might be relevant; that is, if the Natural Resources Conservation Service (NRCS 1986) curve number method is not used for the simulation of infiltration, the method parameters (e.g., Curve Number) are irrelevant.

3. Upper and lower limits of each calibration parameter are defined based on the physical, biological, and chemical characteristics of the waterbody and contributing watershed and values reported in similar modeling studies. This process ensures that the search of optimum parameter values is constrained to realistic parameter ranges (Ambrose et al. 1993, Park et al. 2005, Lin et al. 2007, 2008, García et al. 2010, Camacho et al. 2014). Although using physically, chemically, or biologically implausible ranges could result in a more reliable model performance, these out-of-range calibrations must

Table 8-2. Principal Parameters for Hydrologic Calibration in TMDL Studies.

Watershed model	Parameter	Parameter definition	Source
AGNPS/ AnnAGNPS	CN	Curve number	Chahor et al. (2014), Bingner and Theurer (2001)
	n	Manning coefficient	
ANSWERS-2000	—	Clay and silt content	Beasley et al. (1980), Bouraoui (1994)
DWSM	CNAF	Uniform Curve Number adjustment factor	Borah et al. (2002), Gao et al. (2015)
	COND	Effective lateral saturated hydraulic conductivity	
	FAFC	Uniform friction adjustment factor for channels	
	FAFO	Uniform friction adjustment factor for overland planes	
GSSHA	d_r	Specified root depth	Downer and Ogden (2004)
	K_{gw}	Hydraulic conductivity of the media	
	K_{rb}	Riverbed hydraulic conductivity	
	K_S	Saturated hydraulic conductivity	
	θ_S	Saturated water content	
	ψ_b	Bubbling pressure	

(Continued)

Table 8-2. (*Continued*)

Watershed model	Parameter	Parameter definition	Source
	e_{gw}	Porosity	
	n_M	Channel Manning's coefficient	
	Λ	Pore distribution index	
GWLF	CN	Curve number	Haith et al. (1992), Lee et al. (2000)
	KU	Cover coefficient for calculation of the evapotranspiration	
	—	Baseflow recession	
	S	Deep seepage coefficient	
	R	Groundwater recession coefficient	
HEC-HMS	CN	Curve number	USACE (2016)
	—	Imperviousness	
	K	Saturated hydraulic conductivity	
	t_C	Time of concentration	
	t_L	Lag time	

C_P	Storage coefficient	
—	Recession factor	
I_a	Initial abstraction	
$\phi-\theta_i$	Volume moisture deficit	
S_f	Wetting front suction	
—	Lag	
HSPF/LSPC		USEPA (2000)
LZSN	Lower-zone nominal soil moisture storage	
AGWRC	Base groundwater recession	
DEEPFR	Fraction of groundwater inflow to deep recharge	
BASETP	Fraction of remaining evapotranspiration from baseflow	
AGWETP	Fraction of remaining evapotranspiration from active groundwater	
CN	Curve number	
IRC	Interflow recession parameter	
INTFW	Interflow inflow parameter	
INFILT	Index to mean infiltration rate	

(Continued)

Table 8-2. (Continued)

Watershed model	Parameter	Parameter definition	Source
	INFILD	Ratio of maximum/mean infiltration capacities	
	UZSN	Nominal upper-zone soil moisture storage	
	CEPSC	Interception storage capacity	
	LZETP	Index to lower-zone evapotranspiration	
	TSNOW	Temperature at which precipitation becomes snow	
	SNOWCF	Snow gauge catch correction factor	
	NSUR	Surface Manning's coefficient	
KINEROS	MK_S	Saturated hydraulic conductivity	Woolhiser et al. (1990), Hantush and Kalin (2005), Goodrich et al. (2012)
	Mn	Manning's coefficient	
	Θ_i	Initial soil moisture	
	MG	Infiltration suction	
MIKE SHE	n_C	Channel Manning's coefficient	DHI (2017a, b), Jaber and Shukla (2012)
	n_O	Surface Manning's coefficient	

(Continued)

D_2	Detention storage
C_{dr}	Leakage coefficient
K_S	Saturated hydraulic conductivity
K	Hydraulic conductivity
Θ_{FC}	Soil moisture at the field capacity
Θ_W	Soil moisture at the wilting point
—	Capillary thickness
LAI	Leaf area index
L_R	Root depth
C_{int}	Canopy interception
k_C	Crop coefficient
MC	Drain level
—	Drain time constant
ρ_b	Soil bulk density
S_S	Specific storage coefficient
S_y	Specific yield

Table 8-2. (Continued)

Watershed model	Parameter	Parameter definition	Source
STEPL	CN	Curve number	Park et al. (2014)
	—	Soil infiltration fraction	
SWAT	CN2	Curve number	Neitsch et al. (2011) and Arnold et al. (2012)
	AWC	Available water capacity	
	ALPHA_BF	Baseflow alpha factor	
	SFTMP	Mean air temperature at which precipitation is equally likely to be rain as snow / freezing rain	
	EPCO	Plant uptake compensation factor	
	ESCO	Soil evaporation compensation factor	
	CH_N	Channel Manning's coefficient	
	OV_N	Surface Manning's coefficient	
	CH_K2	Channel conductivity	
	SLSOIL	Slope length for lateral subsurface flow	
	SNOCOVMX	Minimum snow water content that corresponds to full snow cover	

SNO50COV	Fraction of SNOCOVMX that provides 50% cover	
SMTMP	Snowmelt base temperature	
TIMP	Snow temperature lag factor	
SOL_K	Saturated hydraulic conductivity	
SURLAG	Surface runoff lag coefficient	
DDRAIN	Depth of subsurface drains	
GW_DELAY	Groundwater delay	
GWQMN	Threshold depth of water in shallow aquifers required for the return flow to occur	
GW_REVAP	Revap coefficient	
REVAPMN	Threshold depth of water in shallow aquifers required for revap	
RCHRG_DP	Deep aquifer percolation factor	
SWMM	Width	Width of overland flow path	Rossman (2015a, b)
	Imperv	Imperviousness	
	Dstore	Depression storage	
	CN	Curve number	

(Continued)

Table 8-2. (*Continued*)

Watershed model	Parameter	Parameter definition	Source
	Ψ	Suction head	
	K	Soil hydraulic conductivity	
	Θ_d	Initial soil moisture	
	$A1$	Groundwater flow coefficient	
	T_{dry}	Drying time	
	N	Surface Manning's coefficient	
WARMF	E_C	Evaporation magnitude	Chen et al. (1998),
	—	Evaporation skewness	Herr and Chen (2012)
	—	Imperviousness	
	T_S	Snow formation temperature	
	M_0 and M_f	Snow melting rates	
	—	Precipitation weighting factor	
	—	Temperature lapse	

	Altitude temperature lapse
Z	Soil layer thickness
Θ	Soil initial moisture
θ_{fc}	Soil field capacity
θ_S	Soil porosity
K_h and K_V	Soil hydraulic conductivity
n_C	Channel Manning's coefficient
n_O	Surface Manning's coefficient
	Detention storage
	Wind speed multiplier

Source: Adapted from Ahmadisharaf et al. (2019).

Notes: USLE = universal soil loss equation, RUSLE = revised universal soil loss equation.

Table 8-3. Principal Parameters for Water Quality Calibration.

Watershed model	Parameter	Parameter definition	Constituent	Source
AGNPS/ AnnAGNPS	—	Root mass	Sediment	Chahor et al. (2014), Bingner and Theurer (2001)
	—	Crop residue		
	$RUSLE_C$	RUSLE cover management factor		
	$RUSLE_P$	RUSLE support practice factor		
	K	Soil erodibility factor		
	—	Canopy cover	Nutrients	
ANSWERS-2000	DF	Overland flow detachment rate	Sediment and nutrients	Beasley et al. (1980), Bouraoui (1994)
	DR	Rainfall detachment rate		
DWSM	FDCI	Flow detachment coefficient	Sediment	Borah et al. (2002), Gao et al. (2015)
	RDC	Rainfall detachment coefficient		
GSSHA	K_{eff}	Soil erodibility factor	Sediment	Downer and Ogden (2004), Downer et al. (2014)
	—	Maximum degradation value		
	$USLE_C$	USLE cover management factor		

Model	Parameter	Description	Output	Reference
GWLF	$USLE_K$	USLE soil erodibility factor	Sediment	Haith et al. (1992), Lee et al. (2000)
	$USLE_P$	USLE support practice factor		
	—	Sediment delivery ratio	Sediment	
	$USLE_C$	USLE cover management factor		
	$USLE_K$	USLE soil erodibility factor		
	$USLE_P$	USLE support practice factor		
	—	Enrichment ratio	Sediment and Nutrients	
HEC-HMS	$USLE_C$	USLE cover management factor	Sediment	Pak et al. (2015)
	—	Fraction of gravel		
	—	Enrichment ratio		
	—	Channel active layer factor		
HSPF/LSPC	JGER	Exponent in soil matrix scour equation	Sediment	Saleh and Du (2004), USEPA (2006)
	JSER	Exponent in sediment washoff equation		
	KGER	Coefficient in soil matrix scour equation		
	KRER	Coefficient in the soil detachment equation		

(Continued)

Table 8-3. (*Continued*)

Watershed model	Parameter	Parameter definition	Constituent	Source
	KSER	Coefficient in the sediment washoff equation		
	KIMP	Phosphate immobilization factor	Phosphorus	
	KDSP	Phosphate desorption factor		
	KADP	Phosphate adsorption factor		
	UKPLP	Factor to adjust plant phosphorus uptake from the surface layer		
	SKPLP	Factor to adjust plant phosphorus uptake from the surface layer		
	KDSAM	Ammonium desorption factor	Nitrogen	
	KIMNI	Nitrate immobilization factor		
	SLMPF	Percolation factor to adjust solutes from the surface to upper-layer storage	Nutrients	
	ULPF	Percolation factor to adjust solutes from upper-to-lower-layer storage		
	ACQOP	Bacteria accumulation on land	Bacteria	Paul et al. (2004), Mishra et al. (2018, 2019)
	FSTDEC	First-order decay rate		

	IOQC	Interflow bacteria concentration		
	SQOLIM	Maximum bacteria accumulation on land		
	WSQOP	Rate of surface runoff that removes 90% of stored bacteria from a pervious land surface		
KINEROS	CF	Rainsplash parameter	Sediment	Woolhiser et al. (1990), Goodrich et al. (2012)
	q_m	Transport capacity		
	CG	Hydraulic erosion transfer coefficient rate		
MIKE SHE*	θ	Effective porosity	Any pollutant	DHI (2017a, b), Jaber and Shukla (2012)
	ρ_b	Soil bulk density		
	α	Dispersivity		
	—	Sorption and desorption		
	—	Source strength		
	μ	Degradation rate		
STEPL	—	Pollutant loading rate	Any pollutant	Park et al. (2014)
	—	Sediment delivery ratio	Sediment	
SWAT	PRF	Peak rate adjustment factor	Sediment	Neitsch et al. (2011), Arnold et al. (2012)
	SPCON	Coefficient in sediment transport equation		

(Continued)

Table 8-3. (*Continued*)

Watershed model	Parameter	Parameter definition	Constituent	Source
	SPEXP	Exponent in sediment transport equation		
	USLE_C	Minimum value for the cover and management factor for the land cover		
	USLE_K	USLE soil erodibility factor		
	USLE_P	USLE support practice factor		
	RCN	Nitrogen concentration in the rain	Nitrogen	
	ERORGN	Organic nitrogen enrichment ratio		
	NPERCO	Nitrate percolation coefficient		
	ANION_EXCL	Porosity fraction from which anions are excluded		
	BC1	Constant rate for biological oxidation of ammonia		
	BC2	Constant rate for biological oxidation of nitrite to nitrate		
	BC3	Local constant rate for hydrolysis of organic nitrogen to ammonium		

Code	Description	Category	Reference
RS4	Local settling rate for organic nitrogen		
PSP	Phosphorus availability index	Phosphorus	
PHOSKD	Phosphorus soil partitioning coefficient		
PPERCO	Phosphorus percolation coefficient		
BC4	Local constant rate for organic phosphorus mineralization		
RS5	Local settling rate for organic phosphorus		
ERORGP	Phosphorus enrichment ratio		
BACTKDQ	Bacteria soil partitioning coefficient	Bacteria	
BACTMIX	Bacteria percolation coefficient		
BCNST	Direct-source concentration		
CFRT_KG	Bacteria loading rate		
WDPQ	Bacteria die-off coefficient in soil		
WDPRCH	Bacteria die-off coefficient in stream		
C1 and C2	Washoff function coefficients	Any pollutant	Rossman (2016)
C1, C2 and C3	Buildup function parameters		

SWMM

(Continued)

Table 8-3. (*Continued*)

Watershed model	Parameter	Parameter definition	Constituent	Source
WARMF	λ	Soil thermal conductivity	Temperature	Herr and Chen (2012)
	λ_S	Snow thermal conductivity		
	K	Convective heat factor		
	—	Minimum negative density gradient		
	D_M, A and A_2	Wind mixing diffusion coefficients		
	D_E, E_M and A_3	Density gradient diffusion coefficients		
	C	Cropping factor	Sediment	
	K	Soil erosivity		
	—	Soil sand, silt, and clay fractions		
	K and b	Detachment velocity coefficients		
	—	Initial bed sediment depth		
	—	Bed sand, silt, and clay fractions		
	LAI	Leaf area index	Nutrients	
	—	Vegetation composition		
	—	Mineral composition		

Symbol	Description	Category
K	Mineral weathering rates	
—	Initial pore water concentrations	
α	Adsorption coefficient	
—	Soil mineral content	
—	Fertilization rates	
k	Reaction rates	
K_N and K_P	Half-saturation constants	Phytoplankton
T_L, T_O and T_U	Temperature tolerant ranges	
—	Phytoplankton chemical composition	
—	Chlorophyll-a/carbon ratio	
G_{Max}	Maximum growth rate	
—	Aeration factor	Dissolved oxygen
K_{SOD}	Sediment oxygen demand	

*MIKE-SHE could be coupled with another software by the Danish Hydraulic Institute, ECOLAB, to define and simulate any water quality constituents. The list of parameters could be, therefore, more comprehensive.

Source: Adapted from Ahmadisharaf et al. (2019).

Notes: USLE = Universal soil loss equation, RUSLE = Revised universal soil loss equation.

remain questionable and must not be used in TMDL determination, allocation, and implementation planning, until the *prima facie* out-of-range parameter values can be independently confirmed as realistic.

4. This step consists of assigning values to each parameter by drawing a sample value from the parameter ranges defined in the second step.

5. The model is executed with the set of assigned parameters.

6. Model results are postprocessed, and the performance is evaluated by calculating the goodness-of-fit measures and hypothesis testing for all the constituents of concern. If the model performance is deemed acceptable for the purposes of the study, then the calibration process is stopped. The reliability of all state variables should also be evaluated by hypothesis testing (probability ≥ 0.05). If the simulation is unreliable, another calibration iteration is performed starting at Step 4. After achieving a reliable simulation, the iterations are continued until the probability of error is minimized.

7. Optimal or a reliable parameter set is validated with an independent synoptic dataset. If the validation is not reliable, the modeling team should consider recalibration and revalidation after a second review of the quality control and quality assurance of both synoptic data collection (Martin and McCutcheon 1999). If the second validation is unreliable and the quality assurance rereview shows that all quality control objectives were not met, model selection should be repeated until a reliable confirmation test of validity is achieved. In the absence of a reliable validation, model or method development or redevelopment might be necessary.

In the case of multiple monitoring stations, a multistep calibration can be performed (from upstream to downstream) by repeating the aforementioned multistep calibration process for each station. However, observations at these locations might be dependent (Yuan et al. 2013) and cause biased calibration findings. This is the simplest approach and more advanced calibration methods could be done in the presence of multiple observation gages.

Many goodness-of-fit measures can be found in the literature. Selection of a particular measure depends on the modeling objectives and the availability of monitoring data. These measures have been extensively used since the 1980s as a surrogate likelihood function or calibration criteria (see Chapter 11). Some modelers have tried to match the modeling objectives with a specific statistic and the degrees of freedom and variability of the required synoptic data (McCutcheon et al. 1990, Arnold et al. 2012, Duda et al. 2012, Goodrich et al. 2012, Herr and Chen 2012, Jaber and Shukla 2012). Table 8-4 presents the commonly used goodness-of-fit measures of model performance alongside the recommended hypothesis testing for the determination of model reliability.

Table 8-4. Goodness-of-Fit Measures for Watershed and Receiving Water Modeling.

Name	Formula	Ideal Value	Description	Limitations	Sensitivity
Probability of error from hypothesis testing	H_0: There exists a significant simulation bias. Frequentist inference: reject H_0 if $$\mu_{P-O} = \frac{\sum_{i=1}^{n}(P_i - O_i)}{n}$$ $$se_{P-O} = \sqrt{\frac{\sum_{i=1}^{n}(P_i - O_i)^2}{n(n-1)}}$$ $$z \sim N(0,1)$$ $$t = \frac{\mu_{P-O}}{se_{P-O}}$$ $$P(z < -t) + P(z > -t) \le 0.05$$ Bayesian inference: reject H_0 if 95% credible interval includes 0.	1	Probability of mistakenly finding that mean residual is not significantly different from zero.	Makes restrictive assumptions about distribution of residuals which may not be applicable in complex, nonlinear or stochastic models. A large number of datapoints and model simulation runs when distribution of residuals is not normal.	This statistic is universally and fundamentally useful for reliability testing of simulations globally within a waterbody and comparing reliability between multiple waterbodies and globally comparing goodness-of-fit.

(*Continued*)

Table 8-4. (*Continued*)

Name	Formula	Ideal Value	Description	Limitations	Sensitivity
Nash–Sutcliffe efficiency (NSE)	$$1 - \frac{\sum_{i=1}^{N}(O_i - P_i)^2}{\sum_{i=1}^{N}(O_i - \bar{O})^2}$$	1	1. Degree of association between observed and simulated compares variance of the differences with observations. 2. The predictive power of the model relative to the variability in the observations.	1. $NSE \leq 0$: average of all observations better estimate that calibrated model. 2. Not useful to identify simulation trends and bias, particularly when model consistently underestimates. 3. Questionable estimates when used with short-duration time series.	1. Sensitive to extremes or outliers and multiple maxima in a time series. 2. Biased simulation when $NSE < R^2$.
Model skill score (MSS)	$$1 - \frac{\sum_{i=1}^{n}(O_i - P_i)^2}{\sum_{i=1}^{n}\left(|P_i - \bar{O}| + |O_i - \bar{O}|\right)^2}$$	1	Difference between simulations and observations (denominator) explained by the simulation (numerator).	1. $MSS \leq 0$: average of all observations is a better predictor than the model. 2. Not used to identify the features and bias in simulation, particularly when model consistently undersimulates.	Similar to Nash–Sutcliffe efficiency.

Metric				
Coefficient of determination (R^2) $$\left(\frac{\sum_{i=1}^{n}(O_i - \bar{O})(P_i - \bar{P})}{\sqrt{\sum_{i=1}^{n}(O_i - \bar{O})^2}\sqrt{\sum_{i=1}^{n}(P_i - \bar{P})^2}}\right)^2$$	1	The magnitude of the linear relationship between the simulations and the observations.	1. Cannot quantify the temporal and spectral features of the results. 2. As long as the model results and observations are correlated, this will produce a high value, even if the model predictions are opposite to the observed data.	Sensitive to outliers and insensitive to additive and multiplicative differences.
Index of Agreement (d) $$1 - \frac{\sum_{i=1}^{n}(O_i - P_i)^2}{\sum_{i=1}^{n}(|P_i - \bar{O}| + |O_i - \bar{O}|)^2}$$	1	The degree to which the simulations are error free.	1. A less robust measure than the NSE 2. Can produce inflated estimates even for poor model fits.	Sensitive to large outliers and insensitive to changes in the model parameters.
Kling–Gupta (KGE) $$1 - \sqrt{(r-1)^2 + \left(\frac{\sigma_P}{\sigma_O} - 1\right)^2 + \left(\frac{\bar{P}}{\bar{O}} - 1\right)^2}$$	1	Considers simulation errors in mean, variability, and dynamics.	Assumes linearity and normality in the data.	Addressed limitations of R^2 and NSE.

(Continued)

Table 8-4. (*Continued*)

Name	Formula	Ideal Value	Description	Limitations	Sensitivity
Mean absolute error (MAE)	$\dfrac{\sum_{i=1}^{n}\lvert P_i - O_i\rvert}{n}$	0	The absolute error between the simulations and the observations.	It is difficult to quantify the error for different model applications or compare the error between multiple locations or events.	Sensitive to the number of deviations between the model and the observations.
Percent bias (PBIAS)	$\dfrac{\sum_{i=1}^{n} O_i - P_i}{\sum_{i=1}^{n} O_i}$	0	The offset between the simulations and the observations.	Cannot resolve periods of overprediction and underprediction by the model, such as modeled consistent lower water temperatures in the summer and higher water temperatures in the winter.	Insensitive to trends, periodicity, and other temporal features in the data.

Metric	Equation	Value	Description	Notes
Root-mean squared error (RMSE)	$\sqrt{\dfrac{\sum_{i=1}^{n}(O_i - P_i)^2}{n}}$	0	Average of root mean squared difference between simulation and observations.	1. Difficult to quantify the error for different model applications or compare errors between multiple locations and events. 2. Should not be used to peaked data such as flush events. Sensitive to large outliers in the data.
Ratio of RMSE and standard deviation (RSR) of observed data	$\dfrac{\sqrt{\sum_{i=1}^{n}(O_i - P_i)^2}}{\sqrt{\sum_{i=1}^{n}(O_i - \bar{P})^2}}$	0	The magnitude of the difference between the simulations and the observations relative to the variability in the observations.	Care should be taken when using this measure with peaked data, as it may overestimate the model performance with abrupt maxima. Sensitive to errors in low-intensity events such as base flows and insensitive to errors in high-value events such as storms or first-flushes.

Source: Adapted from Ahmadisharaf et al. (2019).

Notes: P_i = Predicted value at time I, O_i = Observed value at time I, $\bar{P}$ = Average of the predicted values, $\bar{O}$ = Average of the observed values, n = Number of data points, $Stdev_O$ = Standard deviation of observed data, r = Linear correlation between the predicted and the observed values, σ_P = Standard deviation of the predicted values, σ_O = Standard deviation of the observed values.

Statistics such as the mean absolute error (MAE), mean squared error (MSE), and root-mean squared error (RMSE) provide an estimate of the error between the simulations and the observations, whereas the normalized root-mean squared error (NRMSE), ratio of RMSE and standard deviation of observed data (RSR), and percent error (PE) estimate how important are these errors relative to the magnitude of the observations. In general, MAE, RMSE, NRMSE, and PE constitute indicators of model prediction error, and the smaller their values, the greater the agreement between the simulations and the observations (Stow et al. 2003). Because RMSE is slightly biased when large outliers exist, MAE should be preferred in general. A widely used measure to quantify the deviation of model predictions from observations is percent bias (PBIAS). This measure could be used to estimate the bias in simulations.

Another widely used measure is the coefficient of determination (R^2), the square of the Pearson's product-moment correlation coefficient, which describes the proportion of the total variances in the observed data that can be explained by the model. The R^2 is insensitive to additive and proportional differences between the simulated and the observed values but is more sensitive to outliers than to the values near the mean. This oversensitivity could lead to a bias toward extreme values.

To overcome the limitations associated with the use of R^2, alternate measures of global fit have been proposed. Three widely used measures include Nash–Sutcliffe efficiency (NSE) (Nash and Sutcliffe 1970), model skill score (MSS), Index of Agreement (d) (Willmott 1981), and Kling–Gupta efficiency (KGE) (Gupta et al. 2009). NSE compares the variance of the errors against the observations (how well the plot of observations versus simulations fit the 1:1 line), whereas d compares the variance of the errors against a reference variance or "potential error." A negative or near-zero NSE or MSS indicates a poor model performance and the mean of the observations is a better predictor than the model. Negative values of NSE could also imply large mass balance errors in the model (Gupta and Kling 2011) and the model cannot be used to define a cause-and-effect relationship between loads and impaired water quality. The model simulations are biased when NSE $< R^2$ (Aitkin 1973, Tedela et al. 2011).

KGE is based on three components: correlation, variability bias, and mean bias. A KGE value of unity means a perfect model performance. Past research, in general, suggests that a threshold of zero could be used to separate satisfactory and unsatisfactory model performance; a positive KGE refers to a satisfactory model performance, whereas a negative KGE refers to a poor performance (e.g., Sutanudjaja et al. 2018, Towner et al. 2019). Unlike NSE, a negative KGE does not mean that the mean of observations is a better predictor than the model (Knoben et al. 2019). A limitation of KGE is that it assumes linearity, normality, and the presence of no outliers in the data. To overcome these shortcomings, modifications have been made to this metric, including a modified KGE by Kling et al. (2012) and a nonparametric KGE by Pool et al. (2018).

Other statistics for watershed modeling include the peak difference and total mean volume squared error. The pros and cons of some of these goodness-of-fit measures are well discussed in the literature (Martinec and Rango 1989, Krause et al. 2005, Moriasi et al. 2015, among others). In general, the use of multiple measures is recommended (Pechlivanidis et al. 2011). In multiobjective calibrations, the measures should reflect various model behaviors (e.g., error, bias, correlation, and trend) as opposed to a single behavior (e.g., only bias). The relative importance of the selected metrics in a multiobjective calibration would depend on the model application and project objectives.

Determining simulation reliability by hypothesis testing should be performed simultaneously for all waterbody ambient observations, simultaneously for all observations within the impaired waters, or for each location at which flow water quality is measured. The goodness-of-fit statistics are not stationary from one observation location to another because of hydrologic, hydrodynamic, and water quality regime changes throughout a waterbody and the contributing watershed and because of the lack of independence of observations from one location compared with another. Distribution testing contains hypothesis testing, including Bayesian hypothesis testing (Chapter 11) as well as Pearson chi squared and Kolmogorov–Smirnov distribution tests, among others. The universal probability of error in hypothesis testing indicates that the mean difference between simulations and observations is not significantly different from zero. These probabilities are calculated during each calibration and validation iteration, in which hypothesis testing with a probability of <0.05 determines whether a simulation is reliable.

Although some synoptic data for calibration and validation of simulations of sediment, nutrients, DO, biochemical oxygen demand, and flow are available from past TMDL development, typically the necessary synoptic data are unavailable for most water quality constituents such as pathogens (fecal coliform bacteria) and toxic substances such as polychlorinated biphenyls (PCBs). A vital element in model selection and TMDL development is to recognize when synoptic data are not available and to plan the necessary field work with USEPA, other agencies, and stakeholders (Martin and McCutcheon 1999). Typical goodness-of-fit measures such as NSE have been used in pathogen calibration (Ahmadisharaf and Benham 2020, Baffaut and Sadeghi 2010, Cho et al. 2010, Coffey et al. 2013, Hernandez-Suarez et al. 2019, Niazi et al. 2015, Pandey et al. 2012, Parajuli et al. 2009) but with much lower thresholds (e.g., $-6.0 < NSE < 0.8$). This manual recommends advancing the practice of TMDL modeling using additional analyses such as hypothesis testing of simulations to establish reliability (e.g., using a probability of error of 0.05).

Kim et al. (2007) provided bacteria-specific guidelines for model evaluation. A simple comparison of predicted and observed average, geometric mean, median, and exceedance (instantaneous violation) values for pathogens and toxics was recommended. They further introduced a 5-day temporal window concept for the calibration of bacteria models, which has been applied for toxic TMDLs too. A 5-day window has the observation as the central point alongside the 2 days before and after. The method includes a calculation of the percent (PCT) of observed data that fall above (PCT_Above), within (PCT_Within), and below (PCT_Below) the 5-day window minimum-maximum range. The PCT Within is an indicator of agreement with observed data, whereas PCT_Above and PCT_Below represent over- and underprediction, respectively. A higher PCT_Within refers to a better model performance. These researchers recommended that PCT_Above and PCT_Below be close to each other to avoid over- or underprediction. Kim et al. (2007) originally suggested these criteria for bacteria modeling. However, these have been used for other pollutants such as PCB, where observations are limited. The 5-day time span can be modified to shorter or longer periods on a case-by-case basis, as recommended by Kim et al. (2007). Alternatively, Dorner et al. (2006) recommended that order of magnitude estimates should be used for bacteria calibration. Pandey et al. (2012) indicated that more than 95% of the simulated bacteria should be within one order of magnitude of the observations.

We strongly recommend that the modeler thoroughly interprets each goodness-of-fit measure and understands what is exactly quantified. Many of these measures average or aggregate model residuals (Larabi et al. 2018). Goodness-of-fit measures might be biased through the presence of much more low magnitudes (e.g., low flows or pollutant concentrations) than high-magnitude observations in the calibration dataset; that is, although the value of goodness-of-fit measure suggests a satisfactory performance, it is not necessarily so. This could be particularly problematic when the goal is to predict high magnitudes of the desired constituent (e.g., extreme floods). Depending on the model application, a multiobjective calibration (using multiple fit measures) could be beneficial. For example, neither R^2 nor NSE measures the model bias, and if the goal is to quantify the bias, PBIAS, which quantifies bias, can be used as well (Alamdari et al. 2017). Sharifi et al. (2013) found that a likelihood measure based on a combination of NSE and mass balance error produced a better model calibration than using NSE alone. In a multiobjective calibration, the selected goodness-of-fit measures should be weighted carefully to reflect their relative importance in model evaluation. Using KGE could partially address this as it is based on both correlation and bias. The commonly used measures (e.g., R^2 and NSE) have been criticized for overemphasizing the large measurements because of squaring the model errors (Legates and

McCabe 1999, Krause et al. 2005). For this reason, researchers have proposed modified measures, including weighted R^2 (Krause et al. 2005) and NSE measures based on absolute difference (Legates and McCabe 1999), relative deviation (Krause et al. 2005), volumetric efficiency (Criss and Winston 2008), and logarithmic transformation. Another limitation of NSE noted by Schaefli and Gupta (2007) is that it does not provide a reliable basis for comparing the results of various case studies and models; the researchers proposed the benchmark efficiency.

These limitations on the goodness-of-fit measures suggest that the sole application of goodness-of-fit measures is not sufficient to conclude that a model is good enough. Additional analyses such as visual inspection and hypothesis testing should also be explored. Because goodness-of-fit measures are not based on determining the underlying distribution of residuals, hypothesis testing should be performed on model residuals to establish that the residuals are not significantly different from zero (Tedela et al. 2011). After hypothesis testing, the probabilities of error from a statistical test (e.g., t-test, Kolmogorov–Smirnov, and sign tests) in accepting that the mean residual is not significantly different from zero is a sound statistic to evaluate the relative fit. Schnoor (1996) provided examples on the Chi-square goodness-of-fit and paired t-test. The former is based on the sum of squares of residual errors, whereas the latter requires the absolute of the sum of residual errors and the sum of squared errors. Proper transformations (e.g., log or Box–Cox) might be needed to ensure that residual errors belong to distributions (e.g., Gaussian) consistent with the statistical tests. For example, duration curves based on simulations and observations could be compared based on a statistical test to evaluate whether the simulated and observed values are from the same distribution. Larabi et al. (2018) applied a statistical framework, functional data analysis, in which t-test was dynamically coupled with an error measure for streamflow calibration. In addition, Harmel and Smith (2007) provided a modified approach by considering measurement uncertainty with the goal of facilitating enhanced evaluation of hydrologic and water quality models.

8.6 MANUAL CALIBRATION AND AUTOMATIC CALIBRATION

The calibration process previously defined can be conducted manually or using automated tools. Manual calibration is widely used in the practice and is especially useful if model run times are prolonged (in the order of several hours or days). These run times are common in complex studies involving linkage between multidimensional hydrodynamic and watershed models. A manual calibration with best professional judgement can be combined with a literature review on the plausible range of model parameters in the absence of computationally efficient models and fast processors. However, a manual calibration can be tedious and time-consuming and does not guarantee near optimal calibration.

Automatic calibration combining a well-designed manual analysis is typically a more efficient approach because it uses an optimization algorithm that performs numerous iterations to identify the optimal set of parameters, thereby ensuring a thorough exploration of the parametric space. An optimization algorithm for the calibration of deterministic models can be based on local search such as the parameter estimation (PEST) technique or global search algorithms such as the shuffled complex evolution (Duan et al. 1993) and dynamically dimensioned search (Tolson and Shoemaker 2007) methods. According to Hadka and Reed (2013), multiobjective optimization algorithms could be broadly categorized into four groups of indicator-based methods, namely, Pareto-front approximation, space partitioning and dimensionality reduction techniques, aggregate functions, and nature-inspired metaheuristics. Because an optimization could be computationally expensive, efficient adaptive techniques such as the Borg multiobjective evolutionary algorithm (Hadka and Reed 2013) could be applied. Most of the prevalent watershed models do not have built-in optimization capabilities or open-source extension software that can assist with automatic calibration. Exceptions are integrated parameter estimation and uncertainty analysis tool plus (IPEAT+) for SWAT+ (Yen et al. 2019), SWAT calibration and uncertainty programs (SWAT-CUP) (Abbaspour 2015), and an HSPF-enhanced expert system (HSPEXP+) (Mishra et al. 2017). Software packages such as PEST and Rhodium (Hadjimichael et al. 2020) could also be applied to watershed models. Despite the strengths of automatic calibrations, caution should be taken when applying such methods. Following an automatic calibration, a set of manual analyzes is recommended to ensure that the automatic calibration has resulted in the best possible model parameterization. Automatic optimizations can support the calibration when well-crafted objectives are identified. However, the modeler should carefully consider the nature and fundamental processes of the system to ensure that the optimal simulation aligns with the reality.

8.7 VALIDATION

Once a TMDL model is calibrated, the reliability of the obtained parameter set must be evaluated with an independent dataset. Validation testing of scientific models, like those used in TMDL development, is an inductive process that can at best only assign a large probability of correctness to the model even when we apply the model to a dataset independent of the one used for calibration. The purpose of validation is not to validate that the model is completely true but rather to ensure that the model simulations are sufficiently credible for decision-making (Chapra 2003). By definition, a model can never represent a true state.

Continuous models of watersheds and receiving waters may partition long-term monitoring into multiyear subsets of unequal duration usually segmenting wetter than normal years from drier than normal years to differentiate the datasets as much as possible to improve the validation testing. The most extensive dataset in the duration and number of variables measured is usually reserved for calibration. When possible, the earliest years of record are reserved for validation to ensure independence. For marginal durations of monitoring, the data on hand may be used for calibration, reserving the data being collected for validation in the future. In cases where validation must be deferred, the use of a phased TMDL assessment may be necessary. Worth noting is the three-tiered hierarchy of validation proposed by Chapra (2003):

1. Application to a case almost identical to the calibration case,
2. Application to a case with different meteorology than the calibration case, and
3. Application to a case with significantly different loadings.

Resource conservation modelers have experimented with split-sample validation (Arnold et al. 2012, Duda et al. 2012, Goodrich et al. 2012, Herr and Chen 2012, Jaber and Shukla 2012) and split-location validation (Arnold et al. 2012, Goodrich et al. 2012). Split-sample validation testing partitions time series of observations at a location. These data are rarely independent, and the partitioning serves to mask the variation in water quality and hydrologic observations, thereby improving the chances that the differences in smaller sets of observations and simulations are not significantly different. Split-location validation reserves data from an adjacent watershed. However, the responses in the adjacent watersheds to the stormwater and NPS pollution loads dominated by meteorologic conditions will not be independent. The responses of a watershed are certainly dependent on the contributing sub-watersheds, so that reserving validation data internally in a watershed from which the calibration data are collected does not result in an independent validation. Example validation approaches include leave-one-out (LOO) cross-validation.

8.8 EVALUATION CRITERIA FOR MODEL PERFORMANCE

USEPA (2002) guidance for quality assurance project plans (QAPPs) recommends a careful definition of the model performance expectations and the quantitative and qualitative criteria that will be used to determine if a model is able to satisfy regulatory or scientific objectives. In practice, the criteria to accept or reject a model are defined by consensus among modelers, stakeholders, and policy makers. The criteria of acceptability ultimately reflect a balance between the objectives of the modeling studies and the inherent limitations existing in watershed modeling.

To facilitate the interpretation of calibration and validation results, researchers have provided qualitative classifications of model performance based on the values of goodness-of-fit. These grades summarize the levels of model performance achieved during decades of watershed model applications and consider model complexity and error. The grades and the statistics should be used only as a complementary information to assess the model performance.

The performance grading reported in the literature is summarized in Tables 8-5 through 8-9. We emphasize that these are not absolute boundaries to categorize the model performance. The threshold values of the goodness-of-fit measures can be adjusted on watershed model, spatial and temporal scale, simulated constituent (e.g., sediment), data availability, magnitude of observations (e.g., low-flows), and watershed size and project objectives/restrictions (Moriasi et al. 2015). It is also recommended that other considerations (e.g., errors in observed data) and analyses (e.g., analysis of residuals and statistical significance) be done in addition to the goodness-of-fit measures (Ritter and Muñoz-Carpena 2013, Harmel et al. 2014). All these evaluations are critical in addition to the quantitative metrics to derive a defensible model. The use of a single metric is not recommended. An example that the sole use of a goodness-of-fit measure could be misleading is that a model can be systematically way off but still generate a high R^2. Further, because hydrologic and water quality calibrations are done separately, the performance metrics do not capture the cumulative nature of the error. If the hydrologic model is erroneous and the pollutants are

Table 8-5. Model Performance Criteria for Daily and Monthly Timescales Based on the Percent Difference Between Modeled and Observed Values.

Grade	Streamflow	Sediment	Water temperature	Nutrients	Pesticides/ toxics
Very Good	<10%	<20%	<7%	<15%	<20%
Good	10%–15%	20%–30%	7%–12%	15%–25%	20%–30%
Satisfactory	15%–25%	30%–45%	12%–18%	25%–35%	30%–40%
Unsatisfactory	>25%	> 45%	>18%	>35%	>40%

Source: Ahmadisharaf et al. (2019).

Table 8-6. Model Performance Criteria Based on the Coefficient of Determination (R^2).

Source	Santhi et al. (2001)	Donigian (2002) and Moriasi et al. (2012)		Moriasi et al. (2015)		
Constituent	Streamflow, nutrients, and sediment	Streamflow		Streamflow	Sediment and phosphorus	Nitrogen
Timescale	Monthly	Monthly	Daily	Daily, monthly, and annual	Monthly	Monthly
Grade			Range			
Very Good	—	>0.85	>0.80	>0.85	>0.80	>0.70
Good	>0.60	0.75–0.85	0.70–0.80	0.75–0.85	0.65–0.80	0.60–0.70
Satisfactory	—	0.65–0.75	0.6–0.70	0.60–0.75	0.40–0.65	0.30–0.60
Unsatisfactory	<0.60	<0.65	<0.60	<0.60	<0.40	<0.30

Source: Donigian (2002), Maréchal (2004), Moriasi et al. (2012, 2015) and Ahmadisharaf et al. (2019).

Table 8-7. Model Performance Criteria Based on Nash–Sutcliffe Efficiency (NSE).

Source	Santhi et al. (2001)	Maréchal (2004) and Allen et al. (2007)	Moriasi et al. (2007)	Ritter and Muñoz-Carpena (2013)	Moriasi et al. (2015)		
					Streamflow	Sediment	Nutrients
Constituent	Streamflow, nutrients, and sediment	Nutrients	Streamflow, nutrients, and sediment	General			
Timescale	Monthly			Daily, monthly, and annual	Monthly		
Grade				Range			
Very Good	>0.50	>0.65	>0.75	>0.90	>0.80	>0.80	>0.65
Good	—	0.50–0.65	0.65–0.75	0.80–0.90	0.70–0.80	0.70–0.80	0.50–0.65
Satisfactory	—	0.20–0.50	0.50–0.65	0.65–0.80	0.50–0.70	0.45–0.70	0.35–0.50
Unsatisfactory	<0.50	<0.20	<0.50	<0.65	<0.50	<0.45	<0.45

Source: Santhi et al. (2001), Maréchal (2004), Moriasi et al. (2007), Allen et al. (2007), Ritter and Muñoz-Carpena (2013) and Ahmadisharaf et al. (2019).

Table 8-8. Model Performance Criteria Based on Percent Bias (PBIAS).

Source	Moriasi et al. (2007)			Maréchal (2004) and Allen et al. (2007)	Moriasi et al. (2015)		
Constituent	Streamflow	Sediment	Nutrients	Nutrients	Streamflow	Sediment	Nutrients
Timescale	Monthly				Daily, monthly, and annual		
Grade				Range			
Very Good	<±10%	<±15%	<±25%	<±10%	<±5%	<±10%	<±15%
Good	±10%–±15%	±15%–±30%	±25%–±40%	±10%–±20%	±5%–±10%	±10%–±15%	±15%–±20%
Satisfactory	±15%–±25%	±30%–±55%	±40%–±70%	±20%–±40%	±10%–±15%	±15%–±20%	±20%–±30%
Unsatisfactory	>±25%	>±55%	>±70%	>±40%	>±15%	>±20%	>±30%

Source: Maréchal (2004), Moriasi et al. (2007), Allen et al. (2007), Ahmadisharaf et al. (2019).

Table 8-9. Model Performance Criteria for Bacteria/Toxic Modeling.

Average[a]	Geometric mean[a]	Median[a]	Exceedance rate[a]	PCT_Within[b]	PCT_Above[b]
<100%	<100%	<100%	<10%	>70%	Close to PCT_Below

[a]Based on the percent (PCT) difference between modeled and observed values.
[b]Based on the 5-day temporal windows.
Source: Ahmadisharaf et al. (2019).

primarily transported by the runoff, then the disparity is cumulative. There may be also insufficient data to calibrate/validate the water quality, whereas the hydrologic simulation may benefit from a denser monitoring record.

8.9 STATE-OF-THE-ART AND STATE-OF-THE-PRACTICE

Model calibration and validation approaches are presented in this chapter to be used as a guide in applications of models in TMDL studies. The focus is on watershed models, although the same is applicable to receiving-water models as well. The modeling process starts with the model selection (Chapter 11), setup, and precalibration. Required data, including meteorologic, pedologic, geologic, geomorphologic, hydrologic, and topographic datasets, are compiled and specified to begin the calibration process. A summary of these data sources is provided in this chapter. Prior to evaluating the model, a thorough investigation should be done on the watershed characteristics and important physical, chemical, and biological processes. Precalibration checks are strongly recommended to identify primary goals (e.g., simulated constituent and spatiotemporal resolution), limitations of the project (e.g., data availability), and watershed characteristics. These checks essentially lead to a more efficient model calibration. A sensitivity analysis needs to be conducted to identify the most sensitive parameters, which are selected for adjustment during the calibration. This should not be limited to local sensitivity analysis as the interrelationship between the parameters is often not detected. Global sensitivity analysis (e.g., Sobol method), which is not typically done in practice, should be performed to provide a fuller extent of the important parameters. Key calibration parameters in the simulation of different constituents for 14 prevalent watershed models are provided in this chapter. The model should then be calibrated, first against observed hydrologic (e.g., streamflow) datasets and then against water quality (e.g., pollutant concentration) datasets by adjusting selected model parameters.

A warmup period is recommended to reduce the model dependence of initial conditions. The calibration should then be followed by a series of validation tests, where the model is used to reproduce conditions independent from the calibration event. Guidelines are provided to grade the results of calibration and validation for streamflow and various pollutants. The focus of this chapter is on deterministic modeling, and guidelines for stochastic modeling are provided in Chapter 9.

State-of-the-practice to evaluate a watershed model performance often relies on goodness-of-fit measures. However, these measures alone are not sufficient, particularly if they are not thoroughly interpreted. State-of-the-art to evaluate model performance demands more efforts. Substantial advances are still needed. It is recommended that the goodness-of-fit measures presented in Tables 8-5 through 8-9 be thoroughly interpreted before drawing any conclusions on model performance. The performance measures should reflect error, bias, correlation, and trend; a multiobjective optimization should be preferred over a single-objective optimization. Thorough visual analyses are helpful alongside the goodness-of-fit measures. Hypothesis testing (e.g., via t-test or Wilcoxon sign test) should be used to ensure that the errors are not significantly different from zero. Model error cannot be determined unless the simulations fall within a very small domain of the observations. Understanding the errors in observed data and model structure helps in interpreting the simulations and explaining poor model performance. Advances in computational power should be exploited to apply complex automatic optimization algorithms instead of manual calibration, the conventional model parameterization approach in practice.

ACKNOWLEDGMENTS

Reviews, edits, and comments provided by Steven C. McCutcheon, Deva K. Borah, and G. Padmanabhan in this chapter are greatly appreciated.

DISCLAIMER

This document was not reviewed by the USEPA. The views expressed in this article are those of the authors and do not necessarily represent the views or the policies of USEPA.

REFERENCES

Abbaspour, K. C. 2015. *SWAT-CUP: SWAT calibration and uncertainty programs—A user manual*. Dübendorf, Switzerland: Eawag Swiss Federal Institute of Aquatic Science and Technology.

Ahmadisharaf, E., and B. L. Benham. 2020. "Risk-based decision making to evaluate pollutant reduction scenarios." *Sci. Total Environ.* 702: 135022.

Ahmadisharaf, E., R. A. Camacho, H. X. Zhang, M. Hantush, and M. M. Yusuf. 2019. "Calibration and validation of watershed models and advances in uncertainty analysis in TMDL studies." *J. Hydrol. Eng.* 24 (7): 03119001.

Aitkin, A. S. 1973. "Assessing systematic errors in rainfall-runoff models." *J. Hydrol.* 20 (2): 121–136.

Alamdari, N., D. J. Sample, P. Steinberg, A. C. Ross, and Z. M. Easton. 2017. "Assessing the effects of climate change on water quantity and quality in an urban watershed using a calibrated stormwater model." *Water* 9 (7): 464.

Allen, J. I., P. J. Somerfield, and F. J. Gilbert. 2007. "Quantifying uncertainty in high-resolution coupled hydrodynamic-ecosystem models." *Journal of Marine Systems* 64(1-4), 3–14.

Ambrose, R. B., T. A. Wool, and J. L. Martin. 1993. *The water quality analysis simulation program, WASP5, Part A: Model documentation.* EPA Center for Exposure Assessment Modeling. Athens, GA: USEPA.

Aquatic Informatics. 2017. *AQUARIUS WebPortal version 2017.1 user manual.* Vancouver, BC, Canada: Aquatic Informatics.

Arnold, J. G., D. N. Moriasi, P. W. Gassman, K. C. Abbaspour, M. J. White, R. Srinivasan et al. 2012. "SWAT: Model use, calibration, and validation." *Trans. ASABE* 55 (4): 1491–1508.

ASCE. 2017. *Total maximum daily load analysis and modeling: Assessment of the practice.* Prepared by TMDL Analysis and Modeling Task Committee of the Environmental and Water Resources Institute of ASCE. Reston, VA: ASCE.

Baffaut, C., and A. Sadeghi. 2010. "Bacteria modeling with SWAT for assessment and remediation studies: A review." *Trans. ASABE* 53 (5): 1585–1594.

Beasley, D. B., L. F. Huggins, and E. J. Monke. 1980. "ANSWERS: A model for watershed planning." *Trans. ASAE* 23 (4): 938–944.

Bicknell, B., J. Imhoff, J. Kittle Jr, T. Jobes, and A. Donigian Jr. 2005. *Hydrological simulation program: Fortran (HSPF) user's manual for release 12.2.* Athens, GA: USEPA.

Bingner, R., and F. Theurer. 2001. *AnnAGNPS technical processes: Documentation version 3.* Oxford, MS: Agricultural Research Service, US Dept. of Agriculture.

Borah, D. K., E. Ahmadisharaf, G. Padmanabhan, S. Imen, and M. M. Yusuf. 2019. "Watershed models for development and implementation of total maximum daily loads." *J. Hydrol. Eng.* 24 (1): 03118001.

Borah, D. K., R. Xia, and M. Bera. 2002. "DWSM—A dynamic watershed simulation model." In *Mathematical models of small watershed hydrology and applications*, edited by V. P. Singh and D. K. Frevert, 113–166. Highlands Ranch, CO: Water Resources Publications.

Bouraoui, F. 1994. "Development of a continuous, physically-based, distributed parameter, nonpoint source model." Ph.D. thesis, Virginia Tech, Dept. of Civil and Environmental Engineering.

Bowie, G. L., W. B. Mills, D. B. Porcella, C. L. Campbell, J. R. Pagenkopf, G. L. Rupp et al. 1985. *Rates, constants, and kinetics formulations in surface water quality modeling.* 2nd ed. EPA/600/3-85/040. Athens, GA: Environmental Research Laboratory, Office of Research and Development, USEPA.

Camacho, R. A., J. L. Martin, J. Diaz, W. H. McAnally, H. Rodriguez, P. Suscy, and S. Zhang. 2014. "Uncertainty analysis of estuarine hydrodynamic models: An evaluation of input data uncertainty in the Weeks Bay estuary, Alabama." *Appl. Ocean Res.* 47: 138–153.

Chahor, Y., J. Casalí, R. Giménez, R. L. Bingner, M. A. Campo, and M. Goñi. 2014. "Evaluation of the AnnAGNPS model for predicting runoff and sediment yield in a small Mediterranean agricultural watershed in Navarre (Spain)." *Agric. Water Manage.* 134: 24–37.

Chapra, S. C. 2003. "Engineering water quality models and TMDLs." *J. Water Resour. Plann. Manage.* 129 (4): 247–256.

Chen, C. W., J. Herr, and L. Ziemelis. 1998. *Watershed analysis risk management framework—A decision support system for watershed approach and TMDL calculation.* Palo Alto, CA: Electric Power Research Institute.

Cho, K. H., Y. Pachepsky, J. H. Kim, A. Guber, D. Shelton, and R. Rowland. 2010. "Release of Escherichia coli from the bottom sediment in a first-order creek: Experiment and reach-specific modeling." *J. Hydrol.* 391 (3–4): 322–332.

Clough, J. S. 2018. *AQUATOX (Release 3.2) Modeling environmental fate and ecological effects in aquatic systems. Vol. 1: User's manual.* Rep. No. EPA/600/B-18/233. Washington, DC: Office of Research and Development, USEPA.

Coffey, R., Dorai-Raj, S., O'Flaherty, V., Cormican, M., Cummins, E., 2013. "Modeling of pathogen indicator organisms in a small-scale agricultural catchment using SWAT." *Hum. Ecological Risk Assessment: Int. J.* 19, 232–253.

Criss, R. E., and W. E. Winston. 2008. "Do Nash values have value? Discussion and alternate proposals." *Hydrol. Processes Int. J.* 22 (14): 2723–2725.

Daggupati, P., N. Pai, S. Ale, K. R. Douglas-Mankin, R. W. Zeckoski, J. Jeong et al. 2015. "A recommended calibration and validation strategy for hydrologic and water quality models." *Trans. ASABE* 58 (6): 1705–1719.

DHI (Danish Hydraulic Institute). 2017a. *MIKE SHE. Vol. 2: Reference guide.* Hørsholm, Denmark: DHI.

DHI. 2017b. *MIKE SHE. Vol. 1: User guide.* Hørsholm, Denmark: DHI.

Donigian, A. 2002. "Watershed model calibration and validation: The HSPF experience." In *Proc., Water Environ. Fed.* 2002 (8): 44–73.

Dorner, S. M., W. B. Anderson, R. M. Slawson, N. Kouwen, and P. M. Huck. 2006. "Hydrologic modeling of pathogen fate and transport." *Environ. Sci. Technol.* 40 (15): 4746–4753.

Downer, C. W., and F. L. Ogden. 2004. "GSSHA: A model for simulating diverse streamflow generating processes." *J. Hydrol. Eng.* 9 (3): 161–174.

Downer, C.W., N. R. Pradhan, F. L. Ogden, and A. R. Byrd. 2014. "Testing the effects of detachment limits and transport capacity formulation on sediment runoff predictions using the US Army Corps of Engineers GSSHA model." *J. Hydrol. Eng.* 20 (7): 04014082.

Duan, Q. Y., V. K. Gupta, and S. Sorooshian. 1993. "Shuffled complex evolution approach for effective and efficient global minimization." *J. Optim. Theor. Appl.* 76 (3): 501–521.

Duda, P., P. Hummel, A. Donigian Jr, and J. Imhoff. 2012. "BASINS/HSPF: Model use, calibration, and validation." *Trans. ASABE* 55 (4): 1523–1547.

Gao, P., D. Borah, and C. Yi. 2015. "Storm event flow and sediment simulations in a Central New York watershed: Model testing and parameter analyses." *Trans. ASABE* 85 (5): 1241–1252.

García, A., J. A. Juanes, C. Álvarez, J. A. Revilla, and R. Medina. 2010. "Assesment of the response of a shallow macrotidal estuary to changes in hydrological and wastewater inputs through numerical modelling." *Ecol. Modell.* 221 (8): 1194–1208.

Gitau, M. W., and I. Chaubey. 2010. "Regionalization of SWAT model parameters for use in ungauged watersheds." *Water* 2 (4): 849–871.

Goodrich, D., I. Burns, C. Unkrich, D. Semmens, D. Guertin, M. Hernandez et al. 2012. "KINEROS2/AGWA: Model use, calibration, and validation." *Trans. ASABE* 55 (4): 1561–1574.

Gupta, H. V., and H. Kling. 2011. "On typical range, sensitivity, and normalization of mean squared error and Nash-Sutcliffe efficiency type metrics." *Water Resour. Res.* 47: W10601.

Gupta, H. V., H. Kling, K. K. Yilmaz, and G. F. Martinez. 2009. "Decomposition of the mean squared error and NSE performance criteria: Implications for improving hydrological modelling." *J. Hydrol.* 377 (1–2): 80–91.

Hadjimichael, A., D. Gold, D. Hadka, and P. Reed. 2020. "Rhodium: Python library for many-objective robust decision making and exploratory modeling." *J. Open Res. Software* 8 (1): 12.

Hadka, D., and P. Reed. 2013. "Borg: An auto-adaptive many-objective evolutionary computing framework." *Evol. Comput.* 21 (2): 231–259.

Haith, D. A., R. Mandel, and R. S. Wu. 1992. *GWLF, generalized watershed loading functions, version 2.0, user's manual.* Ithaca, NY: Cornell University.

Hantush, M. M., and L. Kalin. 2005. "Uncertainty and sensitivity analysis of runoff and sediment yield in a small agricultural watershed with KINEROS2." *Hydrol. Sci. J.* 50 (6): 1171.

Harmel, R. D., and P. K. Smith. 2007. "Consideration of measurement uncertainty in the evaluation of goodness-of-fit in hydrologic and water quality modeling." *J. Hydrol.* 337 (3): 326–336.

Harmel, R., P. Smith, K. Migliaccio, I. Chaubey, K. Douglas-Mankin, B. Benham et al. 2014. "Evaluating, interpreting, and communicating performance of hydrologic/water quality models considering intended use: A review and recommendations." *Environ. Modell. Software* 57: 40–51.

Hernandez-Suarez, J. S., S. A. Woznicki, and A. P. Nejadhashemi. 2019. "Multi-site watershed model calibration for evaluating best management practice effectiveness in reducing fecal pollution." *Hum. Ecol. Risk Assess. Int. J.* 26 (10): 2690–2715.

Herr, J., and C. Chen. 2012. "WARMF: Model use, calibration, and validation." *Trans. ASABE* 55 (4): 1387–1394.

Jaber, F., and S. Shukla. 2012. "MIKE SHE: Model use, calibration, and validation." *Trans. ASABE* 55 (4): 1479–1489.

Kim, S. M., B. L. Benham, K. M. Brannan, R. W. Zeckoski, and G. R. Yagow. 2007. "Water quality calibration criteria for bacteria TMDL development." *Appl. Eng. Agric.* 23 (2): 171–176.

KISTERS. 2013. *WISKI hydrological data management software (user manual).* Citrus Heights, CA: KISTERS.

KLEMEŠ V. 1986. "Operational testing of hydrological simulation models." *Hydrol. Sci. J.* 31 (1): 13–24.

Kling, H., M. Fuchs, and M. Paulin. 2012. "Runoff conditions in the upper Danube basin under an ensemble of climate change scenarios." *J. Hydrol.* 424–425: 264–277.

Knoben, W. J., J. E. Freer, and R. A. Woods. 2019. "Inherent benchmark or not? Comparing Nash–Sutcliffe and Kling–Gupta efficiency scores." *Hydrol. Earth Syst. Sci.* 23 (10): 4323–4331.

Krause, P., D. P. Boyle, and F. Base. 2005. "Comparison of different efficiency criteria for hydrological model assessment." *Adv. Geosci.* 5: 89–97.

Larabi, S., A. St-Hilaire, F. Chebana, and M. Latraverse. 2018. "Using functional data analysis to calibrate and evaluate hydrological model performance." *J. Hydrol. Eng.* 23 (7): 04018026.

Lee, K. Y., T. R. Fisher, T. E. Jordan, D. L. Correll, and D. E. Weller. 2000. "Modeling the hydrochemistry of the Choptank River Basin using GWLF and Arc/Info: 1. Model calibration and validation." *Biogeochemistry* 49 (2): 143–173.

Legates, D. R., and G. J. McCabe. 1999. "Evaluating the use of "goodness of fit" measures in hydrologic and hydroclimatic model validation." *Water Resour. Res.* 35 (1): 233–241.

Lin, J., L. Xie, L. J. Pietrafesa, J. S. Ramus, and H. W. Paerl. 2007. "Water quality gradients across Albemarle-Pamlico estuarine system: Seasonal variations and model applications." *J. Coastal Res.* 231: 213–229.

Lin, J., L. Xie, L. J. Pietrafesa, H. Xu, W. Woods, M. A. Mallin et al. 2008. "Water quality responses to simulated flow and nutrient reductions in the Cape Fear River Estuary and adjacent coastal region, North Carolina." *Ecol. Modell.* 212 (3–4): 200–217.

Linsley, R. K., M. A. Kohler, and J. L. H. Paulhus. 1975. *Hydrology for engineers.* 2nd ed. New York: McGraw-Hill.

Maréchal, D. 2004. "A soil-based approach to rainfall-runoff modelling in ungauged catchments for England and Wales." PhD Thesis, Cranfield University, UK. 157 pp.

Martin, J. L., and S. C. McCutcheon. 1999. *Hydrodynamics and transport for water quality modeling.* Boca Raton, FL: CRC Press.

Martinec, J., and A. Rango. 1989. "Merits of statistical criteria for the performance of hydrological models." *J. Am. Water Resour. Assoc.* 25 (2): 421–432.

McCutcheon, S. C. 1989. *Water quality modeling: Vol. I, river transport and surface exchange.* Boca Raton, FL: CRC Press.

McCutcheon, S. C., Z. Donwei, and S. Bird. 1990. *Model calibration, validation and use,* 5.1–5.77. Manual for Performing Waste Load Allocations, Book III (Estuaries), Part 2, EPA-823-R-92-003. Washington, DC: USEPA.

Mishra, A., E. Ahmadisharaf, B. L. Benham, M. L. Wolfe, S. C. Leman, D. L. Gallagher et al. 2018. "Generalized likelihood uncertainty estimation and Markov chain Monte Carlo simulation to prioritize TMDL pollutant allocations." *J. Hydrol. Eng.* 23 (12): 05018025.

Mishra, A., B. R. Bicknell, P. Duda, T. Donigian, and M. H. Gray. 2017. "HSPEXP+: An enhanced expert system for HSPF model calibration—A case study of the Snake River Watershed in Minnesota." *J. Water Manage. Model.* 25: C422.

Moriasi, D., J. Arnold, M. Van Liew, R. Bingner, R. Harmel, and T. Veith. 2007. "Model evaluation guidelines for systematic quantification of accuracy in watershed simulations." *Trans. ASABE* 50(3), 885-900.

Moriasi, D., M. W. Gitau, N. Pai, and P. Daggupati. 2015. "Hydrologic and water quality models: Performance measures and evaluation criteria." *Trans. ASABE* 58 (6): 1763–1785.

Nash, J. E., and J. V. Sutcliffe. 1970. "River flow forecasting through conceptual models. Part I—A discussion of principles." *J. Hydrol.* 10 (3): 282–290.

Neitsch, S. L., J. G. Arnold, J. R. Kiniry, and J. R. Williams. 2011. *Soil and water assessment tool theoretical documentation version 2009.* College Station, TX: Texas Water Resources Institute.

Niazi, M., C. Obropta, R. Miskewitz. 2015. "Pathogen transport and fate modeling in the Upper Salem River Watershed using SWAT model." *J. Environ. Manage.* 151, 167–177.

NRCS (National Resources Conservation Services). 1986. *Urban hydrology for small watersheds.* Conservation Engineering Division, NRCS, Tech. Release 55. Washington, DC: USDA.

Pandey, P. K., M. L. Soupir, M. Haddad, and J. J. Rothwell. 2012. "Assessing the impacts of watershed indexes and precipitation on spatial in-stream E. coli concentrations." *Ecol. Indic.* 23: 641–652.

Pak, J., K. Ramos, M. Fleming, W. Scharffenberg, and S. Gibson. 2015. "Sensitivity analysis for sediment transport in the hydrologic modeling system (HEC-HMS)." In *Proc., Joint Federal Interagency Conf.* April 19–23, 2015, Reno, Nevada. Accessed November 13, 2021. http://www.sedhyd.org/2015/proceedings.

Parajuli, P. B., K. Douglas-Mankin, P. L. Barnes, and C. Rossi. 2009. "Fecal bacteria source characterization and sensitivity analysis of SWAT 2005." *Trans. ASABE* 52 (6): 1847–1858.

Park, K., H.-S. Jung, H.-S. Kim, and S.-M. Ahn. 2005. "Three-dimensional hydrodynamic-eutrophication model (HEM-3D): Application to Kwang-Yang Bay, Korea." *Mar. Environ. Res.* 60 (2): 171–193.

Park, Y. S., D. H. Kum, Y. H. Jung, J. P. Cho, K. J. Lim, and K. S. Kim. 2014. "Simulation of the best management practice impacts on nonpoint source pollutant reduction in agricultural area using STEPL WEB model." *J. Korean Soc. Agric. Eng.* 56 (5): 21–27.

Paul, S., P. Haan, M. Matlock, S. Mukhtar, and S. Pillai. 2004. "Analysis of the HSPF water quality parameter uncertainty in predicting peak in-stream fecal coliform concentrations." *Trans. ASAE* 47 (1): 69–78.

Pechlivanidis, I. G., B. M. Jackson, N. R. McIntyre, and H. S. Wheater. 2011. "Catchment scale hydrological modelling: A review of model types, calibration approaches and uncertainty analysis methods in the context of recent developments in technology and applications." *Global NEST J.* 13 (3): 193–214.

Perdikaris, J., B. Gharabaghi, and R. Rudra. 2018. "Reference time of concentration estimation for ungauged catchments." *Earth Sci. Res.* 7 (2): 58–73.

Pool, S., M. Vis, and J. Seibert. 2018. "Evaluating model performance: towards a non-parametric variant of the Kling-Gupta efficiency." *Hydrol. Sci. J.* 63(13-14), 1941-1953.

Pushpalatha, R., C. Perrin, N. Le Moine, and V. Andréassian. 2012. "A review of efficiency criteria suitable for evaluating low-flow simulations." *J. Hydrol.* 420–421: 171–182.

Refsgaard, J. C., and H. J. Henriksen. 2004. "Modelling guidelines— Terminology and guiding principles." *Adv. Water Resour.* 27 (1): 71–82.

Ritter, A., and R. Muñoz-Carpena. 2013. "Performance evaluation of hydrological models: Statistical significance for reducing subjectivity in goodness-of-fit assessments." *J. Hydrol.* 480: 33–45.

Rossman, L. A. 2015a. *Storm water management model reference manual. Vol. I.* Cincinnati, OH: National Risk Management Research Laboratory, Office of Research and Development, EPA.

Rossman, L. A. 2015b. *Storm water management model user's manual, version 5.1.* Cincinnati: National Risk Management Research Laboratory, Office of Research and Development, USEPA.

Rossman, L. A. 2016. *Storm water management model reference manual. Vol. III.* Cincinnati, OH: National Risk Management Research Laboratory, Office of Research and Development, USEPA.

Saleh, A., and B. Du. 2004. "Evaluation of SWAT and HSPF within BASINS program for the upper North Bosque River watershed in central Texas." *Trans. ASAE* 47 (4): 1039–1049.

Santhi, C., J. G. Arnold, J. R. Williams, W. A. Dugas, R. Srinivasan, and L. M. Hauck. 2001. "Validation of the swat model on a large RWER basin with point and nonpoint sources 1." *J. Am. Water Resour. Assoc.* 37 (5): 1169–1188.

Schaefli, B., and H. V. Gupta. 2007. "Do Nash values have value?" *Hydrol. Processes* 21 (15): 2075–2080.

Schnoor, J. L. 1996. *Environmental modeling: Fate and transport of pollutants in water, air, and soil.* Hoboken, NJ: John Wiley & Sons.

Sharifi, A., L. Kalin, M. M. Hantush, S. Isik, and T. E. Jordan. 2013. "Carbon dynamics and export from flooded wetlands: A modeling approach." *Ecol. Model.* 263: 196–210.

Stow, C. A., C. Roessler, M. E. Borsuk, J. D. Bowen, and K. H. Reckhow. 2003. "Comparison of estuarine water quality models for total maximum daily load development in Neuse River Estuary." *J. Water Resour. Plann. Manage.* 129 (4): 307–314.

Sutanudjaja, E. H., R. van Beek, N. Wanders, Y. Wada, J. H. C. Bosmans, N. Drost et al. 2018. "PCR-GLOBWB 2: A 5 arcmin global hydrological and water resources model." *Geosci. Model Dev.* 11 (6): 2429–2453.

Tedela, N. H., S. C. McCutcheon, T. C. Rasmussen, R. H. Hawkins, W. T. Swank, J. L. Campbell et al. 2011. "Runoff Curve Numbers for 10 small forested watersheds in the mountains of the Eastern United States." *J. Hydrol. Eng.* 17 (11): 1188–1198.

Tolson, B. A., and C. A. Shoemaker. 2007. "Dynamically dimensioned search algorithm for computationally efficient watershed model calibration." *Water Resour. Res.* 43 (1): W01413.

Towner, J., H. L. Cloke, E. Zsoter, Z. Flamig, J. M. Hoch, J. Bazo et al. 2019. "Assessing the performance of global hydrological models for capturing peak river flows in the Amazon basin." *Hydrol. Earth Syst. Sci.* 23: 3057–3080.

USACE (United States Army Corps of Engineers). 2010. *HEC-DSS add-in excel data exchange for excel 2007–2010. User's manual.* Davis, CA: USACE. Institute for Water Resources. Hydrologic Engineering Center.

USACE. 2016. *Hydrologic modeling system HEC-HMS: User's manual.* Davis, CA: Hydraulic Engineering Cener.

USEPA (United States Environmental Protection Agency). 1991. *Guidance for water quality-based decisions: The TMDL process.* Washington, DC: USEPA.

USEPA. 2000. *BASINS technical note 6: Estimating hydrology and hydraulic parameters for HSPF.* Washington, DC: Office of Water.

USEPA. 2002. *Guidance for quality assurance project plans for modeling.* Washington, DC: USEPA.

USEPA. 2006. *BASINS technical note 8: Sediment parameter and calibration guidance for HSPF.* Washington, DC: USEPA.

USEPA. 2013. *Better assessment science integrating point and nonpoint sources.* Washington, DC: USEPA.

Willmott, C. J. 1981. "On the validation of models." *Phys. Geogr.* 2 (2): 184–194.

Woolhiser, D. A., R. Smith, and D. C. Goodrich. 1990. *KINEROS: A kinematic runoff and erosion model: Documentation and user manual.* USDA-ARS-77. Fort Collins, CO: USDA.

Yen, H., S. Park, J. G. Arnold, R. Srinivasan, C. J. Chawanda, R. Wang et al. 2019. "IPEAT+: A built-in optimization and automatic calibration tool of SWAT+." *Water* 11 (8): 1681.

Yuan, Y., W. Nie, E. V. Taguas, and S. C. McCutcheon. 2013. "Initial abstraction and curve numbers in semiarid watersheds in southeastern Arizona." *Hydrol. Processes* 28 (3): 774–783.

CHAPTER 9

MODEL UNCERTAINTY ANALYSIS
AND THE MARGIN OF SAFETY

*Mohamed M. Hantush, Harry X. Zhang, Rene A. Camacho-Rincon,
Ebrahim Ahmadisharaf, Yusuf M. Mohamoud*

The margin of safety (MOS) is a required element of total maximum daily loads (TMDLs) that accounts for the uncertainty about the relationship between the pollutant load and the quality of the receiving waterbody. MOS also accounts for uncertainty regarding the accuracy of adopted numerical targets against which simulated water quality parameters are compared. In almost all TMDLs, the MOS is selected or accounted for using explicit and implicit approaches, but often without an explicit determination of the level of protection provided by the TMDL. The latter cannot be determined without conducting an uncertainty analysis of some sort and implementing a risk-based approach. The extent to which approved TMDLs have performed uncertainty analysis as the basis for selecting MOS and whether such analysis would benefit TMDLs deserve attention. This chapter covers the state-of-the-practice on the selection of MOS in TMDLs and the state-of-the-art on model uncertainty estimation and risk-based MOS determination. The chapter provides a summary of the sources of uncertainty, approaches for selecting the MOS, a survey of MOS types implemented in practice, and advanced probabilistic methods that practitioners may find helpful in future TMDL development.

9.1 UNCERTAINTY ANALYSIS

Uncertainty, in general, can be defined as a measure of imperfect knowledge of environmental systems or probable error that can occur during data collection and modeling (e.g., Singh et al. 2007). Model uncertainty specifically refers to the impossibility of representing the real world perfectly by means of a mathematical model (Beven 2009). Models

271

cannot precisely represent the true behavior of the system because of deficiencies in hypotheses and model assumptions, and errors in observed data and model parameters. Uncertainty analysis quantifies the predictive capability of a model, and is, therefore, a necessary step after calibration and validation of the model. This analysis is performed to investigate the impacts of different error sources on the model performance and ultimately to obtain an informed evaluation of the relationship between loads and impaired waters (Walker et al. 2003, Beven 2005, 2009, Shirmohammadi et al. 2006).

Uncertainty is, in general, classified into epistemic and aleatory (Ang and Tang 2007) depending on the nature of the missing or unknown information (e.g., Walker et al. 2003, Refsgaard et al. 2007, Matott et al. 2009). Epistemic uncertainty is attributed to the imperfection in our knowledge to mathematically model the real world or the ability to make predictions. Therefore, epistemic uncertainty is knowledge based and can be minimized systematically through the development of more accurate representations of underlying physical, chemical, and biological processes, improved instrumentation and measurement techniques, and the implementation of better modeling practices. Epistemic uncertainty arises from model structural errors, unknown parameters, errors in initial and boundary conditions, and spatiotemporal variability of system excitations (Beck 1987, van Straten and Keesman 1991, Shirmohammadi et al. 2006, Harmel and Smith 2007, Nguyen and Willems 2016, Ahmadisharaf et al. 2019). Aleatory uncertainty deals with inherent randomness of the underlying phenomenon that manifests as variability in the observed data. This type of uncertainty results from an intrinsic spatiotemporal variability of climatic and hydrologic events, and, hence, is too difficult to reduce. If a model is capable of simulating with precision and accuracy the response of a watershed to rainfall events (i.e., zero epistemic uncertainty), there will still be some level of uncertainty to predict runoff events because of the highly variable and chaotic characteristics of atmospheric circulation and rainfall intensity through a watershed.

In practice, epistemic uncertainty is viewed as the most relevant source and can be reduced through an improved representation of the physical and biochemical processes (Beven and Binley 1992, Reckhow 2003, Refsgaard et al. 2006). Model structure uncertainty is caused by inadequate hypotheses, processes overlooked owing to a lack of complete knowledge of the system, imperfect mathematical representation of critical physicochemical and biological processes impacting water flow and quality, and errors in computer codes. Input data uncertainty is caused by errors in the data used to initiate model runs and gaps in the spatial and time-series data. These errors can be related to the lack of proper instrumentation, inaccurate measurements caused by low equipment precision, inappropriate installation or maintenance of laboratories/field instruments, and input data processing errors (Camacho et al. 2014a). For example, rating curves are often used to provide measured streamflow rates, typically obtained by a stage–flow power relationship that is not perfect and amenable to errors. Further, the stage is often estimated from water pressure, and temperature is known to affect these readings. Measurement errors, scale issues, and inadequate size or gaps in time-series data of the simulated variables can have a significant impact on calibration and model predictive uncertainty. This type of uncertainty is often lumped with model structural errors as an additive noise term or represented by some stochastic process. Finally, parametric uncertainty is caused by unknown parameter values and parameters that cannot be determined independently in terms of measurable variables or by field tests and laboratory experiments. This source of uncertainty is invariably common in water quality studies, whereby a large number of model parameters are typically dealt with in problems of nutrient cycling, oxygen demand, and biomass production (e.g., Camacho et al. 2014b).

In TMDL studies, the design of effective strategies to meet water quality standards and ensure protection of designated uses highly depends on the accuracy of the models in simulating the receiving waterbody responses to pollutant discharges. The adequacy of determined TMDLs and success of mitigation strategies, however, can be adversely impacted by data and modeling errors, including both epistemic and aleatory sources of uncertainty. To address these problems in TMDL studies, the US Clean Water Act Section 303(d)(1)(c) mandated the use of an MOS as a mechanism to compensate for all sources of uncertainty arising from data, analysis, and modeling during the development of a TMDL. MOS, therefore, must be included in all TMDLs to provide a measure of assurance that the impaired waterbody will meet and maintain water quality standards once load reductions are implemented.

9.2 TOTAL MAXIMUM DAILY LOAD MARGIN OF SAFETY

MOS is a required component of the TMDL according to the US Clean Water Act, Section 303(d). It is defined as an unallocated loading capacity (LC) of the waterbody and, thus, should reflect both the reliability of the observed water quality data and the models used to compute the LC. MOS is introduced in the TMDL Equation (9-1) to account for the uncertainty in the relationship between pollutant loads and the quality of the receiving waterbody. It is an unallocated waste assimilative capacity taking into consideration the background water quality contributions. MOS also buffers against uncertainty in regard to the accuracy of the numerical targets, which may exist in the best of circumstances. The variability of the data from which loading was determined and reliability of the models by which the LC was calculated should be accounted for in MOS (Novotny 2003). Because of the uncertainty in observed water quality data and models, a small MOS may result in nonattainment of the water quality standards, but a large MOS can be inefficient and costly. MOS can be incorporated either explicitly as an unallocated waste assimilative capacity or implicitly in the TMDL computations by making conservative modeling assumptions. In most TMDL studies, however, the determination of MOS is subjective and even arbitrary and lacks an explicit relationship with the desired degree of protection to be provided (i.e., hedging against violating water quality standards). Methods for model uncertainty estimation have matured, but existing TMDL rules or guidance are not clear on how this uncertainty should be factored into the calculation of MOS. The process of determining the proper magnitude of MOS in a TMDL is typically negotiated among the developer of the TMDL, the agencies involved (primarily states), and stakeholders. This process will benefit from a formal framework explicitly linking MOS determination to modeling uncertainty. Methods for the selection and estimation of MOS are first discussed in the following section.

9.3 ESTIMATION OF THE MARGIN OF SAFETY

MOS is always incorporated in the TMDL computations, but no guidelines are available for selecting MOS values, except the use of professional judgment and experience. However, statistical and probabilistic methods are nevertheless available and can be implemented to explicitly relate MOS to the uncertainty of TMDL estimates or the estimated risk of violating water quality standards considering multiple sources of uncertainty.

9.3.1 Explicit Margin of Safety

An explicit inclusion of the MOS is performed by setting aside a fraction of the calculated LC to account for uncertainty in the TMDL study (e.g., 5% of the allocated assimilative capacity). This fraction of the calculated load is then subtracted from the LC before allocation to all point sources waste load (WLA) and other nonpoint sources load (LA):

$$TMDL = LC = \Sigma WLA + \Sigma LA + MOS \qquad (9\text{-}1)$$

where LC is calculated as the maximum amount of daily loading that a waterbody can receive without violating water quality standards, and LA also includes background sources. Another explicit approach for the estimation of the MOS includes using more conservative numerical targets than those determined by states (see, e.g., Zhang and Yu 2004). Zhang and Yu (2004) considered 9.5 mg/L as the instream target nitrate concentration instead of 10 mg/L as the water quality standard for nitrate–nitrogen concentration. As will be seen in published TMDL documents, this approach is not uncommon.

The explicit estimation of the MOS, although more complex than the implicit approach, is a preferred one because it provides a more objective account of the main sources of uncertainty in a TMDL study. This evaluation serves as a basis to improve model performance, to optimize data monitoring and collection, and to better understand the role of uncertainty in water quality modeling.

A formula for estimating the MOS is provided by Dilks and Freedman (2004), in which they propose replacing the conservative input values that were used to determine LC with expected values of each parameter. The water quality model is then rerun using the expected input parameter values to determine the LC. The authors proposed the MOS to be the difference between the LC calculated using the model with conservative inputs and the LC using the model with the expected values of inputs:

$$MOS = LC\big|_{\bar{X},\bar{\theta}} - LC\big|_{X^*,\theta^*} \tag{9-2}$$

where $\bar{X}, \bar{\theta}$ are, respectively, the expected input forcing and the parameters, and X^*, θ^* are the corresponding conservative values. However, the level of protection (or safety buffer) provided by the calculated MOS in Equation (9-2) at the very best remains unknown.

9.3.2 Implicit Margin of Safety

MOS can be incorporated implicitly by making conservative assumptions on the assimilative capacity of the receiving waterbody during the calculation of $\sum$WLA and $\sum$LA. TMDL developers should clearly define the conservative assumptions made while formulating the TMDL. Example implicit approaches implemented by states in the development of TMDLs include the use of conservative assumptions in (1) model development, (2) the use of biochemical reaction rates, and (3) the derivation of numerical targets and downplaying the effectiveness of best management practices and restoration activities. Such assumptions may be related to the frequency or magnitude of low-flow conditions, and the magnitude of biochemical processing and cycling rates. For instance, using flow conditions of lower frequency than 7Q10 (the lowest 7-day average flow that occurs on average once every 10 years) during the estimation of the permissible loads may compensate for uncertainty in the records of flow and provide a conservative estimate of the assimilative capacity of the receiving waterbody. 7Q11 or 7Q12 are examples of flow conditions of lower frequency than 7Q10. The use of 7Q10 instead of 7Q2 is another example. Ignoring instream die-off rates of fecal coliform when modeling bacterial transport in a watershed is another example of a conservative assumption whereby anticipated losses are represented in additional implicit MOSs. The uncertainty in translating narrative standard into surrogate numerical target values should also be implicitly accounted for in the MOS.

For the implicit case, therefore, Equation (9-1) becomes

$$TMDL = LC = \Sigma WLA + \Sigma LA \qquad (9\text{-}3)$$

where MOS is implicitly incorporated to the calculated LC on the right-hand side of Equations (9-3). The implicit method is easier to implement but provides a less objective way of accounting for uncertainty than the explicit method and suffers from the following drawbacks (Dilks and Freedman 2004): (1) a lack of guidance on the proper choice of conservative assumptions and input values, (2) an unknown degree of protection, and (3) an unknown magnitude of the resulting MOS.

9.3.3 Risk-Based Margin of Safety

Efforts relating the MOS and required load reduction to rigorous model uncertainty estimation have been marginal in TMDL studies, but even then, they have been limited to the research arena and hypothetical TMDLs. Notable approaches explicitly relating the MOS to a desired degree of protection are those equating the MOS to the standard deviation using first-order error analysis (FOEA) (Zhang and Yu 2004) and Bayesian Monte Carlo (BMC) methods that emphasize estimation of the probability of exceeding or less than the water quality standard (Borsuk and Stow 2000, Borsuk et al. 2002, Hantush and Chaudhary 2014, Chaudhary and Hantush 2017, Camacho et al. 2018, Ahmadisharaf et al. 2019). These approaches furnish a formal methodology for estimating the MOS as a function of an acceptable level of risk and essentially suggest that the MOS can be calculated as the difference between the required reduction of mean load with a 50% degree of protection and the required mean-load reduction at a prescribed but higher degree of protection (Dilks and Freedman 2004, Shirmohammadi et al. 2006). The mean load reduction at a 50% protection buffer is the required load reduction obtained from the model using average parameter values or based on deterministic model applications:

$$MOS(\beta) \approx L_c - L_\beta \qquad (9\text{-}4)$$

where β is the Probability of exceeding the water quality standard (or less than the standard, e.g., in case of oxygen), L_c is the calculated compliance load corresponding to the reference simulation, and L_β is the calculated β-compliance mean load considering random parameters and analysis uncertainty.

Equation (9-4) is essentially that proposed by Hantush and Chaudhary (2014). Note that the MOS here is a function of the acceptable level of risk (β). Figure 9-1 provides a schematic illustration of the meaning of MOS in Equation (9-4). Equation (9-4) reveals three key points. First, the equation evaluates the MOS relative to a baseline simulation that varies from one application to another. For example, in the absence of observed water quality data, a baseline simulation can be based on some average of default model parameter values or the means of a prior parameter distribution (or priori) derived from literature tabulations or expert judgment and experience. In Bayesian inferences, a prior probability distribution reflects

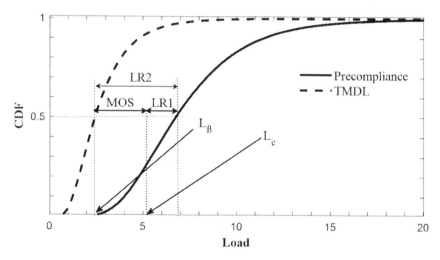

Figure 9-1. Estimation of MOS. The solid line corresponds to the pre-compliance CDF of loading and the dashed line corresponds to compliance loading (TMDL). LR_1 is the required load reduction for the reference simulation. LR_2 is the β-compliance mean-load reduction.
Source: Adapted from Hantush and Chaudhary (2014).

the modeler's belief about the uncertainty of a parameter before conditioning on the observational data.

In the presence of water quality data, a baseline simulation is based on the calibrated model parameter values (as in traditional model calibration) or the means of the posterior parameter distributions (PPDs) obtained after Bayesian conditioning on the observational data. Second, the MOS is a function of risk level because L_β depends on β. Third, Equation (9-4) is essentially a plot of the required LC reduction as a function of β. This plot can be used to determine the required load reduction for an acceptable risk level β. In real-world TMDLs, this would require implementing a probabilistic framework.

Another approach was proposed by Shirmohammadi et al. (2006), whereby LC is considered as the value corresponding to a 50% probability of occurrence (i.e., that obtained from the model with median values of inputs) and the MOS would then be estimated as a percentage of that value. Zhang and Yu (2004) determined the LC using a conservative water quality standard obtained by subtracting the standard deviation for nitrate concentration from the corresponding water quality standard. In their approach, first-order variance analysis (FOVA; also known as FOEA) was implemented to calculate the mean and standard deviation of nitrate–nitrogen using the HSPF model.

Risk-based approaches for estimating a TMDL are more accurate than the traditional approaches because they explicitly account for data and modeling errors in determining the probability of meeting (or violating) the water quality standard. The probability of a water quality percentile exceeding or being less than the standard can be computed analytically (e.g., FOVA for normal distribution) or by means of the Monte Carlo (MC) method for highly nonlinear, complex models. As previously stated, the relationship between the required mean-load reductions and the corresponding risk values can be obtained in the form of a plot and then can be utilized by decision makers and stakeholders to make well-informed decisions on acceptable risk values. It is worth noting that in case a formal uncertainty analysis is conducted and the probability of exceeding the numerical target is estimated, the MOS becomes something of ancillary value because the LC would then be computed based on an explicit, desired degree of protection.

Despite policy and cultural barriers, risk-based TMDL estimation remains a scientifically defensible and transparent approach relating MOS to the risk (probability) that water quality standard may be violated. Approving agencies (USEPA and the state department of environment) and stakeholders can negotiate an acceptable level of risk to assure compliance and protection of the environment, while avoiding unnecessary and costly pollution control measures. Future research may focus on means to eliminate such barriers through effective communication and education on the importance of uncertainty analysis to TMDL estimation and decision-making.

9.4 DETERMINATION OF THE MARGIN OF SAFETY IN CASE-STUDY TOTAL MAXIMUM DAILY LOADS

In a TMDL review study, Dilks and Freedman (2004) investigated how the MOS was determined in 172 TMDLs. A total of 70% of the TMDLs reviewed specified an explicit MOS and 4.3% of the TMDLs reviewed used an implicit MOS. Only one TMDL calculated uncertainty in the analysis and reflected this uncertainty in an MOS. All but this TMDL, the TMDLs that used an explicit MOS considered a safety factor. More recently, Nunoo et al. (2019) employed the natural-language processing method to review the MOS values of TMDLs approved by the USEPA from 2002 to 2016 in an online database system known as the Assessment TMDL Tracking And ImplementatioN System (ATTAINS). One thousand TMDL documents were sampled from among 38,000 approved TMDLs. Only 16% of the sampled explicit MOS values evolved from some form of mathematical estimation process; the remaining 84% selected an arbitrary safety factor, with an MOS value of 10% being the most implemented value. Only two of the sampled TMDLs selected the MOS based on uncertainty analyses.

Table 9-1 lists 17 TMDL documents recently surveyed by the authors, pollutants addressed by the TMDLs, states, computational models, and MOS estimation method. All these documents reported either the implicit method or the explicit method or both for selecting the MOS. None of the studies used uncertainty analysis, formal or informal, as the mean to inform the selection of the MOS. Five of the documents reported the implicit method as the base for selecting the MOS; eight documents reported the use of the explicit method; and the remaining four TMDL studies used both the implicit and explicit methods.

9.5 UNCERTAINTY ANALYSIS METHODS

Despite the plethora of uncertainty estimation methods, the use of uncertainty analysis, formal or informal, remains very limited in TMDLs. Only a handful of TMDL applications have relied on uncertainty analysis as the basis for selecting the MOS, and almost all are research studies. The reluctance to base the MOS explicitly on model uncertainty estimates might be attributed to the following factors: (1) a lack of enforceable guidelines on estimation of the MOS, a process left to the agencies involved and stakeholders to negotiate (Novotny 2003), (2) absence of policy regarding the desired degree of protection to be provided by the MOS (Dilks and Freedman 2004), (3) a thorough uncertainty analysis of process-oriented water quality model is not trivial and can be resource demanding (Chapra 2003), and (4) socioeconomic cost of dealing with MOS values is so large as to make implementation impractical. It seems

Table 9-1. Survey of MOS Methods in Sampled TMDL Reports.

TMDL case study	State	Pollutant(s)	Computational model	MOS estimation method
Fecal coliform TMDL for the Upper North Buffalo Creek Watershed (Murray et al. 2004)	New York	Fecal coliform	WinHSPF	Explicit: reduced water quality target Implicit: assuming continuous source loading
NEOSHO River Basin TMDL, Marion Lake Eutrophication (USEPA 2005a)	Kansas	Total Nitrogen (TN), N, and Total Phosphorus (TP)	GWLF, BATHTUB	Explicit: 10% of the total annual nutrient loads from the watershed
NEOSHO River Basin TMDL, Metals (USEPA 2005b)	Kansas	Metals	Empirical/statistical	Explicit: difference between upper and lower 90% confidence limits of the mean total hardness in each flow range
Dissolved oxygen TMDL for Long Branch, WBID 3030 (Gao 2005)	Florida	TN, TP, biological oxygen demand, and dissolved oxygen deficit	SWMM	Implicit: BOD decay rate and TN and TP attenuation rates = 0; event-based mean concentrations of TN from human land-use categories were all reduced to the level of the upland forest
Walla Walla River basin pH and dissolved oxygen TMDL (WSDE 2007)	Oregon	pH and dissolved oxygen deficit	QUAL2Kw and empirical formula	Implicit: using 7Q10 instead of 7Q2; elevated plant effluent discharge; similar biomass and growth rates under background/reduced nutrient loading scenarios and current conditions; and others

Nutrient TMDLs for the Cahaba River Watershed (ADME 2006)	Alabama	Nutrients, siltation, and pathogens	LSPC, EPDRIV1, CAHABA—Spreadsheet	Implicit: least-impacted reference streams; steady-state model with monthly median flows; requiring TP concentrations to meet growing-season target at the critical compliance points
TMDLs for the Walnut Creek Watershed (OEPA 2010)	Ohio	Fecal coliform, sediment, and habitat quality	Simple mathematical equations, fecal coliform model (SLAPIT)	Implicit: stringent requirement for delisting; lowering 30 day mean geometric mean standard; ignoring die-off between source loading and TMDL end point; 100% of all fecal coliform sources available for wash-off; ignoring land-use buffering capacity efficiency; conservative targets for sediment and habitat
TMDL development—total phosphorus—for Taylorsville Lake (NREPC 2000)	Kentucky	Phosphorus	CE-QUAL-W2	Explicit: 2.6% of loading for the summer period and 10% for other seasons
Kansas/Lower Republican Basin TMDL, Shunganunga Creek (USEPA 2007)	Kansas	Dissolved oxygen deficit	Regression model	Explicit: increasing dissolved oxygen standard from 5.0 to 5.5 mg/L

(Continued)

Table 9-1 (*Continued*).

TMDL case study	State	Pollutant(s)	Computational model	MOS estimation method
TMDLs for the Upper Auglaize River Watershed (OEPA 2004)	Ohio	Habitat, dissolved oxygen, TP, NH_4-N, and bacteria (FC)	Export coefficient (TP), EPA multi-SMP, fecal tool (FCLET)	Implicit: applying stringent requirements for delisting; assumption in P and N target development. Explicit: 56% of bacterial loading capacity; 5% reduction in P and N target values
TMDLs for the Blanchard River Watershed (OEPA 2009)	Ohio	TP, fecal coliform, habitat, and sediment	GWLF, QUAL2K	Implicit: using TP summer target for other seasons; die-off rates ignored in streams; assumptions in runoff-generated loads arising from land application of manure; conservative target values for sediment and habitat. Explicit: 4% of fecal coliform loading capacity
TMDL development for total mercury in the Satilla Watershed (USEPA 2001)	Georgia	Total mercury	WCS and WASP5	Explicit: selecting the highest predicted water column concentration of mercury to determine load reduction; assigning load reduction to point sources. Implicit: conservative assumptions in deriving the estimate of anticipated reductions in emissions to the air

TMDL for the Rawls Creek (SCDHEC 2000)	South Carolina	Fecal coliform	Simple load calculations	Explicit: 12.5% reduction in the state standard for fecal coliform bacteria
TMDL for the Fork Creek (USEPA 2005c)	South Carolina	Fecal coliform	BIT spreadsheet, Load-duration method	Explicit: 5% reduction in fecal coliform bacteria standard
TMDLs for the Upper Little Miami River (OEPA 2001)	Ohio	NH_4, dissolved oxygen deficit, sediment, and habitat	GWLF, QHEI, and QUAL2E	Implicit: setting the point-source inputs at the full design or permit value; high-end background value for nutrients; assuming very low-flow condition (7Q10); using moderately high instream temperatures
TMDL for turbidity in the Upper Birch Creek (USEPA 1996)	Alaska	Turbidity and sediment	Simple load calculations	Explicit: setting aside 10% of computed loading capacity Implicit: ignoring settling from the water column
Fecal coliform TMDL for the Tallabinnela Creek, Tombigbee River Basin (MDEQ 2006)	Florida	Fecal coliform	Simple mass balance	Explicit: 10% of average daily loading capacity

that practitioners find it easier to propose a safety factor as a buffer against errors in the data and uncertainty in the selected models. However, this can be a costly proposal as uncertainty deserves to be incorporated with some rigor in TMDL development (NRC 2001, Reckhow 2003) to avoid potential failures to meet the standards and improve water quality economically.

This section provides a summary of widely used probabilistic methods that have a promising potential to be used in TMDL development and a robust estimation of MOS.

Uncertainty analysis has been performed in watershed modeling studies using different methods, the most notable being FOVA (also known as FOEA), Kalman filtering, MC analysis, Bayesian inference methods such as BMC, Markov chain Monte Carlo (MCMC), importance sampling (IS) (e.g., Gelman et al. 2004, Del Moral et al. 2006), generalized likelihood uncertainty estimation (GLUE) (Beven and Binley 1992), sequential uncertainty fitting (SUFI-2) (Abbaspour et al. 2004, 2007), management objectives constrained analysis of uncertainty (MOCAU), stochastic analysis of model residuals (SAMR), and probabilistic collocation method (PCM) (Guzman et al. 2015). Table 9-2 summarizes the uncertainty analysis applied in previous water quality modeling studies. Most of these methods require repeated model simulations, which represents a serious limitation, particularly in studies dealing with multidimensional models with long computational time. The FOVA, GLUE, and BMC methods have been successfully applied in TMDL research studies, primarily because of their ease of implementation and lower computational expenses compared with other methods. These methods are further discussed in the forthcoming sections.

SUFI-2 is a sequential uncertainty estimation algorithm built in SWAT-CUP essentially as a calibration tool in the popularly used Soil and Water Assessment Tool (SWAT) (Abbaspour et al. 2007) for modeling watershed hydrology and diffuse source pollutant loading. The algorithm utilizes two statistics, namely, the P-factor to control the percentage of observations that are bounded by the simulations, and the R-factor for the 95% prediction interval (2.5% to 97.5% percentiles).

Several TMDL studies have considered statistical models including linear regression. This chapter does not address the uncertainty estimation of regression models. Confidence intervals for the coefficients of linear regression models and prediction limits for model estimates or new forecasts can be computed formally using the rules of mathematical probability in any of the statistics and applied probability textbooks. Interested readers and modelers may refer to Neter et al. (1985, Sections 3.4, 3.5, 7.6, and 7.7) and Ang and Tang (2007, Section 8.2.3) on formulas for the estimation of regression model parameter confidence limits and prediction intervals.

Table 9-2. Uncertainty Analysis Methods Applied in Water Quality
Modeling Studies.

Uncertainty analysis method	Water quality model	Simulated pollutant(s)	Reference
BMC	GRDOM	BOD	Dilks et al. (1992)
BMC	HSPF	Dissolved oxygen	Patil and Deng (2011)
BMC, GLUE, LHS, and MC	MFG	TSS	Olson (2017)
FOVA (or FOEA)	HSPF	Nutrients	Zhang and Yu (2004)
FOVA (or FOEA)	STORM	TSS	Park and Roesner (2012)
GLUE	WARMF	Diazinon	Zheng and Keller (2008)
GLUE	Stormwater quality model	Dissolved oxygen and BOD	Mannina and Viviani (2010)
GLUE	HSPF	FC	Ahmadisharaf and Benham (2020)
GLUE and LHS	HSPF	FC	Jia and Culver (2008)
GLUE and MC	SWAT	Nutrients	Shirmohammadi et al. (2006)
GLUE and MCMC	HSPF	FC	Mishra et al. (2018b)
MC	HSPF	TSS	Mitsova-Boneva and Wang (2007)
MC and TPMC	HSPF	FC	Mishra et al. (2018a)
MCMC	SWAT	Nutrients	Zheng and Han (2016)

(Continued)

Table 9-2 (*Continued*). Uncertainty Analysis Methods Applied in Water Quality Modeling Studies.

Uncertainty analysis method	Water quality model	Simulated pollutant(s)	Reference
MOCAU	WARMF	TSS and Diazinon	Zheng and Keller (2008)
MRBC	SWAT	Nutrients	Han and Zheng (2016)
PCM	WARMF	Diazinon	Zheng et al. (2011)
SAMR	HSPF	FC	Chin (2009)
SCE	HSPF	TSS	van Griensven and Meixner (2007)

Source: Adapted from Ahmadisharaf et al. (2019).

Notes: TN = Total nitrogen, TP = Total phosphorus.

9.5.1 First-Order Variance Analysis

The First-Order Variance Analysis (FOVA) method provides an estimate of model uncertainty by calculating the first two moments (mean and variance) of the model outputs from the mean and variance of model parameters and input variables. The first two moments can be used to construct confidence intervals around the outputs assuming normality of the model residual errors. To compute the mean and variance of an output variable Y, FOVA starts with evaluating the first-order Taylor expansion of the model $F(X, \theta)$, which simulates the evolution of Y; that is, $Y = F(X, \theta)$ (Melching 1992, Blumberg and Georgas 2008, Camacho et al. 2014a). F represents a mathematical model representation of Y (e.g., dissolved oxygen), X is a matrix of p input or forcing variables (e.g., BOD, ammonia, and nitrate), and θ is a vector of q model parameters (e.g., channel Manning coefficient, bed slope, BOD decay rate, and reaeration rate). The expansion of $F(X, \theta)$ is performed around the calibrated model parameters (θ_0) and inputs (X_0), typically assuming that they are statistically independent. The means of model outputs after truncating higher-order terms and taking the expectation are $Y_0 = F(X_0, \theta_0)$, where $X_0 = (X_{1o}, X_{2o}, ..., X_{po})$ and θ_0 are the calibrated inputs and parameters, respectively. The variances of model output Y are estimated from the Taylor expansion after truncating higher-order terms as follows (e.g., Blumberg and Georgas 2008):

$$Var(Y) = \sigma_{Y^2} = \sum_{i=1}^{p} \left[\frac{\partial F}{\partial X_i} \Big|_{X_i=X_{io}} \sigma_{Xi} \right]^2 + \sum_{i=1}^{q} \left[\frac{\partial F}{\partial \theta_i} \Big|_{\theta_i=\theta_{io}} \sigma_{\theta i} \right]^2 \quad (9\text{-}5)$$

where σ_Y^2 is a direct estimate of the output uncertainty, and σ_{Xi}^2 and $\sigma_{\theta i}^2$ are the variances of the ith input variable and model parameter, respectively. For correlated parameters or input variables, a more general expression of Equation (9-5) can be found elsewhere (Singh et al. 2007, Ang and Tang 2007, Camacho et al. 2014a). The derivative term $\partial F/\partial X_i$ in Equation (9-5) can be numerically evaluated using a simple difference scheme such as forward differencing [i.e., $\Delta F = F(X_{i0} + \Delta X_i) - F(X_{i0})$], where $F(X_{i0} + \Delta X_i)$ is the model estimation obtained after perturbing the input variable X_i around the calibrated value by a magnitude ΔX_i. Similar is the case for $\partial F/\partial \theta_i$. Equation (9-5) can be expressed alternatively in terms of the coefficients of variation (CVs) (i.e., $CV_Y \equiv \sigma_Y/Y_0$, $CV_{Xi} \equiv \sigma_{Xi}/X_{io}$, $CV_{\theta i} \equiv \sigma_{\theta i}/\theta_0$):

$$CV_Y^2 = \Sigma_{i=1}^{p} \left[(DSC_i^{F_{Xi}=X_{io}}) CV_{Xi} \right]^2 + \Sigma_{i=1}^{q} \left[(DSC_i^{F_{\theta i}=\theta_{io}}) CV_{\theta i} \right]^2 \quad (9\text{-}6)$$

where DSC represents dimensionless sensitivity coefficients that quantify the relative importance of changes in the input variable X_i and model parameter θ_i on the model estimations. These coefficients can be computed via the following formula (Blumberg and Georgas 2008):

$$DSC_i^{F_{Xi}=X_{io}} = \left[\frac{\left(\dfrac{\partial F}{\partial X_i} \right)}{\left(\dfrac{F(X_i)}{X_i} \right)} \right]_{X_i=X_{io}} \quad \text{and} \quad DSC_i^{F_{\theta i}=\theta_{io}} = \left[\frac{\left(\dfrac{\partial F}{\partial \theta_i} \right)}{\left(\dfrac{F(\theta_i)}{\theta_i} \right)} \right]_{\theta_i=\theta_{io}} \quad (9\text{-}7)$$

The implementation of FOVA can be summarized as follows (Melching 1992, Zhang and Yu 2004, Camacho et al. 2014a):

- Identify the model parameters and input and output variables of interest.
- Obtain model outputs using baseline values of the model parameters and input forcing variables. Typically, the baseline values are selected as the calibrated values of model parameters (θ_0) and inputs (X_0).
- Perturb each input variable and model parameter of interest by a small amount (e.g., 10%) and run the model with the perturbed values. Use the corresponding simulated model outputs to compute the DSC with Equation (9-7).

- Provide an estimate for the standard deviation σ or alternatively the coefficient of variation CV for each input variable and model parameter. This step may require literature search or expert judgment.
- Calculate the variance or the coefficient of variation of the outputs using Equation (9-5) or Equation (9-7).
- For TMDL studies, use the output variance to identify the most conservative water quality condition [e.g., calibrated output of dissolved oxygen minus one or multiple standard deviation(s)] and compute the input load required to meet the water quality standard for such conditions. The difference between the load calculated using the calibrated output (baseline conditions) and the load calculated using the uncertainty estimate from FOVA can be used as an estimate of MOS.

The truncation of higher-order terms leading to first- or second-order estimates of the mean and variance and overlooking potential statistical dependence among model parameters and inputs limit the application of FOVA. The assumption that the variance of the model given by Equation (9-5) is an accurate approximation of the true variance of the model outputs over the wide range of X and θ does not always hold. In nonlinear systems, this assumption is limited by errors introduced because of truncating higher-order terms in the Taylor expansion around X_0 and θ_0 (Melching 1995, Melching and Yoon 1996, Zhang and Yu 2004). In addition, it is often necessary to assume that the model parameters and input variables are statistically independent, and if they are, correlations between parameters and input variables must be known in advance and prescribed as inputs to the method. For all practical purposes, the latter is typically not the case. Finally, normality of the model outputs is a requirement for the estimation of model output predictive interval. Despite all these limitations, studies have shown that FOVA can produce acceptable results (Burges and Lettenmaier 1975, Scavia et al. 1981, Malone et al. 1983, Yen et al. 1986, Melching 1992, Bobba et al. 1996, Camacho et al. 2014a, Bolster and Vadas 2013, Kuria and Vogel 2015).

9.5.2 Monte Carlo Method

The Monte Carlo (MC) method is a technique that relies on repeated model runs to approximate probabilistic distribution and statistical properties of the output of a modeling system, given the probabilistic distributions of the inputs (Singh et al. 2007). This method is straightforward and provides an effective approach for uncertainty estimation (Helton and Davis 2003), especially for complex models and highly nonlinear systems. A well-known trait of MC analysis is its simplicity and ease of use

(Hanson 1999, Le Maître and Knio 2010, Rajabi and Ataie-Ashtiani 2014). Once the uncertain parameters and input variables are assigned probability distributions, the method starts by drawing a large number of random samples and the model is run repeatedly to generate corresponding model outputs, thereby propagating the uncertainty of inputs to the outputs. In other words, a complex stochastic problem is reduced to purely deterministic analysis with the simulated outputs analyzed statistically (Madani and Lund 2011). The generated model outputs can be used to construct probability distributions of the model outputs and estimate the summary statistics (e.g., mean, standard deviation, percentiles, etc.). The MC method is nonintrusive, so that the users can apply existing models to conduct simulations with minimal modification of software codes (Helton and Davis 2003). It is generic, needs fewer assumptions than the other propagating tools (Brown and Heuvelink 2006), and is robust for discontinuities (Wiener 1938, Peng and Zhang 2012). In addition, the MC method is flexible, and unlike FOVA, it can handle highly nonlinear and complex models (Hantush and Kalin 2005, Rajabi and Ataie-Ashtiani 2014). However, the application of the MC method outside of a Bayesian framework is recommended only when observational data are not available.

Despite the aforementioned capabilities, high computational cost could be a stumbling block. To overcome this problem, it is often recommended that a sampling efficiency technique be implemented in concert (Janssen 2013). Latin hypercube sampling (LHS) (McKay et al. 1979) is an example that can improve the sampling efficiency of the MC simulation (Helton and Davis 2003). It divides the entire multidimensional parameter space into multiple nonoverlapping hypercubes and draws a random number within each hypercube, hence leading to a more uniform sampling from the parameter-space hypercube and less model runs than the standard MC simulation (Melching 1995, Janssen 2013). As such, it is a more structured and efficient sampling method to achieve numerical convergence. LHS has been widely applied do deal with environmental and water resource problems, yet its applications to TMDL studies are rare.

9.5.3 Bayesian Monte Carlo Analysis

Bayesian methods utilize Bayes' theorem to modify formally the prior assumptions on model parameters and to update the probability distributions of the parameters and model outputs as additional information becomes available. The provision for combining judgmental information with observational data in the estimation of parameters and model outputs is a major advantage of the Bayesian approach over the classical statistical approach. Hence, these methods are suited for model calibration and provide a formal approach for predictive uncertainty estimation.

The BMC method is a probabilistic method like IS,GLUE, and MCMC aims to obtain the posterior (conditional) PPDs of model parameters/ inputs and modeled system variables of interest (Kennedy and O'Hagan 2001, Engeland et al. 2005, Liu and Gupta 2007, Stow et al. 2007, Ames and Lall 2008, Hantush and Chaudhary 2014). The conditional median, mean value, and other percentiles can be used as estimates of model predictive uncertainty, and, hence, to compute the MOS in TMDLs (e.g., Zhang and Yu 2004, Patil and Deng 2011, Hantush and Chaudhary 2014). Besides its shear simplicity, the BMC method offers three main advantages over FOVA. First, in addition to parametric uncertainty, it accounts for model structural and observational errors (Hantush and Chaudhary 2014). Second, the method is not limited to normally/lognormally distributed model outputs. Third, as additional observational data become available, the Bayes rule can be implemented to update estimates of PPDs of both model parameters and simulated outputs. MC-based methods, however, can be computationally expensive, particularly for higher-dimensional parameter spaces.

To describe the BMC method, consider the problem of calculating the uncertainty associated with the outputs (Y) (e.g., dissolved oxygen) of a watershed model generically described by the model $Y = F(X, \theta)$. The model outputs are subject to multiple sources of uncertainty because of errors in input datasets (X), model parameters (θ), and model structure. These uncertainties and observational errors cause the model outputs (Y) to deviate from observations (O). A generic expression relating model outputs to observations and modeling errors can be expressed by

$$O = Y + \varepsilon \qquad (9\text{-}8)$$

where ε is a vector of random errors. In what follows, the errors are assumed statistically independent, homoscedastic, and normally distributed.

Within a Bayesian framework, model parameters and inputs are treated as random variables with prescribed probability distributions. BMC is essentially a sequential algorithm that updates these distributions through the Bayes theorem as new observational data become available, thereby allowing for the estimation of model output predictive interval.

The implementation of the BMC algorithm starts with proposing prior probability distributions for the uncertain input datasets $P(X)$ and model parameters $P(\theta)$. These prior distributions can be defined by the modeler using expert judgment and literature review. In some cases, the distributions of observable inputs (e.g., point-source BOD concentrations) can be defined from laboratory or field equipment precision/error reports assuming that the measurements are normally distributed (or any other suitable distribution). In practice, however, the prior distributions of inputs are difficult to determine, particularly if the inputs cannot be directly observed, and often estimated from other variables or averaged at different spatial and temporal scales.

The uncertainty in model parameters (θ) is also difficult to determine a priori, given the inevitable lack of a complete knowledge of the system under consideration. However, it is not uncommon if there is no prior factual information on the parameter to propose uniform prior distributions (i.e., diffuse priors) to avoid applying special importance to a specific parameter value. This way, the problem is reduced to estimating the initial range values of each model parameter, which can be done using literature review, expert judgment, and knowledge about the system under analysis. Triangular priors can also be proposed if the most likely value of a parameter can be inferred from literature and experience. It should be noted, however, that in the case of an overwhelming amount of observed data, the choice of the priors becomes increasingly irrelevant and conditioning on the observational data supersedes prior judgment while updating probability distributions using the Bayesian equation (9-9).

The second step in the BMC method consists of updating the prior distributions of model parameters and outputs as additional information becomes available (i.e., O). In the case of uncertain model parameters, the updated distributions are denoted by $P(\theta|O)$, indicating that the distributions are now conditional or newly informed by the observations. The distributions denoted by $P(\theta|O)$ are generically known as posterior distributions and are calculated using the Bayes theorem as follows:

$$P(\theta|O) = \frac{P(O|\theta)P(\theta)}{\int P(O|\theta)P(\theta)d\theta} \tag{9-9}$$

where $P(O|\theta) \equiv L(\theta)$ is the likelihood function that expresses the conditional probability of the data observed given the parameter vector θ, and $P(\theta)$ is the prior probability of the parameter set θ, often initially selected equal to $1/N$, where N is the number of sampled parameter sets in the MC simulation (equal weights are assigned to θs a priori). The denominator in Equation (9-9) is a normalizing constant which ensures that the sum of posterior probabilities over the N parameter sets is equal to unity:

$$P(\theta|O) = k L(\theta)P(\theta) \tag{9-10}$$

To define the likelihood function, it is necessary to propose a statistical structure for the residuals between the simulations and the observations (ε) [Equation (9-8)]. Several likelihood functions can be constructed based on the degree of bias, correlation, and seasonal or other trend variations in the series of residuals (Maranzano and Krzysztofowicz 2004, Schoups and Vrugt 2010, Hantush and Chaudhary 2014). In the simplest case, if the residuals are independent, identically distributed Gaussian variates, $\varepsilon_t \sim N(0, \sigma_\varepsilon^2)$, the likelihood function is given by

$$L(\boldsymbol{\theta}) = (2\pi\sigma_\varepsilon^2)^{-\frac{n}{2}} exp\left[-\frac{1}{2\sigma_\varepsilon^2}\varepsilon^T\varepsilon\right] \tag{9-11}$$

where σ_ε^2 is the variance of the residual errors, ε is $(n \times 1)$ vector of model residual errors, and n is the number of observations. σ_ε^2 can be estimated formally by Maximum Likelihood Estimation (Hantush and Chaudhary 2014).

The likelihood function of multiple model state variables is the product of likelihoods of each state variable (e.g., Dilks et al. 1992, Camacho et al. 2015):

$$L(\boldsymbol{\theta}) = \Pi_{j=1}^{m}\left[(2\pi\sigma_{\varepsilon j}^2)^{-\frac{n_j}{2}} exp\left(-\frac{1}{2\sigma_{\varepsilon j}^2}\varepsilon_j^T\varepsilon_j\right)\right] \tag{9-12}$$

where m is the number of model simulated state variables, and n_j is the size of the observational data of the simulated output j.

The probability density function (PDF) of a new observation o_k (prediction) is mathematically calculated by invoking the total probability theorem:

$$\begin{aligned} f(o_k|O) &= \int_\Theta f(o_k|\boldsymbol{\theta})P(\boldsymbol{\theta}|O)d\boldsymbol{\theta} \\ &= k\int_\Theta f(o_k|\boldsymbol{\theta})L(\boldsymbol{\theta})P(\boldsymbol{\theta})d\boldsymbol{\theta} \end{aligned} \tag{9-13}$$

where $f(o_k|O)$ is the PDF of the new observation o_k given the present observations O, $f(o_k|\boldsymbol{\theta}) \sim N(y_k, \sigma_\varepsilon^2)$ is the conditional PDF of o_k given $\boldsymbol{\theta}$; and $y_k = F(\boldsymbol{X}_k, \boldsymbol{\theta})$. The conditioning on X_k is implicit in Equation (9-13).

The cumulative distribution function (CDF) of o_k is similar to Equation (9-13) but with $f(o_k|O)$ and $f(o_k|\boldsymbol{\theta})$ to be replaced by the corresponding CDFs, $F(o_k|O)$ and $F(o_k|\boldsymbol{\theta})$. $F(o_k|O)$ can be inverted to obtain percentiles of choice and prediction limits for new observations (e.g., 5th and 95th). These uncertainty bounds can be used to identify the most adverse water quality condition and to estimate the permitted loads to meet specific water quality standards at an acceptable risk level. Analytical formulas for posterior cumulative distribution (CDF) of simulated variables and probability of violations (greater/less than numerical targets), expressed in terms of likelihood-weighted model simulations, are given by Hantush and Chaudhary (2014).

9.5.4 Generalized Likelihood Uncertainty Estimation Method

The Generalized Likelihood Uncertainty Estimation (GLUE) Method is essentially a Bayesian method that rejects the notion of a single "optimum parameter set" and embraces the concept of "equifinality" (Beven and Freer 2001, Beven 2006) instead. The equifinality concept implies that different model structures and different parameter combinations (also known as behavioral sets) within a chosen model structure can be equally valid simulators of the observed system behavior. The methodology starts with the generation of an ensemble of parameter sets by sampling random parameter values from their respective prior distributions and conducting MC simulation. A likelihood measure is then computed for each parameter set (θ_i) by a comparison of the simulated outputs with observations using some fit measure such as Nash–Sutcliffe efficiency (Beven and Binley 1992):

$$L(\boldsymbol{\theta}) = 1 - \frac{\sigma_i^2}{\sigma_o^2} \qquad (9\text{-}14)$$

where $L(\theta)$ is a measure of the likelihood of simulating the dataset Y_{obs} given the parameter set θ, σ_i^2 is the variance of residual errors, and σ_O^2 is the variance of observations. $L(\boldsymbol{\theta})$ is used here as a fuzzy measure of the probability of how well the parameter set allows the model to describe the data. In a sense, it is a generalization to the likelihood function often used in classical Bayesian estimation and, therefore, is referred to as an informal likelihood measure. Once the likelihoods of all parameter sets are computed, parameter sets whose likelihoods exceed or are equal to a prescribed threshold value are retained as *behavioral* sets and parameter sets that fail the test are considered *nonbehavioral* sets and are rejected. Model simulations corresponding to nonbehavioral parameter sets are considered dissimilar to the behavior of the system under study. The likelihood weights of the retained simulations are then normalized so that their sum is 1.0. The normalized likelihood values are then combined with the prior parameter distribution using Bayes theorem [Equation (9-10)] to yield the posterior parameter set probability mass. The normalized likelihoods can be treated as probability masses for the simulated model outputs and can be used to assess the uncertainty associated with the simulations. Sometimes, behavioral parameter sets are given equal weights when generating the probability distributions of model outputs.

Besides their simplicity (non-iterative), particularly in highly nonlinear and complex environmental models, one major advantage of the GLUE and BMC methods is the emphasis on parameter sets (as opposed to individual parameters), whereby covariation among the parameters are reflected implicitly in the value of the likelihood measure associated with each set (Beven and Binley 1992, Schulz et al. 1999, Chaudhary and Hantush 2017). The methodology, however, has drawbacks, the most notable being subjective selection of the likelihood measure and threshold criterion separating the *behavior* and *nonbehavior* parameter sets. Different values of the threshold can lead to different sizes of the output uncertainty band (Schulz et al. 1999, Zheng and Keller 2007). The implication of an arbitrarily selected likelihood measure is that GLUE's uncertainty limits are no longer direct estimates of the probability of observing the data. Thiemann et al. (2001), Mantovan and Todini (2006), Stedinger et al. (2008), and Vrugt et al. (2009) provide a thorough evaluation of the GLUE method.

9.5.5 Markov Chain Monte Carlo

The Markov Chain Monte Carlo (MCMC) method (Gilks et al. 1996) is a formal Bayesian sampler and a class of algorithms for sampling from probability distributions based on constructing a Markov chain that has the desired posterior joint parameter distribution $f(\theta|O)$ as its equilibrium distribution. MCMC methods are iterative methods and start with a proposed a priori distribution of the residual errors. Then, they generate random walk through the parameter space to improve search efficiency and converge to the posterior joint probability distribution to derive the appropriate form for the likelihood function. The mapping from parameter space to likelihood space identifies a range of plausible parameter sets and allows an estimation of both parameter and predictive uncertainty (Schoups and Vrugt 2010).

Sampling from the posterior distribution requires an iterative algorithm. The Metropolis algorithm (Gelman et al. 2004) is the simplest technique and has been applied by Yang et al. (2008) in a watershed model application comparing various uncertainty analysis techniques including this one. The Metropolis–Hastings algorithm (Hastings 1970, Gelman et al. 2004) is one of the most general techniques and has been applied by Mishra et al. (2018a) to prioritize TMDL pollutant allocations in a rural watershed in western Virginia using the HSPF model. The SCEM-UA algorithm utilizes LHS to produce initial parameter sets with parameter values randomly distributed throughout the feasible parameter space (Vrugt et al. 2003). An adaptation of the SCEM-UA algorithm is the DREAM sampling scheme that uses a differential evolution as a genetic algorithm for global optimization. Markov chains (each representing a randomly drawn parameter set) are simultaneously run in parallel. The chains are initialized by LHS and the parameter space using uniform distributions (Vrugt et al. 2009). A third convergence algorithm is DREAM-ZS, which is proposed by Schoups and Vrugt (2010) as a modification of the original DREAM algorithm. This approach uses sampling from an archive of past states to generate candidate points in each individual chain and requires only three parallel chains to summarize the posterior distribution (Pourreza-Bilondi et al. 2017).

Except for Mishra et al. (2018b), there has been no application of the MCMC method to TMDL problems when compared with BMC and GLUE. This may be attributed to the relative simplicity of the latter, particularly in addressing water quality management problems (Borsuk et al. 2002, Zheng and Keller 2008, Patil and Deng 2011, Hantush and Chaudhary 2014, Camacho et al. 2018).

The formulation of the likelihood function is a key differentiator among the statistically rigorous Bayesian methods, BMC, MCMC, and GLUE. BMC and MCMC explicitly account for model residual errors and use formal likelihoods, whereas in GLUE, observational and model structural errors are lumped artificially to parametric uncertainty and informal likelihoods are often used. Formal Bayesian approaches attempt to resolve the effects of various sources of modeling uncertainty (Vrugt et al. 2009) and are more consistent in the application of the rules of mathematical probability (Thiemann et al. 2001). Both MCMC and BMC have a robust formulation that utilizes a formal likelihood function and do not suffer from subjective criteria separating behavioral from nonbehavioral parameter sets in GLUE (Stow et al. 2007), thereby providing a more solid theoretically foundation for estimating the posterior probability distributions of model parameters and outputs. However, MCMC is relatively more difficult to apply than BMC and GLUE because it requires user input in selecting a variance scaling factor that ensures chain convergence and in determining the Markov chain burn-in period (Samanta et al. 2007).

The Bayesian approach using a formal likelihood function could also be used to obtain estimates of MOS as the difference between the load calculated using the expected model prediction and the load calculated at a given risk level. Estimation of MOS using Bayesian methods is currently a topic of investigation. The reader is referred to Borsuk et al. (2002), Shirmohammadi et al. (2006), Hantush and Chaudhary (2014), and Camacho et al. (2018) for an extended discussion on the topic including example applications to TMDLs. A notable trait of the GLUE and BMC methods is the relative ease of obtaining required load reductions as a function of probability of exceeding the numerical target (Borsuk et al. 2002, Chaudhary and Hantush 2017, Camacho et al. 2018). Both methods require less computational effort than MCMC and are less intrusive when it comes to code modification and implementation in readily available computer packages.

9.5.6 Kalman Filtering

Although it has received relatively much less attention than the previously described approaches in watershed and water quality modeling, Kalman filtering (KF), especially the Ensemble Kalman filter (EnKF) (Evensen 2003, De Lannoy et al. 2007, Liu and Gupta 2007), has been extensively used in sequential data assimilation in stochastic groundwater modeling, atmospheric and climate forecasting, land-surface models, marine ecosystem models, and oceanographic-related problems.

KF is a predictor–corrector recursive algorithm that was originally developed for dealing with linear filtering problems (Kalman 1960). Detailed derivation of the recursive algebraic relationships can be found in Jazwinski (1970). The Extended Kalman Filter (EKF) (Lewis 1986) extends the domain of application of KF to nonlinear systems. KF recursions start with a time-update process to predict state variable(s) and associated error covariance(s) after initializing the estimate of the state variable and associated covariance structure, followed by a measurement update (or a correction) to assimilate observed data into the system variable(s) based on the Kalman gain. Applications of KF and EKF have been limited to systems relatively simpler than watersheds (e.g., Bras and Rodriguez-Iturbe 1985, Lettenmaier and Burges 1976, Hantush and Mariño 1994, 1997). However, the introduction of EnKF allows applications of KF to complex watershed-scale problems (e.g., Reichle et al. 2002, De Lannoy et al. 2007, Kim et al. 2007). The EnKF nonlinearly propagates a finite ensemble of model trajectories, from which estimates of the state-variable probability distributions give a complete statistical description of the state variable. These characteristics make EnKF easier to apply than EKF and more suitable for complex and highly nonlinear systems.

In general, for higher-dimension state variables, KF is computationally demanding and requires accurate knowledge of the first two moments of the initial state of the process and measurement noise. Common applications of KF are limited to white process/measurement noise; autocorrelations in the process and measurement noise and cross correlation among the noise terms complicate the analysis. Despite the advantage of EnKF in the nonlinear projection of the state variable, the recursive relationship that it utilizes during the measurement update remains an approximation derived from a linear state-space representation. There is no evidence in the literature of an application of KF to TMDLs, not even at the research level.

9.6 STATE-OF-THE-ART AND STATE-OF-THE-PRACTICE

This chapter reviewed state-of-the-practice on MOS determination in TMDLs and state-of-the-art on methods for model uncertainty estimation that can be applied to risk-based water quality management and TMDLs. The most common methods for selecting or estimating the MOS are the implicit and explicit methods. Surveys of approved or recommended

TMDLs revealed that these methods were implemented without an explicit determination of the risk level involved in TMDL development. Only a handful, among hundreds, of the surveyed studies have conducted formal uncertainty analysis as the basis for MOS selection. Formal uncertainty analysis of water quality data and models can inform a robust determination of MOS along with an explicit estimation of the reliability of TMDL calculations. The degree of protection against water quality violation (i.e., reliability) provided by implicitly or explicitly selected MOS cannot be quantified without conducting some level of uncertainty analysis. This underscores the need for communicating the importance of uncertainty analysis to stakeholders, decision makers, and policy makers responsible for the development of TMDLs (NRC 2001, Reckhow 2003). TMDLs are likely to benefit from model uncertainty determination and implementing risk-based approaches aided by recent advances in statistical and probabilistic methods for model uncertainty estimation. It should be acknowledged that no guidelines currently exist on the selection of an appropriate MOS other than the use of simple implicit and explicit methods provided in the USEPA guidance document. As such, state agencies are not mandated to use uncertainty analysis as the basis for the determination of MOS.

The use of uncertainty estimation methods such as FOVA and Bayesian MC methods (GLUE, BMC, and MCMC) has been limited to research-oriented TMDLs but have the potential to be implemented in real-world TMDL studies. Bayesian MC methods stand out as the most comprehensive in model uncertainty estimation as they deal with nonlinearity and multiple sources of random errors using the probability theory. However, they can be computationally resource demanding when dealing with complex environmental systems (e.g., watersheds) and higher–parameter-space dimensions. More research is needed to improve the efficiency of the application of probabilistic methods and to expand their domain of applicability to more complex environmental systems. Tools are available to be linked to models or to develop codes to conduct Bayesian analysis for model calibration and uncertainty estimation. Such tools are Matlab, WinBUGS (Bayesian inference Using Gibbs Sampling) (Lunn et al. 2009), and Bayesian tools using, among others, R statistical package—general-purpose MCMC and SMC samplers and tools for Bayesian statistics (Wirtschaftsuniversität Wien, 2021). Although it remains a challenge to implement these tools in conjunction with water quality models for TMDLs, the ability to quantify model predictive uncertainty and base the selection of MOS on estimated standard deviations of predicted loadings could be the easiest step, but rigorous enough to start with.

The reviewed probabilistic methods afford a promising potential to be used in developing TMDLs and estimating MOS based on data and modeling uncertainty. From the perspective of TMDL practitioners, the use of more advanced methods in estimating model predictive uncertainty and determining MOS can reduce uncertainty during TMDL development phase and help gain higher confidence in the level of protection provided by the calculated TMDL for ambient water quality.

DISCLAIMER

This chapter was reviewed in accordance with the USEPA policy and approved for publication. The views expressed in this chapter are those of the authors and do not necessarily represent the views or policies of the USEPA.

REFERENCES

Abbaspour, K. C., C. Johnson, and M. T. van Genuchten. 2004. "Estimating uncertain flow and transport parameters using a sequential uncertainty fitting procedure." *Vadose Zone J.* 3 (4): 1340–1352.

Abbaspour, K. C., J. Yang, I. Maximov, R. Siber, K. Bogner, J. Mieleitner et al. 2007. "Modelling hydrology and water quality in the pre-alpine/alpine Thur watershed using SWAT." *J. Hydrol.* 333 (2–4): 413–430.

ADME (Alabama Department of Environmental Management). 2006. *Nutrient total maximum daily loads (TMDLs) for the Cahaba River Watershed.* Montgomery, AL: ADME.

Ahmadisharaf, E., and B. L. Benham. 2020. "Risk-based decision making to evaluate pollutant reduction scenarios." *Sci. Total Environ.* 702: 135022.

Ahmadisharaf, E., R. A. Camacho, H. X. Zhang, M. M. Hantush, and Y. M. Mohamoud. 2019. "Calibration and validation of watershed models and advances in uncertainty analysis in TMDL studies." *J. Hydrol. Eng.* 24 (7): 03119001.

Ames, D. P., and U. Lall. 2008. "Developing total maximum daily loads under uncertainty: Decision analysis and the margin of safety." *J. Contemp. Water Res. Educ.* 140 (1): 37–52.

Ang, A. H.-S., and W. H. Tang. 2007. *Probability concepts in engineering: Emphasis on applications in civil & environmental engineering.* New York: Wiley.

Beck, M. B. 1987. "Water quality modeling: A review of the analysis of uncertainty." *Water Resour. Res.* 23 (8): 1393–1442.

Beven, K. 2005. "On the concept of model structural error." *Water Sci. Technol.* 52 (6): 167–175.

Beven, K. 2006. "A manifesto for the equifinality thesis." *J. Hydrol.* 320 (1–2): 18–36.

Beven, K. 2009. *Environmental modelling: An uncertainty future?* London: Routledge.

Beven, K., and A. Binley. 1992. "The future of distributed models: Model calibration and uncertainty prediction." *Hydrol. Process.* 6 (3): 279–298.

Beven, K., and J. Freer. 2001. "Equifinality, data assimilation, and uncertainty estimation in mechanistic modelling of complex environmental systems using the GLUE methodology." *J. Hydrol.* 249 (1–4): 11–29.

Blumberg, A. F., and N. Georgas. 2008. "Quantifying uncertainty in estuarine and coastal ocean circulation modeling." *J. Hydraul. Eng.* 134 (4): 403–415.

Bobba, A. G., V. P. Singh, and L. Bengtsson. 1996. "Application of first-order and Monte Carlo analysis in watershed water quality models." *Water Resour. Manage.* 10 (3): 219–240.

Bolster, C. H., and P. A. Vadas. 2013. "Sensitivity and uncertainty analysis for the annual phosphorus loss estimator model." *J. Environ. Qual.* 42 (4): 1109–1118.

Borsuk, M. E., and C. A. Stow. 2000. "Bayesian parameter estimation in a mixed-order model of BOD decay." *Water Res.* 34 (6): 1830–1836.

Borsuk, M. E., C. A. Stow, and K. H. Reckhow. 2002. "Predicting the frequency of water quality standard violations: A probabilistic approach for TMDL development." *Environ. Sci. Technol.* 36 (10): 2109–2115.

Bras, R. L., and I. Rodriguez-Iturbe. 1985. *Random Functions and Hydrology.* Reading, MA: Addison-Wesley.

Brown, J. D., and G. B. Heuvelink. 2006. "Assessing uncertainty propagation through physically based models of soil water flow and solute transport." In *Encyclopedia of hydrological sciences,* edited by M. G. Anderson, 1181–1195. Chichester, UK: Wiley.

Burges, S. J., and D. P. Lettenmaier. 1975. "Probabilistic methods in stream quality management." *J. Am. Water Resour. Assoc.* 11 (1): 115–130.

Camacho, R. A., J. L. Martin, J. Diaz, W. H. McAnally, H. Rodriguez, P. Suscy et al. 2014a. "Uncertainty analysis of estuarine hydrodynamic models: An evaluation of input data uncertainty in the Weeks Bay estuary, Alabama." *Appl. Ocean Res.* 47: 138–153.

Camacho, R. A., J. L. Martin, W. McAnally, J. Díaz-Ramirez, H. Rodriguez, P. Sucsy et al. 2015. "A comparison of Bayesian methods for uncertainty analysis in hydraulic and hydrodynamic modeling." *J. Am. Water Resour. Assoc.* 51 (5): 1372–1393.

Camacho, R. A., J. L. Martin, B. Watson, M. Paul, L. Zheng, and J. Stribling. 2014b. "Modeling the factors controlling phytoplankton in the St. Louis Bay estuary, Mississippi and evaluating estuarine responses to nutrient load modifications." *J. Environ. Eng* 141 (3): 04014067.

Camacho, R. A., J. L. Martin, T. Wool, and V. P. Singh. 2018. "A framework for uncertainty and risk analysis in total maximum daily load applications." *Environ. Model. Software* 101: 218–235.

Chaudhary, A., and M. M. Hantush. 2017. "Bayesian Monte Carlo and maximum likelihood approach for uncertainty estimation and risk management: Application to lake oxygen recovery model." *Water Res.* 108: 301–311.

Chapra, S. C. 2003. "FORUM: Engineering Water Quality Models and TMDLs." *J. Water Resour. Plan. Manag.* 247–256.

Chin, D. A. 2009. "Predictive uncertainty in water-quality modeling." *J. Environ. Eng.* 135 (12): 1315–1325.

De Lannoy, G. J. M., P. R. Houser, V. R. N. Pauwels, and N. E. C. Verhoest. 2007. "State and bias estimation for soil moisture profiles by an ensemble Kalman filter: Effect of assimilation depth and frequency." *Water Resour. Res.* 43: W06401.

Del Moral, P., A. Doucet, and A. Jasra. 2006. "Sequential Monte Carlo samplers." *J. R. Stat. Soc., Ser. B* 68 (Pt 3): 411–436.

Dilks, D. W., R. P. Canale, and P. G. Meier. 1992. "Development of Bayesian Monte Carlo techniques for water quality model uncertainty." *Ecol. Model.* 62 (1–3): 149–162.

Dilks, D. W., and P. L. Freedman. 2004. "Improved consideration of the margin of safety in total maximum daily load development." *J. Environ. Eng.* 130 (6): 690–694.

Engeland, K., C. Y. Xu, and L. Gottschalk. 2005. "Assessing uncertainties in a conceptual water balance model using Bayesian methodology." *Hydrol. Sci. J.* 50 (1): 45–63.

Evensen, G. 2003. "The ensemble Kalman filter: Theoretical formulation and practical implementation." *Ocean Dyn.* 53 (4): 343–367.

Gao, X. 2005. *Dissolved oxygen TMDL for Long Branch, WBID 3030.* TMDL Rep. Tallahassee, FL: Florida Department of Environmental Protection.

Gelman, A., J. B. Carlin, H. S. Stern, and D. B. Rubin. 2004. *Bayesian data analysis.* Boca Raton, FL: Chapman and Hall/CRC.

Gilks, W. R., S. Richardson, and D. J. Spiegelhalter. 1996. *Markov Chain Monte Carlo in practice.* London: Chapman & Hall.

Guzman, J. A., A. Shirmohammadi, A. M. Sadeghi, X. Wang, M. L. Chu, M. K. Jha et al. 2015. "Uncertainty considerations in calibration and validation of hydrologic and water quality models." *Trans. ASABE* 58 (6): 1745–1762.

Han, F., and Y. Zheng. 2016. "Multiple-response Bayesian calibration of watershed water quality models with significant input and model structure errors." *Adv. Water Resour.* 88: 109–123.

Hanson, K. M. 1999. "A framework for assessing uncertainties in simulation predictions." *Physica D Nonlinear Phenom.* 133 (1–4): 179–188.

Hantush, M. M., and A. Chaudhary. 2014. "Bayesian framework for water quality model uncertainty estimation and risk management." *J. Hydrol. Eng.* 19 (9): 04014015.

Hantush, M. M., and L. Kalin. 2005. "Uncertainty and sensitivity analysis of runoff and sediment yield in a small agricultural watershed with KINEROS2." *Hydrol. Sci. J.* 50 (6): 1171.

Hantush, M. M., and M. A. Mariño. 1994. "Two-dimensional stochastic analysis and optimal estimation in aquifers: Random recharge." *Water Resour. Res.* 30 (2): 559–569.

Hantush, M. M., and M. A. Mariño. 1997. "Stochastic solution to Inverse problem in ground water." *J. Hydraul. Eng.* 123 (12): 1139–1146.

Harmel, R. D., and P. K. Smith. 2007. "Consideration of measurement uncertainty in the evaluation of goodness-of-fit in hydrologic and water quality modeling." *J. Hydrol.* 337 (3): 326–336.

Hastings, W. 1970. "Monte Carlo sampling methods using Markov chains and their applications." *Biometrika* 57 (1): 97–109.

Helton, J. C., and F. J. Davis. 2003. "Latin hypercube sampling and the propagation of uncertainty in analyses of complex systems." *Reliab. Eng. Syst. Saf.* 81 (1): 23–69.

Institute for Statistics and Mathematics, Wirtschaftsuniversität Wien. 2021. "Bayesian Tools - General-Purpose MCMC and SMC Samplers and Tools for Bayesian Statistics" (https://cran.r-project.org/web/packages/BayesianTools/vignettes/BayesianTools.html).

Janssen, H. 2013. "Monte-Carlo based uncertainty analysis: Sampling efficiency and sampling convergence." *Reliab. Eng. Syst. Saf.* 109: 123–132.

Jazwinski, A. H. 1970. *Stochastic processes and filtering theory.* San Diego: Academic.

Jia, Y., and T. B. Culver. 2008. "Uncertainty analysis for watershed modeling using generalized likelihood uncertainty estimation with multiple calibration measures." *J. Water Resour. Plan. Manag.* 134 (2): 97–106.

Kalman, R. E. 1960. "A new approach to linear filtering and prediction problems." *J. Basic Eng.* 82 (1): 35–45.

Kennedy, M. C., and A. O'Hagan. 2001. "Bayesian calibration of computer models." *J. R. Stat. Soc., Ser. B* 63 (3): 425–464.

Kim, S., Y. Tachikawa, and K. Takara. 2007. "Applying a recursive update algorithm to a distributed hydrologic model." *J. Hydrol. Eng.* 12 (3): 336–344.

Kuria, F., and R. Vogel. 2015. "Uncertainty analysis for water supply reservoir yields." *J. Hydrol.* 529: 257–264.

Le Maître, O. P., and O. M. Knio. 2010. "Introduction: Uncertainty quantification and propagation." In *Spectral methods for uncertainty quantification,* 1–13. Dordrecht, Netherlands: Springer.

Lettenmaier, D. P., and S. J. Burges. 1976. "Use of state estimation techniques in water resources system modeling." *J. Am. Water Resour. Assoc.* 12 (1): 83–99.

Lewis, F. L. 1986. *Optimal estimation with an introduction to stochastic control theory.* New York: Wiley.

Liu, Y., and H. V. Gupta. 2007. "Uncertainty in hydrologic modeling: Toward an integrated data assimilation framework." *Water Resour. Res.* 43: W07401.

Lunn, D., D. Spiegelhalter, A. Thomas, and N. Best. 2009. "The BUGS project: Evolution, critique and future directions." *Stat. Med.* 28 (25): 3049–3067.

Madani, K., and J. R. Lund. 2011. "A Monte-Carlo game theoretic approach for multi-criteria decision making under uncertainty." *Adv. Water Resour.* 34 (5): 607–616.

Malone, R., D. S. Bowles, M. P. Windham, and W. J. Grenney. 1983. "Comparison of techniques for assessing effects of loading uncertainty upon a long term phosphorous model." *Appl. Math. Modell.* 7 (1): 11–18.

Mannina, G., and G. Viviani. 2010. "An urban drainage stormwater quality model: Model development and uncertainty quantification." *J. Hydrol.* 381 (3–4): 248–265.

Mantovan, P., and E. Todini. 2006. "Hydrological forecasting uncertainty assessment: Incoherence of the GLUE methodology." *J. Hydrol.* 330 (1–2): 368–381.

Maranzano, C. J., and R. Krzysztofowicz. 2004. "Identification of likelihood and prior dependence structures for hydrologic uncertainty processor." *J. Hydrol.* 290 (1–2): 1–21.

Matott, L. S., J. E. Babendreier, and S. T. Purucker. 2009. "Evaluating uncertainty in integrated environmental models: A review of concepts and tools." *Water Resour. Res.* 45: W06421.

McKay, M. D., R. J. Beckman, and W. J. Conover. 1979. "Comparison of three methods for selecting values of input variables in the analysis of output from a computer code." *Technometrics* 21 (2): 239–245.

MDEQ (Mississippi Department of Environmental Quality). 2006. *Fecal coliform TMDL for Tallabinnela Creek, Tombigbee River Basin: Lee, Pontotoc, Chickasaw, and Monroe Counties, Mississippi.* Jackson, MS: MDEQ.

Melching, C. S. 1992. "An improved first-order reliability approach for assessing uncertainties in hydrologic modeling." *J. Hydrol.* 132 (1–4): 157–177.

Melching, C. S. 1995. "Reliability estimation." In *Computer models of watershed hydrology*, edited by V. P. Singh, 69–118. Littleton, CO: Water Resources Publications.

Melching, C. S., and C. G. Yoon. 1996. "Key sources of uncertainty in QUAL2E model of Passaic River." *J. Water Resour. Plann. Manage.* 122 (2): 105–113.

Mishra, A., E. Ahmadisharaf, B. L. Benham, D. L. Gallagher, K. H. Reckhow, and E. P. Smith. 2018a. "A two-phase Monte Carlo simulation for partitioning the effects of epistemic and aleatory uncertainty in TMDL modeling." *J. Hydrol. Eng.* 24 (1): 04018058.

Mishra, A., E. Ahmadisharaf, B. L. Benham, M. L. Wolfe, S. C. Leman, D. L. Glalagher et al. 2018b. "Generalized likelihood uncertainty estimation and Markov Chain Monte Carlo simulation to prioritize TMDL pollutant allocations." *J. Hydrol. Eng.* 23 (12): 05018025.

Mitsova-Boneva, D., and X. Wang. 2007. "Exploring the variability in suspended sediment yield using BASINS–HSPF and probabilistic modeling: Implications for land use planning." *J. Environ. Inf.* 9 (1): 29–40.

Murray, T., A. McDaniel, D. Phlegar, and A. Kebede. 2004. "Fecal coliform total maximum daily load for the Upper North Buffalo Creek Watershed City of Greensboro, Guilford County." In *Proc., Water Environment Federation,* January 2005.

NREPC, Kentucky Division of Water. 2000. *Total maximum daily load (TMDL) development—Total phosphorus—For Taylorsville Lake, Spencer County, Kentucky.* Frankfort, KY: Natural Resources and Environmental Protection Cabinet, Kentucky Division of Water.

Neter, J., W. Wasserman, M. H. Kutner. 1985. *Applied Linear Regression Models.* Irwin, Homewood, Illinois.

Nguyen, T. T., and P. Willems. 2016. "The influence of model structure uncertainty on water quality assessment." *Water Resour. Manag.* 30 (9): 3043–3061.

Novotny, V. 2003. *Water quality: Diffuse pollution and watershed management.* Hoboken, NJ: Wiley.

NRC (National Research Council). 2001. *Assessing the TMDL approach to water quality management.* Washington, DC: Water Science and Technology Board, Division of Earth and Life Studies.

Nunoo, R., P. Anderson, S. Kumar, and J.-J. Zhu. 2019. "Margin of safety in TMDLs: A natural language processing aided review of the state of practice." *J. Hydrol. Eng.* 25 (4): 04020002.

OEPA (Ohio Environmental Protection Agency). 2001. *Total maximum daily loads for the Upper Little Miami River.* Draft Report. Columbus, OH: Ohio EPA.

OEPA. 2004. *Total maximum daily loads for the Upper Auglaize River Watershed.* Columbus, OH: Ohio EPA.

OEPA. 2009. *Total maximum daily loads for the Blanchard River Watershed.* Columbus, OH: Ohio EPA.

OEPA. 2010. *Total maximum daily loads for the Walnut Creek Watershed.* Columbus, OH: Ohio EPA.

Olson, C. C. 2017. "Stormwater control measure modeling and uncertainty analysis for total maximum daily load compliance." Ph.D. thesis, Colorado State University, Dept. of Civil and Environmental Engineering.

Park, D., and L. A. Roesner. 2012. "Evaluation of pollutant loads from stormwater BMPs to receiving water using load frequency curves with uncertainty analysis." *Water Res.* 46 (20): 6881–6890.

Patil, A., and Z.-Q. Deng. 2011. "Bayesian approach to estimating margin of safety for total maximum daily load development." *J. Environ. Manag.* 92 (3): 910–918.

Peng, M., and L. Zhang. 2012. "Analysis of human risks due to dam-break floods—Part 1: A new model based on Bayesian networks." *Nat. Hazard.* 64 (1): 903–933.

Pourreza-Bilondi, M., S. Z. Samadi, A.-M. Alkhoond-Ali, and B. J. Ghahraman. 2017. "Reliability of semiarid flash flood modeling using Bayesian framework." *J. Hydrol. Eng.* 22 (4): 05016039.

Rajabi, M. M., and B. Ataie-Ashtiani. 2014. "Sampling efficiency in Monte Carlo based uncertainty propagation strategies: Application in seawater intrusion simulations." *Adv. Water Resour.* 67: 46–64.

Reckhow, K. H. 2003. "On the need for uncertainty assessment in TMDL modeling and implementation." *J. Water Resour. Plan. Manag.* 129 (4): 245–246.

Refsgaard, J. C., J. P. van der Sluijs, J. Brown, and P. van der Keur. 2006. "A framework for dealing with uncertainty due to model structure error." *Adv. Water Resour.* 29 (11): 1586–1597.

Refsgaard, J. C., J. P. van der Sluijs, A. L. Hojberg, and P. A. Vanrolleghem. 2007. "Uncertainty in the environmental modelling process—A framework and guidance." *Environ. Model. Software* 22 (11): 1543–1556.

Reichle, R. H., J. P. Walker, R. D. Koster, and P. R. Houser. 2002. "Extended versus ensemble Kalman filtering for land data assimilation." *J. Hydrometeorol.* 3 (6): 728–740.

Samanta, S., D. Mackay, M. Clayton, E. Kruger, and B. Ewers. 2007. "Bayesian analysis for uncertainty estimation of a canopy transpiration model." *Water Resour. Res.* 43 (4): W04424.

Scavia, D., W. F. Powers, R. P. Canale, and J. L. Moody. 1981. "Comparison of first-order error analysis and Monte Carlo simulation in time-dependent lake eutrophication models." *Water Resour. Res.* 17 (4): 1051–1059.

SCDHEC (South Carolina Department of Health and Environmental Control). 2000. *Total maximum daily load (TMDL), Rawls Creek, South Carolina.* Columbia, SC: SCDHEC.

Schoups, G., and J. A. Vrugt. 2010. "A formal likelihood function for parameter and predictive inference of hydrologic models with correlated, heteroscedastic, and non-Gaussian errors." *Water Resour. Res.* 46 (10): W10531.

Schulz, K. 1999. "Equifinality and the Problem of Robust Calibration in Nitrogen Budget Simulations." *Soil Sci. Soc. Am. J.* 63, 1934–1941.

Shirmohammadi, A., I. Chaubey, R. D. Harmel, D. D. Bosch, R. Muñoz-Carpena, C. Dharmasri et al. 2006. "Uncertainty in TMDL models." *Trans. ASABE* 49 (4): 1033–1049.

Singh, V. P., S. K. Jain, and A. Tyagi. 2007. *Risk and reliability analysis, a handbook for civil and environmental engineers.* Reston, VA: ASCE.

Stedinger, J. R., R. M. Vogel, S. U. Lee, and R. Batchelder. 2008. "Appraisal of the generalized likelihood uncertainty estimation (GLUE) method." *Water Resour. Res.* 44 (12): W00B06.

Stow, C. A., K. H. Reckhow, S. S. Qian, E. C. Lamon, G. B. Arhonditsis, M. E. Borsuk et al. 2007. "Approaches to evaluate water quality model parameter uncertainty for adaptive TMDL implementation1." *J. Am. Water Resour. Assoc.* 43 (6): 1499–1507.

Thiemann, M., M. Trosset, H. Gupta, and S. Sorooshian. 2001. "Bayesian recursive parameter estimation for hydrologic models." *Water Resour. Res.* 37 (10): 2521–2535.

USEPA (US Environmental Protection Agency). 1996. *Total maximum daily load for turbidity in Upper Birch Creek, Alaska.*

USEPA. 2001. *Total maximum daily load (TMDL) development for total mercury in the Satilla Watershed.*

USEPA. 2005a. *Neosho River Basin Total Maximum Daily Load, Marion Lake (Marion Reservoir), Eutrophication.*

USEPA. 2005b. *Neosho River Basin Total Maximum Daily Load, including Shoal Creek, Short Creek, Shawnee Creek, Turkey Creek and Center Creek. Biological impairment from metals.*

USEPA. 2005c. *Total maximum daily load for Fork Creek, Stations: PD-067, PD-068, fecal coliform.*

USEPA. 2007. *Kansas/Lower Republican Basin total maximum daily load. TMDL document for Shunganunga Creek. Watershed assessment, tracking & environmental results.*

van Griensven, A., and T. Meixner. 2007. "A global and efficient multi-objective auto-calibration and uncertainty estimation method for water quality catchment models." *J. Hydroinf.* 9 (4): 277–291.

van Straten, G. T., and K. J. Keesman. 1991. "Uncertainty propagation and speculation in projective forecasts of environmental change: A lake-eutrophication example." *J. Forecasting* 10 (1–2): 163–190.

Vrugt, J. A., H. V. Gupta, W. Bouten, and S. Sorooshian. 2003. "A shuffled complex evolution metropolis algorithm for optimization and uncertainty assessment of hydrologic model parameters." *Water Resour. Res.* 39 (8): 1201.

Vrugt, J. A., C. J. Ter Braak, H. V. Gupta, and B. A. Robinson. 2009. "Equifinality of formal (DREAM) and informal (GLUE) Bayesian approaches in hydrologic modeling?" *Stochastic Environ. Res. Risk Assess.* 23 (7): 1011–1026.

Walker, W. E., P. Harremoes, J. Rotmans, J. P. van der Sluijs, M. B. van Asselt, P. Janssen, and M. P. Krayer von Krauss. 2003. "Defining uncertainty a conceptual basis for uncertainty management in model-based decision support." *Integr. Assess.* 4 (1): 5–17.

Wiener, N. 1938. "The homogeneous chaos." *Am. J. Math.* 60 (4): 897–936.

Wirtschaftsuniversität Wien. 2021. Bayesian Tools - General-Purpose MCMC and SMC Samplers and Tools for Bayesian Statistics. Institute for Statistics and Mathematics. (https://cran.r-project.org/web/packages/BayesianTools/vignettes/BayesianTools.html)

WSDE (Washington State Department of Ecology). 2007. *Walla Walla River Basin pH and dissolved oxygen total maximum daily load.* Lacey, WA: WSDE.

Yang, J., P. Reichert, K. C. Abbaspour, J. Xia, and H. Yang. 2008. "Comparing uncertainty analysis techniques for a SWAT application to the Chaohe Basin in China." *J. Hydrol.* 358 (1–2): 1–23.

Yen, B. C., S. T. Cheng, and C. S. Melchin. 1986. "First-order reliability analysis." In *Stochastic and risk analysis in hydraulic engineering*, edited by B. C. Yen, 1–36. Highlands Ranch, CO: Water Resources Publications.

Zhang, H. X., and S. L. Yu. 2004. "Applying the first-order error analysis in determining the margin of safety for total maximum daily load computations." *J. Environ. Eng.* 130 (6): 664–673.

Zheng, Y., and F. Han. 2016. "Markov chain Monte Carlo (MCMC) uncertainty analysis for watershed water quality modeling and management." *Stochastic Environ. Res. Risk Assess.* 30 (1): 293–308.

Zheng, Y., and A. A. Keller. 2007. "Uncertainty assessment in watershed-scale water quality modeling and management: 2. Management objectives constrained analysis of uncertainty (MOCAU)." *Water Resour. Res.* 43: W08408.

Zheng, Y., and A. A. Keller. 2008. "Stochastic watershed water quality simulation for TMDL development—A case study in the Newport Bay Watershed." *J. Am. Water Resour. Assoc.* 44 (6): 1397–1410.

Zheng, Y., W. Wang, F. Han, and J. Ping. 2011. "Uncertainty assessment for watershed water quality modeling: A probabilistic collocation method based approach." *Adv. Water Resour.* 34 (7): 887–898.

CHAPTER 10

USEPA TOTAL MAXIMUM DAILY LOAD REPORT ARCHIVE AND REPORT SEARCH TOOL

Nigel W.T. Quinn, Saurav Kumar, Rosanna J. La Plante

10.1 INTRODUCTION

The methodology followed for the development of total maximum daily loads (TMDLs) requires the estimation of allowable pollutant loads that can be discharged to a waterbody without violating water quality objectives at a designated compliance monitoring site. Estimation of salt loading accounts for historical point- and nonpoint-source discharges to the waterbody and requires the application of conservative constraints such as the selection of a design flow representative of flow water year type and an appropriate factor of safety. For some watersheds or drainage basins that do not have a dominant point or nonpoint source, the typical TMDL development protocol can lead to recommendations that have a high level of uncertainty. The application of the standard TMDL design criteria that guide model selection can also lead to a suboptimal selection of model. For example, in the western United States, the selection of a design flow equal to the 10% low-flow hydrology in a watershed can be very restrictive, given the greater range of flows from low to high encountered in arid western basins. Having ready access to prior TMDL case studies and reports can be helpful, especially if conducted in watersheds that share characteristics with the watershed being analyzed. It, therefore, follows that having a TMDL report screening tool makes it easier to review TMDLs developed for the same pollutant but for watersheds that might have different hydrology or water chemistry characteristics. These characteristics can also include different flow regimes, water quality conditions, and types of water quality impairment. Most TMDLs have unique characteristics, and standard analytical methodologies may need to be modified or adapted to meet local needs.

Understanding the characteristics of each watershed is crucial in selecting the right model or analytical tool for the development of a TMDL. The selection of the appropriate TMDL model also depends on factors such as the methods for data collection, availability of a model integration framework, availability of data for calibration and model validation, and the scheme or selection of an appropriate MOS for TMDL implementation.

The US Environmental Protection Agency (USEPA) developed the online system, described previously, known as the Assessment and Total Maximum Daily Load Tracking and Implementation System (ATTAINS), for assessing the information about the conditions in the nation's surface waters. (USEPA 2021). The ATTAINS web portal is an invaluable resource of information on TMDL reports and documented impairments impacting US waters. However, ATTAINS has a limitation in that it does not explicitly provide information about the modeling tool(s) used for TMDL development.

Published TMDL reports can be found in USEPA's ATTAINS that archives relevant information for the development of new TMDLs. In addition to tracking the evolution of TMDLS developed in the United States, these reports can facilitate a better understanding of the background data, model(s), and impairment(s) that are needed to implement a credible TMDL. The fundamental challenge is to develop effective and efficient techiques to query, summarize, and disseminate the essential relevant information from these documents.

The large number of TMDL documents (more than 70,000 at the time of completing this Manual of Practice) and the lack of a consistent organization of the background data and model selection process in the reports detract from the benefits of these reports to the analysts responsible for TMDL initiation and development. These TMDL reports are not required to conform to a predefined format, sometimes making it difficult to access essential information. This lack of coherence has constrained efforts on automation of the data acquisition process and the formulation of TMDL model inputs that might be possible with a more structured approach to TMDL report organization. Nevertheless, recent advances in machine learning technology can offer some solutions to these limitations. Natural language processing and other artificial intelligence algorithms can be introduced into the TMDL model selection workflow to create a decision support system (DSS) for accessing essential information from these TMDL reports. Such a DSS can be designed for a high level of transparency that provides a schema for planners and consultants to support typical choices/ assumptions made during the TMDL development process.

The USEPA ATTAINS repository is an independent database repository for all TMDL documents. Hence, mining the text contained in the archived TMDL reports in this repository for specific terms or utilizing the frequency count of a particular term – both factors can be used to assess the relevance and potential utility of each report accessed. The TMDL Report Selection (TRS) tool is a web-based software tool developed to summarize statistics on key TMDL elements derived from TMDL reports published during 1975 to 2017 (ASCE 2017, Quinn et al. 2019). Information related to the use of the TRS tool for a specific TMDL model is provided in this chapter as well as practical examples of searches that were performed and the results obtained. The examples also provide statistics from the TMDL report repository for the period 1975 to 2017 that include the number of reports for the following purposes: (1) reports published in each of the 55 states; (2) reports published during each of the years 1975 to 2017; (3) reports that use any of the selected analytical procedures including simple models, watershed models, and receiving water quality models; (4) reports that address each of the listed impairments; and (5) reports that use each of the selected analytical procedures or models addressing all selected impairments (Quinn et al. 2019, ASCE 2017).

10.2 ACCESSING THE TOTAL MAXIMUM DAILY LOAD DATABASE AND USE OF THE TOTAL MAXIMUM DAILY LOAD REPORT SELECTION TOOL

It is standard practice that all TMDL documents be submitted to USEPA for review and approval/disapproval. If instances where USEPA does not fully approve a TMDL, the agency has authority to develop what it considers to be an "acceptable TMDL." The end result of the TMDL submittal process to USEPA is a repository of all TMDL documents that describe how the TMDL was initiated and developed and that provides guidance for implementation. The document usually includes information related to data collection, the modeling approach and model selection, the development of innovative pollutant management strategies, and stakeholder involvement. The document, typically, also includes guidance for dealing with data and model uncertainty that are important for the estimation of a Margin of Safety assessment for the analysis performed. As of 2018, 71,397 TMDL documents that addressed 75,075 instances of impairment had been incorporated in the USEPA ATTAINS database. This information has proved to be useful to managers and practitioners whose role has been to plan, scientifically defend, and oversee implementation of the proposed TMDL.

10.2.1 USEPA ATTAINS Database

In the current instance, the ATTAINS repository of TMDL reports was used to generate a database of models and other information relevant to TMDL development (TMDL-DB). The records retrieved from the ATTAINS repository included information such as links to the report, document type, impairment category, USEPA Region, and lead state. The TMDL-DB was populated using about 27,068 unique TMDLs (identified by unique TMDL ID) from the ATTAINS repository that represented 76,127 TMDLs developed from 1975 to 2017 (Figure 10-1). Descriptions of models and other pertinent information were accessed from the TMDL reports in the ATTAINS repository with text searches based on *regular expressions* that were able to recognize variations in the names of the models. For example, the well-known watershed models HSPF and LSPC were recognized as the same model in the query, and LDC was associated with load–duration curve and flow–duration curve. Other combinations were similarly attributed to the same modeling technique (Kumar 2017). In addition, the text searching procedure (Figure 10-2) listed the frequency of mention for certain models, the modeling techniques utilized, and other terms associated with TMDL model development and contained in the ATTAINS database. Such queries allow the TMDL analyst to perform an initial screening of suitable models.

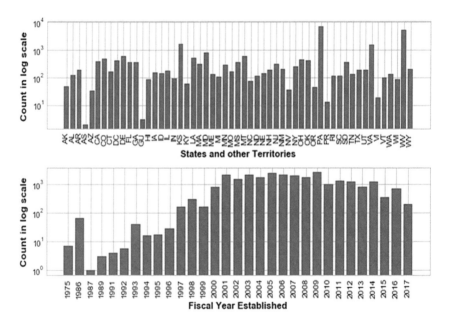

Figure 10-1. Completion date and geographical distribution within the United States of the TMDL reports in the ATTAINS database produced in output from the TRS tool.
Source: Kumar (2017), Quinn et al. (2019).

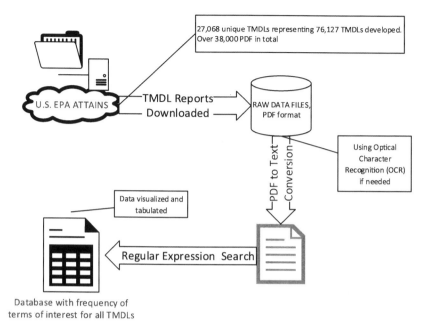

Figure 10-2. Schematic of steps necessary to acquire data from the ATTAINS database for analysis using the TRS tool.
Source: Kumar (2017), Quinn et al. (2019).

10.2.2 Features of the Total Maximum Daily Load Report Selection Tool

The TRS tool (version 1.2) (Kumar 2017) was developed, initially, as a decision-support tool to explore and identify relations between water quality impairments and currently available modeling techniques in the USEPA ATTAINS TMDL database. The tool guides users in the selection of those TMDL reports that have potential to be used as case studies based on documented water quality impairments, modeling techniques, and other characteristics of interest (e.g., the use of remote sensing) through a visual representation of the known associations among the water quality parameters of interest. These associations are based on the number of reports that contain these descriptors. The results may not always yield relevant TMDL project examples for the TMDL under development. In addition, the ATTAINS repository, used to develop these associations, is not comprehensive and does not include all published TMDL reports. Therefore, there is some uncertainty associated with the quantitative assessment of the prevalence of a modeling technique and/or impairment leading the TRS reporting tool to exhibit some bias.

The relationships among impairments, watershed models, receiving water models, and other terms associated with TMDL models are displayed in two interactive visualizations—the chord graph and the matrix graph. When using the chord graph, a connection is established on the circle between any two terms, regardless of categories, when a TMDL report is identified that contains both these terms. For example, if a TMDL report is identified that contains the impairment descriptors "Nutrients" and "Sediment" and models "CE-Qual-W2" and "HSPF," connections are established among all possible binary pairs of the descriptors. Each report marked for attribution to an impairment is based on the original data record contained in the ATTAINS database. A user-configurable "critical-frequency" marks each report that uses a specific modeling technique. In cases where the TMDL report has been identified by the text search algorithm to have used a particular named modeling technique equal to or more than some chosen "critical-frequency" number, the report is validated as having used the particular modeling technique.

10.2.3 Total Maximum Daily Load Report Summary Statistics using the TMDL Report Selection Tool

The number of model citations that can be identified using the TRS tool is summarized in a frequency plot (Figure 10-3). The plot shows that the tool produces good consistency in the number of references to archived TMDL model reports in the ATTAINS database. Most model applications cited showing a frequency count of between 100 and 1,000 on the logarithmic scale of the ordinate axis. Simple models, mass balance models, and spreadsheet models also have high counts with a frequency count in the 500 to 5,000 range. The TRS tool can be used to provide a summary plot of the frequency count for pollutant descriptors that include toxic constituents, nutrients, pesticides, sediment, and nuisance biota (Figure 10-4) with similar success and consistency. The reports with the highest frequency count producing the bulk of the citations were for mercury and pathogens with frequency count being in the 50 to 500 range. Figure 10-5 shows the TRS tool output of the citation frequency for eight constituents and the high-frequency count for mercury and pesticides.

Figure 10-5 shows the frequency count for specific models used for TMDL analyses contained in the ATTAINS TMDL report database. The "inconclusive" label was provided when assessing TMDL reports where it was not clear if a model was used to perform the TMDL analysis. This number is surprisingly high, suggesting that more consistency is needed in describing the use of models in TMDL reports. The number may also reflect the prevalence of other modeling techniques not captured in the text search algorithm.

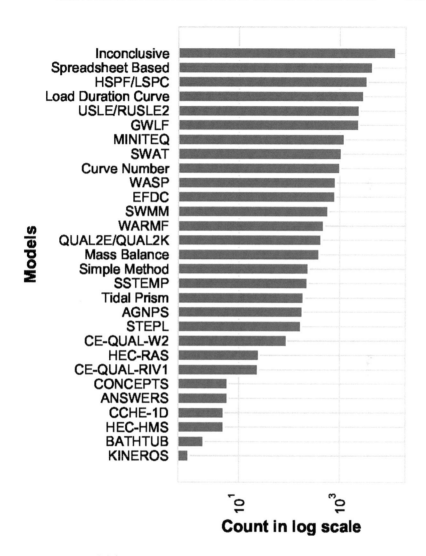

Figure 10-3. Model frequency statistics in output produced by the TRS tool. Source: Kumar (2017), Quinn et al. (2019).

10.2.4 Total Maximum Daily Load Model Development Workflow using the TMDL Report Selection Tool

A typical TMDL model development workflow for use of the TMDL Report Selection Tool (TRS version 1.2) is shown in Figure 10-6. To use the tool, the analyst initially selects the "critical frequency" by moving the graphic slider contained in the TRS Tool user interface. This slider selects the criterion by which TMDL reports are classified with respect to the

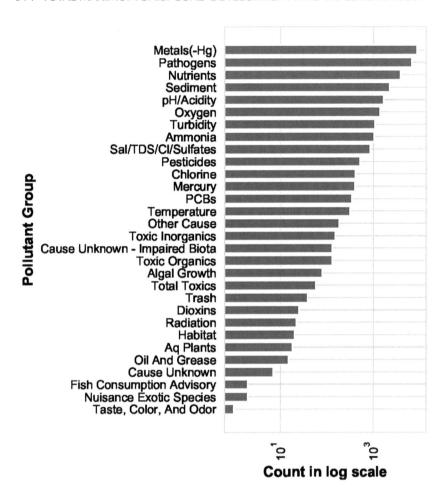

Figure 10-4. Frequency counts for commonly cited constituents that appear in the text of the TMDL reports contained in the ATTAINS repository.
Source: Kumar (2017), Quinn et al. (2019).

frequency count of each parameter name that can be found in one or more TMDL reports that mention the development of models. For example, if 30 is the value selected on the slider, then the same model name (and its derivatives or alternates) needs to occur a minimum of 30 times in the report text, if that report is to appear in the output as being used for that TMDL. As the slider is moved further to the right to a higher number, fewer reports appear in the output and in the report table. The slider does not have an impact on the labeling of the watershed impairment. Impairment labels that are included in the ATTAINS database metadata were assumed to be appropriately classified. Selecting any of the entries

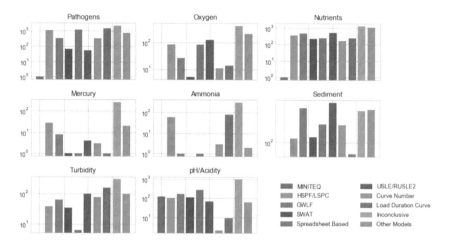

Figure 10-5. TRS tool output that shows the frequency count of models are cited in TMDL reports for the eight constituents listed. These constituents include oxygen (deficit), nutrients, sediment, mercury, ammonia, turbidity, pathogens, and pH/acidity. The category "inconclusive" was previously described as referring to those TMDL reports where uncertainty about the modeling approach followed (Kumar 2017).
Source: Kumar (2017), Quinn et al. (2019).

that are displayed on the circumference of the wheel invokes a chord graphing utility that connects the constituents of major concern with other reported constituents. This visualization tool also shows connections to the set of models that are associated with the same constituents described in the TMDL reports located on the ATTAINS database. Clicking at any time on the "remove filters" button clears the search filters. The TRS Tool produces a data connections matrix that appears below the selection wheel and which uses gray tone shading to show the relative strength of the relationship between any two table entries on both the ordinate and the abscissa axes of the matrix. Where there are multiple instances of correspondence of the entries in the search criterion from the TMDL reports selected, these appear in the matrix in darker tones. A black entry in the matrix would indicate significant correspondence.

10.3 STATE-OF-THE-ART AND STATE-OF-THE-PRACTICE

Previously published TMDL reports should be a starting point for the development of a new TMDL not only because these reports can save time and effort by informing the practitioner of a workable prior approach but also because they infer a deeper understanding of the relationships among

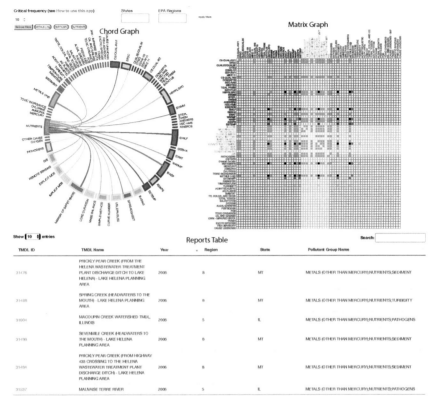

Figure 10-6. The TRS tool user interface shows the chord graphing tool that, when invoked, allows the user to explore connections and relationships between constituents of concern, associated constituents and TMDL reports that contain references to these constituents of concern. The number of reports can be screened by increasing the frequency count requirement in the dialog box, which can save the user time by selecting those reports with the most usage that likely corresponds to the report focus. More than one constituent can be selected with the filter (e.g., mercury and sediment) that will provide a greater number of links in the chord graph.
Source: Kumar (2017), Quinn et al. (2019).

the data, the model selected, and the TMDL load reduction scenarios developed to address impairments. The USEPA ATTAINS TMDL report repository is a valuable asset that has been underutilized owing to the lack of software tools to readily access the data and information contained in prior TMDL reports. The TRS tool is a state-of-the-art tool that promotes a greater use of information describing the state of the practice. Widespread adoption of such a tool would most likely require policy support at the agency level but could lead to longer-term improvements in the future cost-effectiveness and efficiency of TMDL modeling efforts. Use of the TRS tool ought to be an early step in the TMDL model development workflow.

The number of reports can be screened by increasing the frequency count requirement, which can save the user time by selecting those reports with the most usage that likely corresponds to the report focus. More than one constituent can be selected with the filter (e.g., mercury and sediment) (Quinn et al. 2019).

REFERENCES

ASCE. 2017. *Total maximum daily load analysis and modeling: Assessment of the practice*. Reston, VA: ASCE.

Kumar, S. 2017. "TMDL report selection tool (TRS)." Accessed December 2018. https://occviz.com/tmdl/.

Quinn, N. W. T., S. Kumar, R. LaPlante, and F. Cubas. 2019. "Tool for searching USEPA's TMDL reports repository to analyze TMDL modeling state-of-the-practice." *J. Hydrol. Eng.* 24(9): 04019026.

USEPA (US Environmental Protection Agency). 2008. "Integrated modeling for integrated environmental decision making." Washington, DC: USEPA.

USEPA. 2021. ATTAINS. Accessed November 13, 2021. https://www.epa.gov/waterdata/attains.

CHAPTER 11

MODEL SELECTION AND APPLICATIONS FOR TOTAL MAXIMUM DAILY LOAD DEVELOPMENT

Vamsi K. Sridharan, Steven C. McCutcheon, Nigel W. T. Quinn, Harry X. Zhang, Saurav Kumar, Ebrahim Ahmadisharaf, Xing Fang, Andrew Parker

11.1 INTRODUCTION

This chapter presents an approach to model selection for total maximum daily load (TMDL) determination, allocation, and implementation planning to attain water quality standards in impaired waterbodies. The determination of a TMDL is the numerical quantification of the total allowable load or waste assimilative capacity of the receiving waterbody (Chapter 1). Total allowable point and nonpoint-source loads are allocated in order to achieve the TMDL goal and water quality standard (Chapters 1 and 12). Implementation planning quantitatively describes how load reductions for both point and nonpoint sources or are to be achieved to meet the numeric or narrative water quality criteria of the impaired waterbody (Chapter 12).

In each of the steps in the TMDL analysis, models play an essential role. Models are vital in (1) determining or developing a TMDL, (2) allocating load reductions for each pollutant source, (3) setting or revising National Pollution Discharge Elimination System (NDPES) permits issued by the USEPA or by states that have been authorized by the USEPA to issue such permits, (4) planning implementation of the TMDL, (5) evaluating whether and how state and other water quality criteria can be achieved, and (6) checking whether federal, state, and other jurisdictional antidegradation requirements are in compliance.

The choice of an appropriate TMDL model or method depends on the pollutant causing the impairment, the spatial and temporal distribution of the loading, the hydrologic, hydrodynamic, and water quality processes that must be simulated, the degree of reliability with which those processes must be represented, and the scientific basis and capabilities of the available models. Apart from these technical considerations, there are also practical considerations such as modeling and data collection skill and experience needed, funding and equipment, and time available that influences model or method choice. All these factors are considered in developing the TMDL model selection protocol presented in this chapter.

Models available for TMDL analysis are discussed in Chapters 2 to 5. Chapter 2 presents watershed models that simulate hydrologic and pollutant fate and transport processes over land areas or catchments and through the stream/sewer conveyance networks. Cope et al. (2020) have shown that comprehensive hydrologic and water quality models, such as HSPF (Chapter 2), have the capability to incorporate the results of receiving water quality models such as WASP, CE-QUAL-W2, and QUAL2K (Chapter 3). Chapter 3 presents receiving water quality models that simulate hydrodynamic and water quality processes within a waterbody. These models are required to analyze water quality or pollutant assimilations in receiving waterbodies, such as lakes and estuaries, that are outside but hydrologically connected to a watershed. In general, TMDL development involves the integration of a watershed model to predict pollutant loads within the watershed and a receiving water quality model to analyze pollutant assimilation in the waterbody. Chapter 4 presents integrated modeling systems and linked models that are needed to represent complex natural systems such as watersheds discharging into lakes or estuaries, as such a system cannot be represented by a single model. Chapter 5 presents alternatives to numerical models, such as simple models and methods for TMDL development. Simple models and methods are typically derived from simple analytical approaches or empirical relationships between the physiographic characteristics of the watershed and pollutant exports, and are often used for load estimates and receiving waterbody analysis when data limitations and budget and time constraints preclude using more detailed models. Chapter 6 discusses critical conditions for streamflow and pollutant loadings and appropriate methods or models to fit such conditions, a consideration of which is required by the USEPA TMDL program.

Sridharan et al. (2021) defined the scientific basis for a structured holistic model selection process by expanding on concepts in Martin and McCutcheon (1999) and based on discussions in the TMDL Analysis and Modeling Task Committee deliberations (ASCE 2017, Borah et al. 2019b). A subgroup of the Task Committee, the authors of this chapter, developed a TMDL model selection protocol that is presented in this chapter. Section 11.2 lists types of models used to develop TMDLs. Section 11.3 presents a holistic approach and a protocol to select practical and dependable models for TMDL development and implementation. In this protocol, rigorous hypothesis testing of the selected model is emphasized, particularly if the model has not already been rigorously peer reviewed. The holistic protocol covers various aspects of model application, from conceptualization and stakeholder collaboration to implementation planning and outreach. These considerations are translated into technical and practical selection criteria and synoptic data requirements. Model evaluation, calibration, validation, and uncertainty estimation are model application steps that influence the selection of the model, and these are described in Sections 11.3 to 11.5. Section 11.5 includes the modeling tasks necessary to support TMDL determination, allocation, and implementation planning. Due diligence on these tasks ensure that the selected TMDL model is appropriate and likely to be approved by the USEPA. Other federal, state, and local agencies and stakeholders have roles in applying best management practices and other controls and oversee the collection of synoptic data for the calibration, validation, and determination of model reliability. The current TMDL modeling practice and potential future developments are presented in Sections 11.6 and 11.7. Finally, a TMDL implementation planning case study is presented in the Appendix.

The protocol presented in this chapter is intended to serve as a minimum standard in selecting and applying models for TMDL development and implementation. As TMDL model performance improves over time, so too would the criteria for their application require regular updating (e.g., WERF 2003, USEPA 2005).

11.2 TYPES OF MODELS AND METHODS FOR TOTAL MAXIMUM DAILY LOAD DETERMINATION

The various models and methods used to develop TMDLs and determine load allocations and reductions for meeting water quality standards were presented in Chapters 2 to 5. These models can be categorized as follows:

1. Watershed models (Chapter 2) that simulate rainfall, runoff, groundwater recharge, erosion, the fate and transport of pollutants flushed by the runoff and adsorbed with sediments, and the transport of water, sediments, and pollutants from the watershed to the receiving waterbody. These models are important for linking the violations of water quality standards in receiving waterbodies to nonpoint-source pollutant loads that may significantly attenuate within the watershed before entering the receiving waterbody. These models are particularly useful when a receiving water quality model (Chapter 3) cannot distinguish all substantial classes of manageable nonpoint sources.

2. Receiving water quality and hydrodynamic models (Chapter 3) that are based on numerical solutions of the governing equations of conservations of mass and momentum of water, heat, and pollutants,

albeit simplified by a range of assumptions. These models are necessary to simulate waste assimilation and determine the assimilative capacity of the impaired waterbody and distinguish all substantial tributary loads, including point- and nonpoint-source loads that do not significantly attenuate within the watershed before entering the receiving waterbody.

3. Integrated models (Chapter 4) link two or more models that simulate water and air transport, water quality, watershed processes, and ecosystem processes. These integrated frameworks typically include geographic information systems and other software used to link models and retrieve and manage large amounts of information. Integrated frameworks are required for TMDL determination, allocation, and implementation planning if

   (a) The domain of a prospective receiving water quality model cannot be discretized to distinguish the impacts of each substantial point-source load, all background loads, and each manageable class of nonpoint-source loads (McCutcheon 1989). When all substantial loads cannot be specified as discrete boundary conditions of the receiving water model, then, watershed, groundwater, or air transport models should be linked to the receiving water model to distinguish all substantial, manageable loads.

   (b) Hydrodynamic or hydraulic models should be linked to water quality models to simulate mixing and transport in large, complex waterbodies or a series of multiple impaired waterbodies and any unimpaired waters that transport pollutants and contribute to the waste assimilative capacity, which include sequentially linked streams, lakes, estuaries, and other coastal waters.

   (c) Best management practices need to be simulated for implementation planning.

4. Simple methods and models (Chapter 5) that include (a) analytical solutions of the governing equations of conservation of momentum, heat, water, and pollutant mass based on a range of simplifying assumptions (Martin and McCutcheon 1999). These methods are usually applied as a spreadsheet and involve simplified mass balances (McCutcheon 1989), loading methods based on mass balances, and load-duration analyses and other uses of the flux equation (i.e., the simple method; Schueler 1987), and (b) empirical statistical methods, which may not have a process basis. Such models also have limited forecasting capability.

Models vary in their level of complexity and sophistication. Model complexity is chiefly defined heuristically by how many water quality processes or empirical relationships between loads and impairments should be reliably simulated. Martin and McCutcheon (1999) show how complexity is defined typically by the number of (1) dimensions and spatial scales used to discretize the model domain, (2) state variables that should be simulated, (3) the number of model coefficients and parameters that must be specified, and (4) the range of time scales that should be simulated.

Model sophistication is the degree of development defined by reliable process integrity of the underlying physical, chemical, or biological processes being simulated. A mature model, which has been carefully thought out, with a well-defined scientific basis, and has undergone stringent peer review and evaluation to optimize practicality will, by definition, be able to represent the process that it was intended to represent with higher integrity.

11.3 MODEL SELECTION FOR TOTAL MAXIMUM DAILY LOAD DETERMINATION, ALLOCATION AND IMPLENTATION PLANNING USING A HOLISTIC APPROACH

Model selection is a key precursor to TMDL determination; however, there is limited guidance on how appropriate models should be selected to achieve water quality management program objectives (NRC 2001, Borah et al. 2019a). An overview of the major considerations for a holistic approach to model selection for TMDL determination, allocation, and implementation planning is presented in this section. The general protocol and information flows are outlined in the TMDL modeling flowchart (Figure 11-1). Elements of the model selection approach are further explained in the subsequent sections: (1) fundamental model selection principles, (2) technical and practical considerations, and (3) stakeholder and expert engagement.

A state, territory, approved tribe, or EPA-required TMDL analysis starts with the most recent biennial priority listing of an impaired waterbody (the topmost input in Figure 11-1) (USEPA 2018). The state agency should determine a TMDL according to the priority ranking of the impaired waterbody on the list of the state's impaired waterbodies (USEPA 2018).

Once the characteristics of the impaired waterbody and the pollutant are compiled (information compilation and Process Flow 1 in Figure 11-1), the critical conditions should be identified, during which the impairment is expected to frequently exceed the water quality standards and that must be simulated reliably by the model (Zhang and Padmanabhan 2019, Camacho et al. 2019). The data requirements and synoptic data collection needed to simulate the water quality during critical conditions should also be identified. These considerations, along with other optional water quality

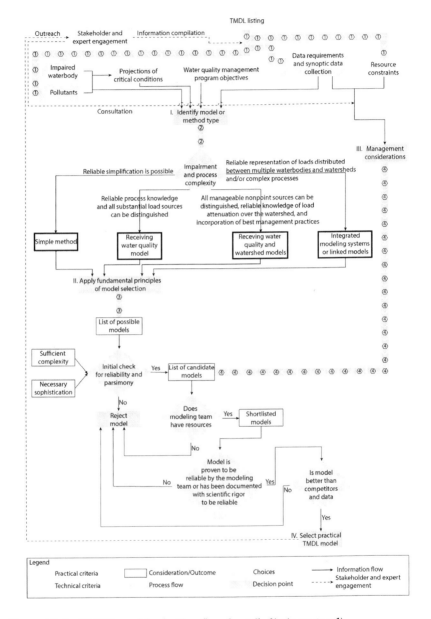

Figure 11-1. TMDL model selection flowchart (holistic protocol).
Source: Adapted from Sridharan et al. (2021).

management objectives, dictate the type of TMDL model or method needed (Decision Point I, Process Flow 2 and first choice, Impairment, and process complexity, in Figure 11-1). When the required synoptic data needed to represent the relationship between loads and impairment are not available, the model selection process should go together with developing and implementing a synoptic data collection program (Figure 11-1).

Figure 11-1 categorizes types of models in the selection protocol (bold boxes). Within a group of similar models, the most parsimonious and sophisticated model should be selected for a specific TMDL. Parsimonious models have only as many model parameters as necessary to provide the minimum process integrity to reliably define the cause-and-effect relationship between loads and impairments (Thomann and Mueller 1987, Thomann 1992). In a sophisticated model, parameters are easily calibrated using a well-designed synoptic data collection program. Typically, sophisticated, well-developed models will have been successfully calibrated for many impaired waters (Martin and McCutcheon 1999).

The TMDL model or method selection then begins by the identification of a tentative list of candidate models or methods (Decision Point II and Process Flow 3 in Figure 11-1) that have sufficient complexity and necessary sophistication. Process Flow 3 then requires the modeling team to identify the list of candidate models that they have experience with (second choice, initial check for reliability and parsimony, in Figure 11-1). Experience can help flatten the learning curve required to master different receiving water quality and watershed models. In addition, most states have preferred TMDL models of known credibility that the state agency has experience in interpreting. The modeling team may also often be required to use a model that the state or third-party contractor has experience with. Until this point, model selection is based exclusively on technical model selection criteria.

At this point, the workflow process in Figure 11-1 requires the consideration of practical constraints (Decision Point III in Figure 11-1) such as constraints on available resources, including funding and time available and resources to collect synoptic data for calibration-validation of the model. The implementing agency will evaluate its in-house modeling resources and may decide to request the USEPA to collaborate in determining the TMDL. The third selection made in Figure 11-1 provides a shortlist of likely reliable TMDL models for which resource limitations can be accounted for to see if expertise/experience, time available, and funding could be expended or the TMDL development reprioritized until the necessary resources are available. Subsequently, the set of shortlisted models is evaluated. Questions that should be asked are as follows: (1) can the model be shown to be reliable by the modeling team or has the model been documented with scientific rigor to be reliable, (2) is the selected model better than its competitors, and (3) are there adequate synoptic data and data collection resources needed for the intended application?

Thus, the flowchart in Figure 11-1 provides a useful and rational protocol to select the most parsimonious, practical model available (Decision Point IV in Figure 11-1). Most of the choices and the final decision in Figure 11-1 can be applied iteratively in more complex applications where multiple iterations through the flow chart may be required.

Model selection is a site-specific tradeoff among reliability, complexity, and sophistication. The following, competing principles could guide the selection of TMDL models:

- Models and methods should provide defensible and parsimonious cause-and-effect relationships between all substantial pollutant loads and violations of the water quality standards.
- Only models that have undergone reliable calibration and validation should be used.
- The most parsimonious model should be selected and applied. At the same time, an oversimplified model should not be used in a quest to reduce the number of calibration parameters. Similarly, a complex but unsophisticated model, which requires too many parameter specifications that cannot be reliably measured or calibrated with synoptic data should not be used.
- The expertise of the modeling team that interprets the simulations is a vital consideration (McCutcheon 1983).
- State-of-the-art codes with excessively large data requirements and a large number of calibration parameters may perform poorly for reasons that are not readily apparent. Models that incorporate current scientific understanding of process integrity through empirical relationships or statistical regressions based on adequate synoptic data collection are likely to be more useful in circumstances when more sophisticated models fail to produce satisfactory results.
- Multiple models should be evaluated in the model selection protocol (Figure 11-1) so that the choice of the TMDL model is both defensible and credible. There may be cases when it might not be possible to simulate the water quality processes associated with the pollutant reliably, such as in the case of emerging contaminants flushed with diatomaceous sediments. This might be owing to a lack of data or a lack of understanding of the underlying process itself. In such cases, it is vital to correctly represent the hydrology and hydrodynamics to improve the reliability in estimating impairment, as it is the flow of water carries the pollutant.

11.3.1 Fundamental Model Selection Principles

The fundamental principles of model or method selection are reliability and parsimony. A reliable calibrated model is scientifically defensible based on sophisticated and parsimoniously represented process integrity, or for simple regression methods, based on extensive synoptic data collection. In practice, the reliability of each calibrated TMDL model or method should be explicitly determined by hypothesis testing (defined subsequently). However, in recent decades, our understanding of underlying physical, chemical, and biological processes has sufficiently advanced so that many mature models will likely satisfy these fundamental principles. When considering models for which rigorous documentation includes sufficient proof that a model is reliable and parsimonious, such as in the case of hydrologic models simulating rainfall, runoff, flow routing, soil erosion, sediment transport, and fate and transport of pollutants with runoff and pollutants adsorbed onto sediments (e.g., models reviewed in Borah and Bera 2003; Borah et al. 2019a, b), these fundamental requirements may be accepted as having been satisfied. However, there are still circumstances when it will be necessary to apply these principles. These situations can include emergent contaminants, complex coupled processes such as habitat degradation and bioaccumulation and amplification in aquatic food webs, and contaminants such as trash for which well-understood physical processes have not yet been incorporated into process-based models. Even when applying the fundamental model selection principles for these types of pollutants, some of the physical processes driving loading, such as the dynamics of runoff, erosion, sedimentation, and atmospheric deposition, are typically well represented in contemporary numerical models. One should not have to retest those components of TMDL models that simulate well-understood processes reliably for these fundamental criteria but rather shift focus to the water quality aspects of the model corresponding to the processes that are poorly understood.

This manual of practice recommends that reliability be quantified for each TMDL determination, allocation, and implementation plan by hypothesis testing (Schueler 1987, McCutcheon et al. 1990, Tedela et al. 2012). Hypothesis testing either performed by the modeling team or reported in the scientific reviews of a model allows the modeling team to be confident that the applied model reliably simulates the synoptic observations of water quality.

To decide if a TMDL model calibration or validation is reliable by hypothesis testing, the null hypothesis must be rejected. The null hypothesis is that the mean of the residuals (differences between observations and simulations) is significantly different from zero (a definable simulation bias exists) with a probability of error in making this decision that is typically selected as 0.05. The alternate hypothesis is that the mean of the residuals is not significantly different from zero (Chapter 8). If the probability that the model residuals are different from zero is less than or equal to 5%, that is, it is not just random chance that the model can simulate the water quality, then the null hypothesis can be rejected and the alternative accepted.

Bayesian hypothesis testing may be useful for nonparametric residual testing, where a very large number of residuals between simulation results and observed data are generated and a distribution of residual means is obtained by sampling subsets of these residuals with replacement. If 95% of all the residuals include zero, then the null hypothesis can be rejected. This approach has several advantages over the conventional two-tailed test. First, if the model parameters and initial and boundary conditions are fully represented in the replicate simulations, then we can be fairly confident that the mean residual is representative of the true population of residuals. Second, this approach is distribution free a priori. The distribution of residuals is empirically determined from the replicate simulations.

However, practical considerations limit the use of the Bayesian approach. Often, there may be too many parameters in the model so that it may be impractical to perform simulations ranging over the entire range of parameter values and initial and boundary conditions. Also, the modeling team's computing restrictions may limit the number of simulations that can be performed within a reasonable amount of time. For these reasons, hypothesis testing depends on both the complexity of the model and resource limitations.

11.3.2 Technical and Practical Considerations in Model Selection

Several technical and practical considerations affect the TMDL model selection process (Figure 11-1). Technical considerations include the characteristics of the impaired waterbody and the pollutants causing impairment, including the point and nonpoint-source loads. Practical considerations include data availability and resource constraints.

A primary consideration in selecting the modeling approach to determine a TMDL is the pollutant(s) that will be managed by the load allocation process (USEPA 2005) (Figure 11-1). All point-source and all manageable nonpoint-source loads should be identified (USEPA 2006). The selected model should reliably explain cause-and-effect relationship between the loads and the impairment. Sometimes, multiple pollutants may interact to produce complicated impairment scenarios. In some cases, the pollutants can be addressed in separate simulations. However, often the impairment may involve interdependent processes within the same waterbody or watershed. In such cases, either a suite of linked models or a complex model capable of representing multiple phenomena may be required. For example, in the Sacramento–San Joaquin Delta in California, a TMDL was implemented to improve oxygenation conditions in a 32 km (20 mi) long deep-water shipping channel for endangered migrating salmon. This required a significant reduction in algal loading from the contributing watersheds. Algae in the shallow river system settled in the deeper, wider ship channel turning to periphyton (a biological material attached to submerged surfaces) and exerted an oxygen demand. However, a policy to reduce agricultural return flows to the lower San Joaquin River to reduce nutrients that stimulated riverine algae growth caused an increase in river salinity at a salinity TMDL compliance monitoring station just above the river interface with the tidal estuary. In this instance, control actions that were best suited to cost-effectively address one TMDL made it more difficult to achieve numeric water quality criterion. The WARMF model (Herr and Chen 2012) (Chapter 2) was chosen to study the effects of management actions on both salinity and algal growth in both the river and estuary. The model applied a simplified one-dimensional hydrologic routing approach in the river that was sequentially linked to a one-dimensional hydrodynamic and salt transport model for the Delta. A cascade of models was, thus, necessary to address the complexity of the system and simulate the fate and transport of more than one pollutant responsible for impairment.

The characteristics of the impaired waterbody for which the TMDL is developed are an important consideration in selecting the model (Figure 11-1). When only point-source loads are present or when all manageable nonpoint sources can be reliably accounted for, a TMDL may be determined for a single stream segment. When there are nonpoint sources that attenuate within the watershed before reaching the impaired waterbody, then the entire basin, including tributary watersheds, may be included in the TMDL determination. The type of watershed and distribution of loads is also an important consideration in model selection. For example, estuarine and lacustrine waters receive pollutant loads from both upstream and downstream sources. In some cases, such as in the Willamette River in Oregon, distributed loading may occur in the tributary watersheds (Annear et al. 2004). In Florida, as the water table is typically high in the aquifers and delayed seepage of infiltration occurs, there is significant interaction between surface flow and groundwater, and so delayed loads owing to long subsurface residences may occur (Borah et al. 2019a). Hydraulic best management practices implemented within the watershed also impact the terrestrial attenuation of loads and should be a consideration in model selection. In all these cases, the relationship of the impaired waterbody with other waterbodies and watersheds should be considered.

A combination of the characteristics of the pollutant and the waterbody will determine the critical conditions that must be simulated. Critical conditions can include the lowest 7-day average flow at a return period of 10 years (7Q10), or the highest water temperature during the summer months or other combinations (see Chapter 6). Critical conditions should be heuristically projected before or during model selection. Otherwise, the selection protocol will go through many needless iterations. A reliable projection of critical conditions may result in static or pseudo dynamic models being selected for TMDL determination. If the projection of critical conditions is not possible or highly uncertain, a dynamic model should be selected. For instance, if the goal is to understand and mitigate eutrophication in a small pond or lake associated with seasonal stratification and overturning dynamics, then a vertical 1D model like BATHTUB (Walker 2006) (Chapter 5) may be appropriate. However, in a narrow, deep lake or reservoir, a 2D model such as CE-QUAL-W2 (Cole and Wells 2018) (Chapter 3) might be needed. If the lake bathymetry has significant spatial variability, a 3D model such as the environmental fluid dynamics code (EFDC) (Hamrick and Wu 1997, Tetra Tech 2002, Zou et al. 2006) (Chapter 3) should be considered.

The determination of the TMDL should also optionally address the jurisdictional water quality management program objectives along with the legally required objectives. The optional goals of a water quality management plan typically are based on stakeholder consensus and other public policies. In multijurisdictional TMDL determinations such as those for the Chesapeake Bay, the San Francisco Bay–Delta estuary, and the Colorado River basin, the jurisdictional policies and stakeholder goals vary across county, state, or even international boundaries.

Particularly, riparian water rights are an important consideration in cross-county or interstate TMDLs. For example, Oregon ranchers in the John Day River basin expressed widespread concern about riparian water rights being affected by the recommendations in the temperature TMDL implementation by the Oregon Department of Environmental Quality (ODEQ 2010a). The agricultural landowners in ten rural counties across which the impairments were listed were concerned that proposed flow restoration should have only been voluntary (ODEQ 2010b), and that Oregon water rights were not taken into account in the load-reduction allocation and implementation planning (ODEQ 2010b). The ODEQ selection of an exceptional stream temperature model developed in-house and supported by long-term synoptic data collection in the John Day River basin allowed the department to demonstrate that the stakeholder concerns during two public comment periods (ODEQ 2010b) would be satisfactorily addressed. Other optional state water quality goals not required by the Clean Water Act and USEPA regulations include long-term systematic climate change, land-use and land-cover shifts, and changing demographic and socioeconomic patterns. In the case of the John Day River basin temperature TMDL, several valid stakeholder concerns about the long-term effects of climate change on changing water temperature could not be addressed in the TMDL development (ODEQ 2010b). These complex considerations can take time and effort to resolve and need to be considered in the TMDL allocation and implementation planning.

There can also be cases of determining, allocating, and implementing TMDLs for shared waters across international boundaries, such as the case of PCBs in Lake Ontario (LimnoTech 2011). In this case, allocations were included for the Canadian portion of the watershed and activities were being conducted to address the pollution in Canada. Without a true partnership with our neighbors, there is presumably little to no assurance that reductions will be integrated into permits or other regulatory frameworks.

Climate impacts, land-use and land-cover changes, as well as population and demographic variability, all create an uncertainty in the hydrologic, water-use, and environmental landscape of a region (Hoyer and Chang 2014). In coastal regions, the threat of sea-level rise should also be considered. A successful TMDL implementation will require modeling flexibility and should incorporate projections of uncertainty for these potential stressors as well as provide an analysis of synoptic data collection and potential management actions to address and minimize these uncertainties (Herron 2017). When the environmental conditions change significantly, or the watershed characteristics change because of urbanization and associated stormwater management practices, for example, then, a model selected in an earlier TMDL determination, allocation, and implementation may no longer be applicable. In such cases, the TMDL model choice should be periodically updated and the TMDL should be revisited as applicable.

Synoptic data collection is often overlooked in model or method selection. Synoptic data are required to determine model or method reliability by hypothesis testing as well as for calibration and validation of the model. Monitoring data are collected for many purposes and are almost never adequate for water quality and watershed model calibration (Martin et al. 1991). One means of accommodating resource limitations in synoptic data collection is to use a phased TMDL (EPA 2006). In this approach, first synoptic data collection is undertaken to resolve the key physical, chemical, and biological processes associated with loading and impairment, and a simple method such as a load–duration curve can be used to reliably allocate nonpoint-source load reductions. In such an approach, a model suitable for the data currently available may be applied, with every effort expended to collect the required synoptic data. When new data become available, the allocation and implementation planning should be further refined. The final phase should use the collected synoptic data for calibration and validation and also use the calibrated model(s) to allocate load reductions and implementation. In practice, the implementing agency may identify a specific model during the procurement process for contracting the TMDL determination, allocation, and implementation planning. In many situations though, it is up to the third-party contractor to propose a model. Ideally, a model selection document is prepared that compares the applicability of multiple models in TMDL development. Typically, a model is proposed and justified. Then, the implementing agency has the opportunity to accept the recommended approach or propose an alternative.

Apart from these technical considerations, available resources play a vital role in model selection. Although complex and sophisticated models allow for a more comprehensive and disaggregated watershed modeling, resources are not always sufficient to carry out these analyses. Advanced models might also be computationally intensive, which might be a burden for state agencies with limited computing resources if the agency is itself performing the TMDL modeling. Resources permitting, state agencies may enlist the services of third-party consultants during the procurement phase to overcome these limitations. However, even third-party contractors may have optimized a workflow for a specific model and may be unfamiliar with a different model. Similar considerations also play out in other aspects of TMDL determination. For example, if complex stochastic modeling for an explicit estimation of the MOS is called for, the resources and expertise may be unavailable to do so (Ahmadisharaf et al. 2019). Although the Clean Water Act (CWA) and USEPA regulations do not list the relevant resources such as budget, time, and analyst skills as criteria in TMDL model selection, it is nonetheless useful to consider these limitations during the model selection process (Figure 11-1).

A holistic process for TMDL model selection is iterative in nature. The best practice should promote the selection of reliable models that adequately represent the effects of pollutant loading in the watershed and the receiving waterbody. The state agency should strive to collect relevant synoptic data required to support the development, calibration, and validation of the chosen model.

11.3.3 Stakeholder and Expert Engagements

Throughout the TMDL determination, allocation, and implementation planning process, engaging with stakeholders and experts in an open and constructive manner is useful for establishing scientific defensibility and credibility of the TMDL (dashed lines in Figure 11-1). Stakeholders can include local communities, nongovernmental organizations, environmental and economic development groups, interstate organizations, and dischargers represented in industry and trade associations who all derive beneficial uses from an impaired waterbody. Experts can include environmental and industry groups and research institutions with expertise in developing and applying TMDL models.

The state agency or third-party contractor may develop data collection, modeling, and monitoring workflows with the support of stakeholders to achieve the TMDL goals. Optimal stakeholder engagement—either through the short public comment periods for a simple TMDL or through a more active engagement for more complex TMDLs—will result in a successful TMDL plan. Stakeholder engagement is an iterative process that occurs throughout the model selection workflow as well (Figure 11-1). Such an engagement includes the following:

- Information compilation: Early engagement with the local community, watershed stakeholders, and regulatory agencies could aid in identifying a problem.
- Scientific consultation: While developing the TMDL plan, scientific and management experts could be consulted to determine the modeling needs, physical, chemical, and biological processes that can be reliably represented, management actions being planned, and allocations and enforcements that are feasible.
- Outreach: Once the TMDL model has been determined, stakeholders should be engaged by explaining the rationale behind the modeling choices. In some cases, third-party reviews may be sponsored by the stakeholders. Stakeholders or their consultants may also scrutinize the model and TMDL plan to evaluate the potential impacts of the allocation and implementation plans on the local community.

Early stakeholder involvement and active engagement in the TMDL process ensures that a wide variety of opinions are considered in the analysis of pollutant control and management options. Experts have domain expertise and are aware of watershed characteristics and implementation constraints (e.g., feasibility of pollutant-reduction strategies). Experts' domain knowledge also covers the physical characteristics of the watershed and the management practices that are currently being implemented, as well as those that have already been tried in the past. Leveraging local knowledge is, therefore, useful in TMDL determination, allocation, and implementation planning.

Watersheds are becoming increasingly complex at the urban–rural interface, with water quality problems becoming more complex with emerging contaminants for which numeric water quality criteria are still not well-established. Best management practices for distributed nonpoint-source loadings from agricultural and animal husbandry activities and residential waste management systems such as septic tanks should be designed with active stakeholder engagement for long-term success. In the case of emerging contaminants such as personal care products and endocrine disruptors, public education and outreach and nonstructural best management practices such as public policy initiatives will be crucial in managing these contaminants. Thus, public participation will become increasingly essential. The success of best management practices for these types of watershed load attenuation efforts depends on participatory stakeholder engagement.

In rare instances, stakeholder involvement is mandatory. For example, in California, the "Little Hoover" Commission (LHC 2009), an independent state oversight agency created in 1962, mandated that all environmental regulatory actions such as TMDLs must involve stakeholder participation through one or more public comment periods. Often, stakeholder engagement is an optional practice. When stakeholder engagement is more participatory in nature, the modeling team can benefit from insights that can pare down unviable load-reduction allocations. Ideally, complex interjurisdictional TMDLs, TMDLs for emerging contaminants, and active participatory engagement with stakeholders can be very beneficial to the modeling team. A recent salinity TMDL being implemented in the San Joaquin River basin of California is led by a stakeholder group called CVSALTS (Quinn 2020). In such cases, actively engaging with stakeholders can also ensure community buy-in and potentially reduce costly and time-consuming litigations that are detrimental to a water quality management program.

11.4 MODEL EVALUATION, CALIBRATION–VALIDATION, AND UNCERTAINTY ESTIMATION

Sound model selection requires at least a qualitative assessment of the prima facie credibility of available models, followed by progressively more in-depth evaluations until a practical TMDL model is selected, as shown in Figure 11-1. The fundamental principles of model selection and other considerations require an evaluation of several sources of information. The primary source to support these choices is the model documentation. Other sources include any model peer reviews, peer-reviewed papers on model development and applications, reports on applications and TMDL documents approved by the USEPA (Chapter 1), among others. Some of these sources provide governing equations and other relationships that relate loading to impairments, other information on process integrity and forecasting capability, data requirements, and any statistical analysis of simulations at other sites that may confer limited credibility. Other sources provide information on ease of use, required expertise, and other resources that typically require management support.

Once a model has been selected, the modeling team should also try to evaluate its performance. As TMDLs become increasingly more common for emerging contaminants for which the underlying science is less mature and where numeric water quality criteria have not yet been established, TMDL model review will also help test the claims of its developers and to objectively prepare the model for legal and expert scrutiny (Moriasi et al. 2012).

A typical review comprises an evaluation of the processes represented in the model, its calibration, validation, and sensitivity and uncertainty analyses, and its application. Model meta-evaluation and review of various alternatives for model selection and application occurs at three levels: (a) the modeling team evaluates the credibility and defensibility; (b) there is an external confirmation of the model selection commissioned by the state or stakeholder contractors; and (c) after the model selection and application, the USEPA approval process for the TMDL document evaluates the model applied (USEPA 2002) (see Chapter 1).

- Evaluation by the modeling team: The modeling team evaluates the potential credibility *prima fascia* of candidate models and methods from published peer reviews and TMDL or other water quality management applications (Figure 11-1). This type of "meta-analysis" could review past model applications for similar impairments. Examples of meta-analyses that may be useful for model selection include Borah and Bera (2003, 2004) and Moriasi et al. (2007, 2012, 2015).

  Once a model has been selected, the selected model should be reviewed by the model development team. This can most often be performed by directly comparing the *model* results with some benchmarks. This can take the form of a simplified set of test cases for which there is a degree of confidence in the results. These test cases include a set of analytical solutions and benchmark synoptic observations (McCutcheon 1983), each of which tests a particular aspect of the model. For instance, an appropriate test of the hydrological, sediment erosion, and water quality components of a TMDL model could include tests of unit hydrograph routing, erosion or deposition rates under constant flow conditions, and the hydrodynamic responses of simplified hydrologic systems. This comparison allows the modeling team to gain an understanding of what the model is doing and what its capabilities and limitations are. Chapter 8 provides a table to qualitatively convert relative goodness-of-fit statistics into indications of anticipated model reliability for similar waterbodies. This type of evaluation scales with the complexity of the model selected and the TMDL.

- Evaluation by external experts: Occasionally, complex TMDL determination, allocation, and implementation planning may benefit from independent analyses of model selection. These expert engagements can be conducted in at least two ways. For example, the effort to establish the Chesapeake Bay TMDLs initially convened a series of workshops circa 1990 that invited most of the expert water quality modelers from the United States and developed lists of hydrodynamic, water quality, and watershed models anticipated to be useful for the Bay, large tributaries, and the watershed. Most states in the 1990s and 2000s developed lists of applicable models and confirmed model selection by telephone consultation with experts from the USEPA Center for Exposure Assessment Modeling (CEAM),

US Army Corps of Engineers (USACE), and a few other agencies. Currently, consultation on a model selection may be possible through ad hoc model development communities. Finally, the USEPA, states, and a few stakeholders may hire independent experts to confirm a model selection by meta-analysis.

- Evaluation of the final TMDL document by the USEPA: The USEPA (2002) evaluates a submitted TMDL document based on the following 11 criteria: (1) identification of waterbody and pollutants, (2) water quality standards, (3) loading capacity, (4) load allocations, (5) waste load allocations, (6) margin of safety, (7) seasonal variation, (8) reasonable assurances that proposed that nonpoint-source load reductions will be met, (9) monitoring plan, (10) implementation planning, and (11) public participation (USEPA 2002, 2005) (Chapter 1). The United States Government Accountability Office (USGAO 2013) found Criteria 8, 9, and 10 to be vague or optional (USGAO 2013). In the absence of strict evaluation requirements, and different standards applied in different regions of the country, the best practice is to use defensible TMDL models that can reliably simulate the water quality using cause-and-effect relationships. This will allow a reliable evaluation of load-reduction allocations and implementation planning scenarios so that states can provide reasonable assurances of nonpoint-source reductions.

The modeling team must specify either in the water quality management document or in separate reports the following with appropriate documentation (Chapra 2003; Moriasi et al. 2012, 2015) to facilitate well-documented model support as well as high-quality model review:

- Physical processes that are being simulated by the model and the process integrity. This includes the sensitivity to state variables, parameters, and initial and boundary conditions.
- Range of spatial and temporal scales and resolution of the TMDL model, and the numerical schemes and approximations applied.
- Simulation uncertainty for specific waterbodies.
- Stage of model development and the level of user support.
- Availability of auxiliary software to manage large amounts of information.
- Additional documentation about the scientific defensibility of the model.

11.4.1 Performance Evaluation

Chapter 8 provides a review of model calibration and validation (for a summary, see Section 11.4.3) to universally determine calibrated simulation reliability that is comparable among different waterbodies. This section highlights how model selection should consider model calibration and validation after the selection.

Model evaluation is used to determine if the calibrated water quality simulations, compared with synoptic observations, are reliable. This can typically be achieved by hypothesis testing or by comparing the simulated water quality to the observed synoptic data. If the simulations are unreliable, the modeling team has two options: either select another model and retest for reliability or revise the model to achieve better process integrity and retest for reliability. If neither option results in reliable simulations, the modeling team should perform further evaluation and testing of the models. If none of the alternatives are satisfactory, the modeling team many consider using the average of all observations to forecast water quality. Use of the average of all observations is paramount to concluding that loading cannot be scientifically linked to the violations of the water quality standards. If one of the evaluated models or methods represents water quality better than the calculated average of all data, the modeling team may be able to use such simulations to start a phased TMDL determination.

Model performance evaluation is also useful while calibrating a model to optimize the model parameters for the specific watershed or waterbody. Finally, performance evaluation using a variety of measures is useful for qualitatively and quantitatively assessing the reliability of the model once the calibration and validation are complete. Documenting model reliability also provides the USEPA scientific evidence when it is apparent that the agency should collaborate with the state to develop a reliable new model or redevelop an existing model, especially for emerging contaminants and difficult-to-analyze pollutants like fecal coliform bacteria.

11.4.1.1 Performance Evaluation during Model Selection. If model selection (Figure 11-1) and calibration fail to provide a reliable model, then the Nash–Sutcliffe efficiency (NSE) or Model Skill Score (MSS) is useful to determine if the best unreliable simulation is better than the average of all the observations. These performance measures are specifically well-suited to evaluate how well a model is performing relative to not having a model at all.

The dimensionless Nash–Sutcliffe efficiency is (Moriasi et al. 2007)

$$\text{NSE} = 1 - \frac{\sum_{i=1}^{N}(O_i - P_i)^2}{\sum_{i=1}^{N}(O_i - \bar{O})^2} \qquad (11\text{-}1)$$

where O_i and P_i are the observed and simulated water quality parameter values for N samples at a given location, and $\bar{O}$ is the mean of the observations. The NSE represents how well a simulation represents variation in the observations compared with the mean of the observations. If the simulation could perfectly represent the variability in the observations, NSE $= 1$. A value of NSE $= 0$ proves that the simulation is no better than the mean of all observations in simulating the variability in the observations. A negative NSE establishes that the simulation is worse than the mean of the observations at simulating the observed variability.

The dimensionless MSS is (Willmott 1981)

$$MSS = 1 - \frac{\sum_{i=1}^{N}(O_i - P_i)^2}{\sum_{i=1}^{N}\left(|P_i - \bar{O}| + |O_i - \bar{O}|\right)^2} \tag{11-2}$$

The MSS quantifies how much of the potential error between a simulation and the observation (the denominator) is explained by the simulation (the numerator). If the model could perfectly simulate the variability in the observations, all the variability would be because of fate and transport processes, and MSS $= 1$. A value of zero establishes that the model accounts for all of the variability between the simulation and the observations. A negative MSS proves that the simulation is more in error than the mean of the observations. MSS, therefore, quantifies how well a model performs in relation to measurement precision.

Critically, NSE, MSS, and all other relative goodness-of-fit statistics listed in Chapter 8 are only comparable at a specific spatial location. Comparing these statistics across spatially inhomogeneous hydrologic and water quality regimes is incorrect and inconsistent. It is also not possible to draw any quantitative conclusions across inhomogeneous regimes. Hypothesis testing is comparable across spatially inhomogeneous hydrologic and water quality regimes and across inhomogeneous regimes because these comparisons are based on a universal normal distribution when there are a large number of observations (typically, $N \geq 30$) or the Student t distribution when there are a small number of observations (typically, $N < 30$) or a nonparametric empirical distribution of model errors in the case of Bayesian hypothesis testing.

11.4.1.2 Performance Evaluation during Model Calibration and Validation. The best scientific practice in model calibration is to create the analytical likelihood from the synoptic data. Then, given a particular set of model parameters that need to be determined, find the values of the parameters that maximize this likelihood. When the errors in the data are distributed normally, the sum of squared errors is exactly the analytical logarithm of the likelihood. However, in most practical applications, most parameters errors are not distributed normally. Also, the interaction of multiple parameters and submodels all with different distributions of errors renders specification of the analytical likelihood function impractical. For more than 30 years, water quality and watershed modelers have heuristically experimented with numerous, relative, goodness-of-fit statistics. These simple statistics have in effect been crude surrogates for the likelihood function. Several of the goodness-of-fit statistics listed in Chapter 8 have been applied as surrogates for the likelihood function. More recently, with the advent of significant computing resources, Bayesian methods have been used to produce a very large number of simulations and empirically construct the likelihood surface from the synoptic data.

11.4.2 General Purpose Performance Measures for Qualitative Assessment

Model performance is typically evaluated in a formal review using measures (Table 8-4) such as statistical tools and other evaluation criteria (Tables 8-5 to 8-9) that provide well-understood metrics of model performance (Moriasi et al. 2015). A critical aspect of model review is the use of proper performance measures with the appropriate evaluation criteria. A TMDL model may be evaluated at a single point or at multiple points within a waterbody. Sometimes, model results are regressed with the data to infer patterns in the model performance. Regressions between the model results and the data only quantify the relative covariance between the simulations and the observations and do not capture systematic temporal differences between the model and the data. These measures assume a linear relationship between the two datasets. This problem is exacerbated when the time resolution of the data and the *model* is very fine, that is, on the order of minutes to hours. Therefore, when dealing with fine-resolution models, it is always a good practice to first estimate the lag between the model results and the observations by performing an autocorrelation analysis and subsequently comparing the lagged model results with the observations (e.g., MacWilliams et al. 2015, Sridharan et al. 2018). Statistical and graphical performance measures can be employed to visualize model performance at a single point. For multiple locations, both statistical and graphical performance measures can be customized to provide a more holistic qualitative picture of model performance (e.g., Moriasi et al. 2007, Jolliff et al. 2009, Ganju et al. 2016, Sridharan et al. 2018). In addition, maps of the available data and model results may be combined in visual displays to help assess model performance (Moriasi et al. 2012). However, it is critical to calibrate and validate models using likelihood functions that have sound theoretical basis or statistical performance measures that have been shown to reasonably mimic the likelihood function (Chapter 8). Graphical performance measures should serve as tools to visualize model results and not as evaluation metrics. A "looks as good as the data" attitude is never "good enough for government work."

Thorough evaluations, including recommended performance measures and acceptable evaluation criteria for commonly used TMDL models are listed in Benham et al. (2006), Borah and Bera (2003, 2004), Moriasi et al. (2012, 2015), and Chapra (2003). Many of these performance measures are also presented in Section 8.5 of this Manual in the context of goodness-of-fit measures to evaluate model performance during the calibration process.

11.4.3 Model Calibration, Validation, and Sensitivity Analysis

This section provides a concise overview of TMDL model calibration, validation and sensitivity analyses to define technical criteria that must be considered in model selection. The objective of model calibration and validation is to establish a reliable cause-and-effect relationship between measured or estimated pollutant loads and the resulting water quality impairments. Calibration should use reliable synoptic data to iteratively select a set of model parameters for a specific receiving water quality model and any auxiliary watershed model that simulates cause-and-effect relationships. Validation requires a separate synoptic data set that is independent of the data used for calibration to confirm the reliability of the calibrated simulations.

New automated calibration methods are now available with the advent of readily accessible high-performance computing resources. This has allowed more complex and sophisticated models to be calibrated in a quantitative manner by evaluating model performance over different parameter values. The calibration methods can handle large datasets (Eberhart and Shi 2001, Plummer 2003) regardless of the number of model parameters. They can be adapted to deterministic models that produce identical results each time they are run with a specific set of parameter values (Doherty 2007) as well as stochastic models whose results vary over multiple instances even with the same set of parameter values (Dancik et al. 2010). More recently, calibration workflows such as the model-independent Parameter Estimation Uncertainty Analysis (PEST) (Doherty 2007) and hierarchical Bayesian modeling have either been integrated directly into model packages or code wrappers are available in which multiple model instances can be run during a calibration workflow.

Critical to model selection, this manual of practice strongly recommends that all model and method calibration and validation (or confirmation) be hypothesis-tested to establish simulation and forecasting reliability (Schueler 1987, McCutcheon et al. 1990, Thomann and Mueller 1987, Tedela et al. 2012). Alternately, the modeling team should choose such models that have been demonstrated rigorously to simulate reliably the cause-and-effect relationships between loading and impairment.

For model selection, the extensive heuristic site-specific estimates of the relative goodness of fit remains useful for determining the credibility of model applications to different impaired waters. Chapter 8 lists the more frequently used relative goodness-of-fit statistics and provided qualitative ranges to heuristically estimate past application credibility.

A sensitivity analysis identifies the dominant physical, chemical, and biological process parameters, model parameters such as the grid size and time-marching scheme, and system inputs such as different loads, variability in the flow, and management actions that contribute to the desired model output. If the model is identified as not being sensitive to certain parameter settings, then these can be set to suitable values from the literature or by exercising the modeling team's best professional judgment. Parameters that are identified as strongly influencing the model can then be adjusted during calibration with more care.

11.4.4 Model Uncertainty Estimation

Uncertainty estimation quantifies the epistemic and random variability owing to algorithmic approximations, ambiguity, nonuniqueness in parameterization, and measurement error in water quality, hydrodynamics, hydrology, meteorology, and loading and other boundary conditions. Uncertainty estimation is useful for determining the MOS (mathematically defined in Equation (1-1) (See more details in Chapter 9). The MOS is incorporated either implicitly or explicitly in TMDL computations. The implicit heuristic guesses, reliance on the belief that model calculations may be conservative, or dependence on safety factors incorporated into water quality standards and the probabilistic determination of violations are difficult to scientifically reproduce. Explicit margins of safety that can be estimated using probabilistic methods as a function of risk of violating water quality standards are scientifically repeatable. Either an implicit or explicit MOS must be incorporated into the model selection process. When nonpoint-source loads are expected to increase over time, a reserve capacity for load increases in the future may be included in the MOS (USEPA 2018). Incorporating rigorous model uncertainty analysis in TMDL development will improve an implementing agency's ability to make decisions in a robust and defensible manner, thereby supporting effective water quality management.

11.5 MODELING TO DETERMINE, ALLOCATE, AND IMPLEMENT TOTAL MAXIMUM DAILY LOAD

Once the model selection has been completed, the TMDL is determined by simulating the water quality under a variety of environmental conditions, particularly during the critical conditions, and estimating the degree to which the impairment exceeds the numerical water quality criteria. If possible, the critical conditions should be projected by modeling the water quality under extreme flow and loading conditions and synoptic data should be collected under such circumstances. This will help in the successful calibration of the model and is more defensible than merely extrapolating water quality simulations to critical conditions.

The second step is to determine the necessary load-reduction allocations from the reliably enumerated point sources and quantified manageable nonpoint sources. These allocations should be driven by the pollutant load reductions that are needed to attain the numeric water quality criteria rather than on the basis of whether there is regulatory authority to manage the loads. In addition, many states do not have effective regulations to manage NPS pollution (Craig and Roberts 2015). Grant funding from the USDA's Natural Resources Conservation Service (NRCS) and USEPA Section 319 is typically used to manage NPS loads to meet TMDL goals for pollutant load reduction. It is important to consider whether the proposed reductions are technically feasible. For example, if the watershed has several wastewater treatment plants, it will likely have some combination (scenarios) of waste load allocations.

The third step is to run the calibrated model(s) under critical conditions with the proposed load-reduction scenarios to forecast the water quality. For point source dominated TMDLs, these should include a "worst-case scenarios" in which all point sources are at their peak loads, for example, municipal wastewater treatment plants have the maximum allowable permitted effluent limits and are operating at their maximum design capacities. After performing the necessary runs, the model results are analyzed to ascertain whether the numeric water quality criteria are exceeded in each proposed scenario. One or more proposed feasible reduction plan(s) may be deemed likely to meet the waste assimilation target. If more than one plan can satisfy the water quality objectives, typically the most cost-effective plan is identified as the preferable scenario in the TMDL study through a stakeholder engagement process. In some cases, none of the proposed scenarios may result in compliance with the water quality objectives or standards. In these cases, the model ought to be run under the natural condition of the watershed to test whether the water quality criterion is exceeded. The natural condition of the watershed is a hypothetical condition in which there are no point sources and land use is one hundred percent forest. If the natural condition results are in exceedance, then the water quality objective is not realistic, unless exceptions to compliance are accepted. Under such circumstances, the USEPA allows the narrative water quality standards of the state to apply (USEPA 2015).

The planning of TMDL scenario simulations for allocations of load reductions is typically an iterative process that the state agency or third-party contractor working on TMDL development uses to assess alternate load-reduction combinations. By engaging with stakeholders, the fairest and most efficient allocations among the various scenarios considered to achieve water quality standards for an impaired waterbody can be achieved. The USEPA provides various supporting documents online for TMDL studies (USEPA 2019a). Examples of case studies for different water quality constituents (bacteria, dissolved oxygen, nutrients, temperature, aluminum, mercury, and turbidity) are provided online by USEPA.

11.6 FUTURE INNOVATION IN TOTAL MAXIMUM DAILY LOAD MODELING

Broader access to denser and more real-time monitoring owing to the availability of reduced cost in-situ sensors will improve our understanding of key physical chemical and biological processes, as well as shed light on the fate and transport dynamics of emerging contaminants. In addition, remote sensing information can provide a rich spatially detailed input to models. These trends in increasing data coverage will lead to new innovations in model development that could include fundamental changes in how watersheds are represented, how hydrology is predicted, and ultimately how models are applied.

Over the past two decades, the majority of TMDL modeling advances have ranged from development of the first GIS-based modeling framework, BASINS (Lahlou et al. 1996) (Chapter 4), to updates and improvements to previously developed models such as SWMM, WASP, HSPF, and EFDC (Chapters 2 and 3). Several of these advances coincided with the surge of TMDLs developed following a series of lawsuits initiated in the 1990s. An exhaustive list of TMDLs approved by the USEPA may be obtained through the Assessment, Total Maximum Daily Load (TMDL) Tracking and Implementation System (ATTAINS) database hosted by the USEPA (USEPA 2020a). The USEPA CEAM continues to distribute models and software focused on quantifying contaminants in waterbodies, including new developments (USEPA 2020b). The USEPA also convenes a Water Quality Modeling Workgroup to support the application of core surface water quality modeling tools aimed at CWA programs. The Workgroup has recently identified models that are frequently used for TMDL and related applications, with the focus being to address gaps and identify future activities. The selected models were developed by a range of entities and, in general, have a track record of being regularly updated. Ten models included in the Workgroup's list are also included in the summary of the commonly used models reported by the TMDL Report Selection (TRS) tool in this MOP (Chapter 10). These models are AGNPS, BATHTUB, CE-QUAL-W2, EFDC, HSPF/LSPC, QUAL2Kw, SWAT, SWMM, WARMF, and WASP (Chapters 2, 3, and 5).

Most of these models have had releases in the last several years, and their advances are indicative of TMDL model advancement trends in general. Recent updates to the models noted here fall into three general categories: (1) usability improvement and visualization upgrades, (2) corrections and code updates, and (3) technical advances. The most common improvements to models have focused on their usability (USDA-NRCS 2019). These updates range from enhancing output options (e.g., WASP, CE-QUAL-W2, WAMF, and AGNPS) to developing GIS user-friendly interfaces for pre- and post-processing (e.g., EFDC, SWAT). In some cases, models have been completely restructured or recoded to facilitate integration of new scientific modules (SWAT and WARMF) (Texas A&M University 2019) or to increase flexibility for multicore processing and interfacing with modern technology (HSP^2 version of HSPF) (RESPEC 2019). For example, the WARMF model has been adapted to accept and link to real-time data in California for TMDL-related forecasting applications. Another common update to these models has been correcting technical issues that developers have been alerted to by the user community. These have been addressed largely by making changes to the model source code and offering updates on model-specific websites.

Technologically, watershed models have focused on ease of use, code modernization, and inclusion of technical advances. The underlying structure of these models and the numeric algorithms are still relatively simple to ensure stability of model results, robustness, and alignment to calibration and validation data sources. Typical simplifying assumptions include computational grids that are structured and spatial discretization methods and temporal advancement algorithms that avoid the formation of fronts and propagation of instabilities within the model domain. Sediment transport models are typically empirical (e.g., RUSLE2 in Chapter 5, GWLF in Chapter 2) or have robust representations of more complex underlying physical processes (e.g., DWSM, KINEROS, and GSSHA in Chapter 2).

Watershed model extensions have been developed to address specific alternatives in implementation planning that have been challenging to industry practitioners. For example, to reflect the recent emphasis on green solutions, SWMM now includes a representation of specific green practices (USEPA 2019b) in the RUNOFF module simulating catchment processes. Although existing tools, such as SUSTAIN (Shoemaker et al. 2009; Chapter 5), are available and well-suited for local-scale best management practice analyses, SWMM has incorporated green practices into a broader watershed modeling framework, albeit limited to catchment scales, to facilitate gray–green hydrology analyses. Recognizing the changing climate and its significant impact on planning at all levels of government and beyond, SWMM has also been updated to simulate future climate change projections more readily (USEPA 2019b). HSPF and its accompanying tools have also been advanced to explicitly consider climate impacts (RESPEC 2019).

Receiving water quality model advances have, in general, focused on adding algorithms to expand the scope of modeling capabilities or improve existing capabilities. For example, WASP (Chapter 3) now includes an organic chemical/nano chemical and solids/nanosolids model (USEPA 2017). CE-QUAL-W2 (Chapter 3) now includes particle tracking algorithms and a built-in sediment diagenesis model. QUAL2KW now simulates unsteady, nonuniform flow in addition to steady flow. Improvement in simulation capabilities for CE-QUAL-W2 include new ice formation/melting routines and wetting and drying of model cells. USACE's HEC-RAS hydrology and hydraulics model (Chapter 3) has been updated to include water quality elements (USACE 2016). The addition of this capability may substantially increase its application in the TMDL field. The WARMF model now includes new modules that support managed seasonal wetland hydrology and the fill and drawdown cycle typical of these catchments. The model is also being used to simulate methylmercury export from wetlands. A manager module was developed specifically for stakeholders and regulators who do not have the time to develop an in-depth knowledge of the model and whose use of the model requires the manipulation of a few key coefficients and substitution of a small range of parameter values. Such advances focused on user-friendliness make more complex models accessible to a larger number of state agencies, but they bear the inherent risk of misapplication by less-experienced users.

User experience improvements will promote a wider application of models and further integration with modern computing technology. Model developers will continue to improve pre- and post-processing interfaces to simplify the modeling process and increase exposure to practitioners. Models will also access the cloud for increased computing power and storage. As noted in the instance of the WARMF model, there is an interest in automating the updating of models both for ongoing real-time water quality management and for water quality forecasting (Herr and Chen 2012). Although quality assurance protocols are still evolving, this innovation has the potential to eliminate some of the start-up and data development steps and associated costs in future TMDL development. These models can also be used in diverse applications such as river basin emergency response. Having a continuously updated flow model can provide long-term benefits for multiple future TMDL development and update endeavors.

Advances in technology and data gathering may address some of the key historical modeling limitations. One area that could benefit from more dense data monitoring and increased computational speed is the simulation of groundwater–surface water interactions, which has long been a challenge for modelers. Simulation of these interactions is critical in watersheds with a shallow groundwater table like Florida. Very few models used in TMDL development efforts allow for a detailed simulation of the underlying groundwater system. USACE has made investments in complex grid-based models that link surface and groundwater, such as GSSHA (USACE 2019) (Chapter 2). The computational intensity and spatial detail required by grid-based models and their pairing with coarser resolution meteorological inputs historically limited their full potential. As GSSHA advances, it may prove useful for TMDL studies in areas driven by shallow groundwater interaction. CE-QUAL-W2 developers have also indicated that future versions will include the simulation of groundwater–surface water interactions. Other technical areas may include more advanced simulation of ecological interactions and a focus on combined impacts (such as resilience to disasters and systemic shifts, in addition to water quality). Aside from deterministic models, there may also be an increase in the use of stochastic models, particularly for biological indicator analysis and related TMDLs or nutrient criteria development. Also, new models will most certainly enter the TMDL field and join the stalwart TMDL models that have been historically applied and improved.

As noted in Chapter 2, Fu et al. (2020) synthesized the present status of watershed water quality modeling, which is used in TMDL analysis, and outlined future research and potential improvements in the representation of freshwater systems pertaining to water quality, including a representation of environmental interfaces, in-stream water quality and process interactions, soil health and land management, and (peri-) urban areas. According to these researchers, the current challenges are quality control of monitoring data, model parameterization and calibration, uncertainty management, scale mismatches, and provisioning of modeling tools. To overcome these challenges, Fu et al. (2020) recommended building stronger collaborations between experimentalists and modelers, bridging gaps between modelers and stakeholders, and cultivating and applying procedural knowledge to better govern and support water quality modeling processes within organizations.

11.7 STATE-OF-THE-ART AND STATE-OF-THE-PRACTICE

The state-of-the-practice in TMDL model selection and TMDL determination, allocation, and implementation planning currently is focused on representing as many processes as required through complex integrated modeling systems. Pollutant loads are typically simulated using either user-friendly spreadsheet tools or watershed models. Receiving water quality processes are simulated using either simple mass balance approaches or steady state or dynamic 1D numerical models. In the case of pathogens, the most common approach over the last 5 years has been to use load–duration curves. For emerging contaminants, heavy metals, and TMDLs determined to meet nonnumeric water quality standards such as habitat restoration or species richness, typically statistical models are being used. In rare instances when surface- or aerial process–based fate and transport models have already been developed, these are used to quantify nonpoint-source loading for the receiving water quality models and methods. In very rare cases, sophisticated 2D and 3D hydrodynamic models are used in lake and estuarine settings. Stakeholder engagement is typically restricted to public comment periods. Model selection rationale is divided between primarily attributed either to reliable process representation or to the prevailing practice. Current practices for stakeholder engagement include one or two public comment periods and responses to public comments received in those periods. In some instances, best management practices are considered in TMDL implementation planning. Ideally, nonpoint-source reduction planning should warrant significant public participation and active stakeholder engagement.

The state-of-the-art is focused on reliably representing physical, chemical, and biological processes using sophisticated numerical receiving water quality, watershed, and atmospheric deposition models (if applicable). Every effort should be expended to collect the synoptic data required to use the most sophisticated and parsimonious models, rather than restricting model usage based on the available data. For emerging contaminants that require statistical models or process-based understanding to be translated into new computer models, rigorous hypothesis testing should be undertaken. To simulate complex dynamic processes such as ecosystem health, new food web dynamics and ecosystem models are available whose application should be more extensively investigated rather than relying on descriptive water quality standards to determine TMDLs. A recent development has been the ready-access to advanced high-performance automatic calibration methods and their increasing utilization by the hydrology and water quality modeling community. These methods should be applied to TMDL models as well. Stakeholder engagement is an important aspect of water quality management, and active engagement with stakeholders through participatory modeling approaches should be encouraged. As watersheds become increasingly urbanized, with water quality problems becoming more complex with emerging contaminants for which numeric water quality criteria have still not been well established, public participation will become essential and will allow state agencies to tackle emergent water quality problems. Participatory modeling for water quality can bestow many benefits to both the state in developing carefully thought-out TMDLs and to local and regional stakeholders who will benefit from the water quality management actions, particularly in poorer and historically marginalized communities. These communities lack resources to determine, allocate, and implement a TMDL to meet water quality standards. Active engagement with these stakeholders to design innovative best management practices in conjunction with a phased TMDL approach can solve the twin problems of water quality management and social justice.

APPENDIX: TOTAL MAXIMUM DAILY LOAD IMPLEMENTATION PLANNING CASE STUDY (ALABAMA)

A case study of the chlorophyll-*a* (Chl-*a*) TMDL determination, allocation, and implementation plan for Locust Fork and Village Creek in Alabama by the Alabama Department of Environmental Management (ADEM 2020) is presented to illustrate the concepts presented in this Chapter using from a real-world TMDL. In the Locust Fork and Village Creek TMDL development, based on the NPDES-permitted effluent flow rate (Q), ADEM grouped the municipal wastewater treatment plants and industrial facilities into three classes. These were Class 1 [$Q \geq 1.0$ million gal. per day (MGD)], Class 2 (0.1 MGD $\leq Q < 1.0$ MGD), and Class 3 ($Q < 0.1$ MGD). The study watershed had 8, 7, and 18 wastewater treatment plants or industrial facilities in Classes 1, 2, and 3, respectively. In this study, 16 scenarios were simulated in which the total phosphorus was reduced (Table A-1). The first three rows in Table A-1 show the information for the calibration (2006 to 2012), natural condition, and the worst-case scenarios. For the industrial point sources, the effluent flow rates were based on the long-term average discharges (ADEM 2020). As there was no prior numeric water quality criterion for total phosphorus, the 90th percentile concentration of the monitored values from submitted discharge monitoring reports was used for the worst-case scenario (Table A-1). The 16 total phosphorus-reduction scenarios (Table A-1) specify either targeted effluent concentrations or effluent load reductions. A load-based limitation would have resulted in an allowable total phosphorus load greater than the historical average total phosphorus load from those facilities. Therefore, the load allocation limitation scenarios (Scenarios 6 to 11 and 13 in Table A-1) were not used in the final TMDL document for total phosphorus reduction.

The dissolved oxygen concentration for waters classified as beneficially useful for fish and wildlife, swimming and other whole-body water-contact sports, and public water supply should be greater than 5 mg/L in Alabama (ADEM 2008). For the Locust Fork and Village Creek nutrient TMDL determinations, the ADEM used a growing season average (April to October) Chl-*a* objective of 18 µg/L at the confluence of Locust Fork after conducting an in-depth evaluation (ADEM 2020) to achieve the dissolved oxygen standard. The last column in Table A-1 lists simulated

Table A-1. Example of Locust Fork and Village Creek (Alabama) TMDL Load-Reduction Scenarios for Total Phosphorus.

| Scenario description | Scenario type | March to October total phosphorus effluent limit | | | Urban nonpoint source | Nonpoint source | Overall GS Avg Chl-a conc. (µg/L) |
| | | Class 1 | Class 2 | Class 3 | TP load percent reduction | TP load percent reduction | (2007–2012) in µg/L |
		Effluent flowrate ≥ 1 MGD	1 MGD > effluent flowrate ≥ 0.1 MGD	Effluent flowrate < 0.1 MGD			
Calibration run		Existing (2006–2012)	Existing (2006–2012)	Existing (2006–2012)	N/A	N/A	15.3
Natural condition (NC)		No point-source dischargers	No point-source dischargers	No point-source dischargers	100% Forested land use	100% Forested land use	1.7
Worst-case scenario		DMR-TP@90th percentile	DMR-TP@90th percentile	DMR-TP@90th percentile	N/A	N/A	44.2
Reduction scenario 1	Ambient conc.	DMR-TP@90th Percentile	DMR-TP@90th percentile	DMR-TP@90th Percentile	36%	36%	44.1
Scenario 2	Ambient conc.	2 mg/L	3 mg/L	3 mg/L	36%	36%	47.2
Scenario 3	Ambient conc.	2 mg/L	2 mg/L	2 mg/L	36%	36%	47.0
Scenario 4	Ambient conc.	1 mg/L	3 mg/L	3 mg/L	36%	36%	34.6
Scenario 5	Ambient conc.	1 mg/L	2 mg/L	2 mg/L	36%	36%	34.2

(Continued)

Table A-1. (Continued)

Scenario description	Scenario type	March to October total phosphorus effluent limit			Urban nonpoint source	Nonpoint source	Overall GS Avg Chl-a conc. (µg/L)
		Class 1	Class 2	Class 3			
		Effluent flowrate ≥ 1 MGD	1 MGD > effluent flowrate ≥ 0.1 MGD	Effluent flowrate < 0.1 MGD	TP load percent reduction	TP load percent reduction	(2007–2012) in µg/L
Scenario 6	Load reduction	1 mg/L	3.79 kg/day	3.79 kg/day	36%	36%	36.0
Scenario 7	Load reduction	0.5 mg/L	3.79 kg/day	3.79kg/day	36%	36%	26.5
Scenario 8	Load reduction	0.3 mg/L	3.79 kg/day	3.79 kg/day	36%	36%	21.8
Scenario 9	Load reduction	0.2 mg/L	3.79 kg/day	3.79 kg/day	36%	36%	19.1
Scenario 10	Load reduction	0.15 mg/L	3.79 kg/day	3.79 kg/day	36%	36%	17.7
Scenario 11	Load reduction	0.10 mg/L	3.79 kg/day	3.79 kg/day	36%	36%	16.2
Scenario 12	Ambient conc.	0.3 mg/L	1 mg/L	5 mg/L	36%	36%	18.5
Scenario 13	Load reduction	0.2 mg/L	1 mg/L	3.79 kg/day	36%	36%	17.4
Scenario 14	Ambient conc.	0.25 mg/L	2 mg/L	5 mg/L	36%	36%	17.6
Scenario 15	Ambient conc.	0.25 mg/L	2 mg/L	6 mg/L	0%	0%	18.0
Scenario 16	Ambient conc.	0.25 mg/L	2 mg/L	6 mg/L	36%	36%	17.7

Source: Adapted from ADEM (2020).

Note: TP = total phosphorus; DMR = discharge monitoring report; Chl-a = chlorophyll-a; conc. = concentration; Avg = average; GS = growing season average Chl-*a* concentrations at the Locust Fork confluence during the growing season for the natural condition, worst-case scenario, and the 16 load-reduction scenarios. Of the 16 scenarios, 6 scenarios had Chl-*a* at or less than the Chl-*a* objective of 18 µg/L, which made it impossible to reduce the growing season average Chl-*a* without significantly reducing the total phosphorus load from the Class 1 facilities. Therefore, the TMDL for total phosphorus in Locust Fork and Village Creek was the monthly average total phosphorus concentration based on Scenario 16 in Table A-1 (ADEM 2020).

When none of the proposed load-reduction scenarios attained the numeric water quality criterion, the model simulations were used to evaluate the waste assimilative capacity during natural conditions. In this case, ADEM water quality criteria (Administrative Code 335-6-10) state that "the minimum dissolved oxygen concentration for waters classified as fish and wildlife, swimming and other whole-body water-contact sports, and public water supply is 5.0 mg/L, except when such levels cannot be achieved as a result of natural conditions." Under these circumstances, the TMDL pollutant allocations are expected to result in the attainment of the prescribed natural dissolved oxygen levels (ADEM 2008).

ACKNOWLEDGMENTS

Reviews, edits, and comments provided by Deva K. Borah and G. Padmanabhan in this chapter are greatly appreciated.

REFERENCES

ADEM (Alabama Department of Environmental Management). 2008. *Final total maximum daily load nutrients & OE/EDO Pepperell Branch AL03150110-0201-700 Nutrients, Sougahatchee Creek Embayment (Yates Reservoir) AL 03150110-0204-101 Nutrients & OE/DO*. Montgomery, AL: Water Quality Branch, Water Division, ADEM.

ADEM. 2020. *Final nutrient total maximum daily loads (TMDLs) for Locust Fork (Waterbody ID AL03160111-0305-102, AL03160111-0308-102, AL03160111-0404-102, AL03160111-0413-112, AL03160111-0413-101) & Village Creek (Waterbody ID AL03160111-0409-100)*. Montgomery, AL: Water Quality Branch, Water Division, ADEM.

Ahmadisharaf, E., R. A. Camacho, H. X. Zhang, M. M. Hantush, and Y. M. Mohamoud. 2019. "Calibration and validation of watershed models and advances in uncertainty analysis in TMDL studies." *J. Hydrol. Eng.* 24 (7): 03119001.

Annear, R. L., M. L. McKillip, S. J. Khan, C. Berger, and S. A. Wells. 2004. *Willamette River basin temperature TMDL model: Boundary conditions and model setup*. Tech. Rep. No. EWR-01-04. Portland, OR: Portland State University.

ASCE. 2017. *Total maximum daily load analysis and modeling: Assessment of the practice*. Prepared by TMDL Analysis and Modeling Task Committee of the Environmental and Water Resources Institute of ASCE. Reston, VA: ASCE.

Benham, B. L., C. Baffaut, R. W. Zeckoski, K. R. Mankin, Y. A. Pachepsky, A. M. Sadeghi et al. 2006. "Modeling bacteria fate and transport in watersheds to support TMDLs." *Trans. ASABE* 49 (4): 987–1002.

Borah, D. K., and M. Bera. 2003. "Watershed-scale hydrologic and nonpoint-source pollution models: Review of mathematical bases." *Trans. ASABE* 46 (6): 1553–1566.

Borah, D. K., and M. Bera. 2004. "Watershed-scale hydrologic and nonpoint-source pollution models: Review of applications." *Trans. ASABE* 47 (3): 789–803.

Borah, D. K., E. Ahmadisharaf, G. Padmanabhan, S. Imen, and Y. M. Mohamoud. 2019a. "Watershed models for development and implementation of total maximum daily loads." *J. Hydrol. Eng.* 24 (1): 03118001.

Borah, D. K., G. Padmanabhan, and S. Kumar. 2019b. "Total maximum daily load analysis and modeling: Assessment and advancement." *J. Hydrol. Eng.* 24 (11): 02019001.

Camacho, R. A., Z. Zhang, and X. Chao. 2019. "Receiving water quality models for TMDL development and implementation." *J. Hydrol. Eng.* 24 (2): 04018063.

Chapra, S. C. 2003. "Engineering water quality models and TMDLs." *J. Water Resour. Plan. Manag.* 129 (4): 247–256.

Cole, T. M., and S. A. Wells. 2018. *CE-QUAL-W2: A two-dimensional, laterally averaged, hydrodynamic and water quality model, version 4.1*. Portland, OR: Dept. of Civil and Environmental Engineering, Portland State University.

Cope, B., T. Shaikh, R. Parmar, S. Chapra, and J. Martin. 2020. *Literature review on nutrient-related rates, constants, and kinetics formulations in surface water quality modeling*. EPA/600/R-19/241. Washington, DC: USEPA.

Craig, R. K., and A. M. Roberts. 2015. "When will governments regulate nonpoint source pollution: A comparative perspective." *BC Envtl. Aff. L. Rev.* 42: 1.

Dancik, G. M., D. E. Jones, and K. S. Dorman. 2010. "Parameter estimation and sensitivity analysis in an agent-based model of *Leishmania major* infection." *J. Theor. Biol.* 262 (3): 398–412.

Doherty, J. E. 2007. *Use of PEST and some of its utilities in model calibration and predictive error variance analysis: A roadmap*. Brisbane, Queensland: Watermark Numerical Computing.

Eberhart, R. C., and Y. Shi. 2001. "Particle swarm optimization: developments, applications and resources." In Vol. 1 of *Proc., 2001 Congress on Evolutionary Computation (IEEE Cat. No. 01TH8546)*, 81–86, doi: 10.1109/CEC.2001.934362.

Fu, B., J. S. Horsburgh, A. J. Jakeman, C. Gualtieri, T. Arnold, L. Marshall, et al. 2020. "Modeling water quality in watersheds: From here to the next generation." *Water Resour. Res.* 56 (11): e2020WR027721.

Ganju, N. K., M. J. Brush, B. Rashleigh, A. L. Aretxabaleta, P. del Barrio, J. S. Grear, et al. 2016. "Progress and challenges in coupled hydrodynamic-ecological estuarine modeling." *Estuaries Coasts* 39 (2): 311–332.

Gao, P. 2008. "Understanding watershed suspended sediment transport." *Prog. Phys. Geogr.* 32 (3): 243–263.

Hamrick, J. M., and T. S. Wu. 1997. "Computational design and optimization of the EFDC/HEM3D surface water hydrodynamic and eutrophication models." In *Next generation environmental models and computational methods*, edited by G. Delich and M. F. Wheeler, 143–156. Philadelphia: Society of Industrial and Applied Mathematics.

Herr, J. W., and C. W. Chen. 2012. "WARMF: Model use, calibration, and validation." *Trans. ASABE* 55 (4): 1387–1396.

Herron, H. 2017. "Climate change and TMDLs." https://www. chesapeakebay.net/.

Hoyer, R., and H. Chang. 2014. "Assessment of freshwater ecosystem services in the Tualatin and Yamhill basins under climate change and urbanization." *Appl. Geogr.* 53: 402–416.

Jolliff, J. K., J. C. Kindle, I. Shulman, B. Penta, M. A. Friedrichs, R. Helber et al. 2009. "Summary diagrams for coupled hydrodynamic-ecosystem model skill assessment." *J. Mar. Syst.* 76 (1–2): 64–82.

Lahlou, M., L. Shoemaker, M. Paquette, J. Bo, S. Choudhury, R. Elmer et al. 1996. *Better assessment science integrating point and nonpoint sources— BASINS. Version 1.0 user's manual (823R96001)*. Washington, DC: Exposure Assessment Branch, Standards and Applied Sciences Division, Office of Science and Technology, EPA.

LHC (Little Hoover Commission). 2009. *Cleaner water: Improving performance and outcomes at the state water boards*. Sacramento, CA: LHC.

LimnoTech. 2011. "Draft TMDL support document for PCBs in Lake Ontario." https://www.dec.ny.gov/docs/water_pdf/lakeontariop cbtmdl.pdf.

MacWilliams, M. L., A. J. Bever, E. S. Gross, G. S. Ketefian, and W. J. Kimmerer. 2015. "Three-dimensional modeling of hydrodynamics and salinity in the San Francisco estuary: An evaluation of model accuracy, X2, and the low–salinity zone." *San Francisco Estuary Watershed Sci.* 13 (1): 1–37.

Martin, J. L., and S. C. McCutcheon. 1999. *Hydrodynamics and transport for water quality modeling*. Boca Raton, FL: CRC Press.

Martin, J. L., W. L. Richardson, and S. C. McCutcheon. 1991. "Modeling studies for planning: The Green Bay project." *J. Am. Water Resour. Assoc.* 27 (3): 429–436.

McCutcheon, S. C. 1983. *The evaluation of selected one-dimensional stream water-quality models with field data.* Waterways Experiment Station Rep. No. E-11. Vicksburg, MS: USACE.

McCutcheon, S. C. 1989. *Water quality modelling: Vol. I, river transport and surface exchange.* Boca Raton, FL: CRC Press.

McCutcheon, S. C., D. Zhu, and S. Bird. 1990. "Model calibration, validation, and use." In *Technical guidance manual for performing waste load allocations. Book III: Estuaries, Part 2: Application of estuarine waste load allocation models,* EPA-823-R-92-003, edited by R. B. Ambrose, J. L. Martin, and S. C. McCutcheon, 40–117. Washington, DC: EPA.

Moriasi, D. N., J. G. Arnold, M. W. Van Liew, R. L. Bingner, R. D. Harmel, and T. L. Veith. 2007. "Model evaluation guidelines for systematic quantification of accuracy in watershed simulations." *Trans. ASABE* 50 (3): 885–900.

Moriasi, D. N., M. W. Gitau, N. Pai, and P. Daggupati. 2015. "Hydrologic and water quality models: Performance measures and evaluation criteria." *Trans. ASABE* 58 (6): 1763–1785.

Moriasi, D. N., B. N. Wilson, K. R. Douglas-Mankin, J. G. Arnold, and P. H. Gowda. 2012. "Hydrologic and water quality models: Use, calibration, and validation." *Trans. ASABE* 55 (4): 1241–1247.

NRC (National Research Council). 2001. *Assessing the TMDL approach to water quality management.* Washington, DC: NRC.

ODEQ (Oregon Department of Environmental Quality). 2010a. *John Day River Basin total maximum daily load (TMDL) and water quality management plan (WQMP).* DEQ-10-WQ-025. Portland, OR: ODEQ.

ODEQ 2010b. *John Day River Basin total maximum daily load (TMDL) and water quality management plan (WQMP): Response to Public Comment.* Portland, OR: ODEQ.

Plummer, M. 2003. "JAGS: A program for analysis of Bayesian graphical models using Gibbs sampling." In Vol. 124 of *Proc., 3rd Int. Workshop on Distributed Statistical Computing,* 1–10, edited by K. Hornick, F. Leisch, and A. Zeileis. Vienna, Austria.

Quinn, N. W. T. 2020. "Policy innovation and governance for irrigation sustainability in the Arid, Saline San Joaquin River Basin." *Sustainability* 12 (11): 4733.

RESPEC. 2019. "RESPEC launches HSP2 tutorials." Accessed October 30, 2021. http://www.respec.com/respec-launches-hsp2-tutorials/.

Schueler, T. S. 1987. *The simple method in controlling urban runoff: A practical manual for planning and designing urban BMPs.* Washington, DC: Washington Metropolitan Water Resources Planning Board, Metropolitan Washington Council of Governments.

Shoemaker, L., J. Riverson Jr., K. Alvi, J. Zhen, S. Paul, and T. Rafi. 2009. *SUSTAIN—A framework for placement of best management practices in urban watersheds to protect water quality.* Washington, DC: National Risk Management Research Laboratory, Office of Research and Development, EPA.

Sridharan, V. K., S. G. Monismith, O. B. Fringer, and D. A. Fong. 2018. "Evaluation of the Delta Simulation Model-2 in computing tidally driven flows in the Sacramento-San Joaquin Delta." *San Francisco Estuary Watershed Sci.* 16 (2).

Sridharan, V. K., N. W. T. Quinn, S. Kumar, S. C. McCutcheon, E. Ahmadisharaf, X. Fang, et al. 2021. "Selecting reliable models for total maximum daily load development: A holistic protocol." *J. Hydrol. Eng.* 26 (10): 04021031.

Tedela, N. H., S. C. McCutcheon, T. C. Rasmussen, C. R. Jackson, E. W. Tollner, W. R. Swank, et al. 2012. "Runoff curve numbers for 10 small forested watersheds in the mountains of the eastern United States." *J. Hydrol. Eng.* 17 (11): 1188–1198.

Tetra Tech. 2002. *Theoretical and computational aspects of sediment and contaminant transport in EFDC.* Tech. Rep. to the US Environmental Protection Agency. Fairfax, VA: Tetra Tech.

Texas A&M University. 2019. "SWAT: Soil & water assessment tool." Accessed October 30, 2021. http://swat.tamu.edu/.

Thomann, R. V. 1992. "Expert critique of case studies." p. 14-1–14-18. In *Technical guidance manual for performing waste load allocations. Book III; Estuaries—Part 4: Critical reviews of coastal embayment and estuarine waste load allocation modeling,* edited by R. B. Ambrose Jr. Washington, DC: EPA.

Thomann, R. V., and J. A. Mueller. 1987. *Principles of surface water quality modeling and control.* New York: Harper and Row.

USACE (United States Army Corps of Engineers). 2016. *HEC-RAS: river analysis system user's manual version 5.0. CPD-68.* Davis, CA: Hydrologic Engineering Center, USACE.

USACE. 2019. "Gridded surface subsurface hydrologic analysis." Accessed October 30, 2021. http://www.erdc.usace.army.mil/Media/Fact-Sheets/Fact-Sheet-Article-View/Article/476714/gridded-surface-subsurface-hydrologic-analysis/.

USDA-NRCS (United States Department of Agriculture-Natural Resources Conservation Service). 2019. "Agricultural non-point sources pollution model." Accessed October 30, 2021. http://www.nrcs.usda.gov/wps/portal/nrcs/detailfull/null/?cid=stelprdb1042468.

USEPA (US Environmental Protection Agency). 2002. "Guidelines for reviewing TMDLs under existing regulations issued in 1992." Accessed October 30, 2021. https://www.epa.gov/sites/production/files/2015-10/documents/2002_06_04_tmdl_guidance_final52002.pdf.

USEPA. 2005. *TMDL model evaluation and research needs.* EPA/600/R-05/149. Cincinnati: National Engineering Research Laboratory.

USEPA. 2006. *Clarification regarding "phased" total maximum daily loads. Memorandum.* Washington, DC: Assessment and Watershed Protection Division.

USEPA. 2015. "Total maximum daily loads with stormwater sources: A summary of 17 TMDLs." Accessed October 30, 2021. https://www.epa.gov/sites/production/files/2015-07/documents/17_tmdls_stormwater_sources.pdf.

USEPA. 2017. "WASP model release notes." Accessed October 30, 2021. http://www.epa.gov/ceam/wasp-model-release-notes.

USEPA. 2018. "Overview of the total maximum daily loads (TMDLs)." Accessed October 30, 2021. https://www.epa.gov/tmdl/overview-total-maximum-daily-loads-tmdls#2.

USEPA. 2019a. "TMDL support documents." Accessed October 30, 2021. https://www.epa.gov/tmdl/tmdl-support-documents.

USEPA. 2019b. "Storm water management model (SWMM)." Accessed October 30, 2021. http://www.epa.gov/water-research/storm-water-management-model-swmm.

USEPA. 2020a. "ATTAINS." Accessed October 30, 2021. https://www.epa.gov/waterdata/attains.

USEPA. 2020b. "Environmental modeling community of practice." Accessed October 30, 2021. https://www.epa.gov/ceam.

USGAO (US Government Accountability Office). 2013. *Clean Water Act: Changes needed if key EPA program is to help fulfill the nation's water quality goals.* Rep. No. GAO-14-80 to Congressional Requestors. Washington, DC: USGAO.

Walker Jr., W. W. 2006. *BATHTUB—version 6.1: Simplified techniques for eutrophication assessment and prediction.* Vicksburg, MI: Environmental Laboratory, United States Army Corps of Engineers Waterways Experiment Station.

WERF (Water Environment Research Foundation). 2003. *Navigating the TMDL process: Evaluation and improvements.* WERF Project 00-WSM-1. Denver, CO: WERF.

Willmott, C. J. 1981. "On the validation of models." *Phys. Geogr.* 2 (2): 184–94.

Zhang, H. X., and G. Padmanabhan. 2019. "Critical condition modeling and analysis in TMDL development and implementation." *J. Hydrol. Eng.* 24 (2): 04018061.

Zou, R., S. Carter, L. Shoemaker, A. Parker, and T. Henry. 2006. "Integrated hydrodynamic and water quality modeling system to support nutrient total maximum daily load development for Wissahickon Creek, Pennsylvania." *J. Environ. Eng.* 132 (4): 555–566.

CHAPTER 12

MODELING FOR TOTAL MAXIMUM DAILY LOAD IMPLEMENTATION

William H. Frost, R. Craig Lott, Rosanna J. La Plante

12.1 INTRODUCTION

Stakeholders with the responsibility to implement a total maximum daily load (TMDL) include communities, state agencies, local governments, and other organizations. Stakeholders together seek the best methods to achieve the pollutant load reductions required to restore the water quality of the impaired waterbody of concern. To achieve this, they need to develop remedial actions that may involve trade-offs among factors such as load reduction, capital and maintenance costs, available land, and ease of implementation. In some circumstances, the same model that was used to develop the TMDL can be used to guide implementation strategies. In other instances, a new decision support model may need to be developed to provide stakeholders with the tool to select among practical load-reduction alternatives. Typically, in both TMDL planning and implementation, models help forecast future water quality conditions. During the planning process, monitoring data are essential for calibrating and developing confidence in model predictions. During implementation, new monitoring stations are often needed to assess compliance with water quality objectives developed for a basin and to provide essential feedback to stakeholders to help allocate pollutant discharge limits and assess fines on those entities contributing to load exceedances.

In addition, the TMDL requires a quantification of load reductions for the load allocation, wasteload allocations, and margin of safety components of the point and nonpoint-source pollutant loads, and these should be identified and quantified in sufficient detail to allow best management practices (BMPs) to be assessed and implemented. Modeling can help estimate the potential effectiveness of BMP implementation.

The overall approach to modeling for TMDL implementation should involve the following steps:

- Identify all potential pollutant sources within the implementer's jurisdiction.
- For stormwater sources, the same TMDL information should be used by the model to simulate runoff loading rates for implementation planning whenever possible.
- Best available local land-cover data and/or runoff loading should be used to calculate baseline untreated and treated loads at the time of implementation. Land-use maps, hydrology, and meteorology data should extend from the time when water quality monitoring recognized the original impairment in the waterbody.
- Approved BMPs and other treatment options that have led to load reductions should be recognized in implementation plans to locate, size, and assess BMPs.
- Models should be recalibrated periodically with new, additional water quality monitoring and updated land-cover data wherever and whenever possible.

This chapter discusses the state-of-the-practice of models used in TMDL implementation planning. It includes examples of watershed-specific models, including ArcView generalized watershed loading function (AVGWLF) for Pennsylvania watersheds, source loading and management model for Windows (WinSLAMM) for Wisconsin watersheds, and the Chesapeake assessment scenario tool (CAST) for Chesapeake Bay watershed TMDL implementation. The applications of two spreadsheet analysis packages are also discussed: the watershed treatment model (WTM) and the spreadsheet tool for estimating pollutant load (STEPL). These case studies are described in more detail in Frost et al. (2019). The generalized watershed loading function (GWLF), the base of the AVGWF, is described in Chapter 2, and WTM and STEPL are described in Chapter 5 as well.

12.2 CHOICE OF MODELS FOR TOTAL MAXIMUM DAILY LOAD IMPLEMENTATION

As previously noted, ideally the same model used in TMDL development can also be used for TMDL implementation and assessment (Chapters 2 to 5). However, this is not always the case. For example, receiving water models would not be particularly useful in selecting between load-reduction strategies and BMPs to achieve the requisite TMDL objectives. Other models may be needed that take advantage of the data resources generated by initial TMDL model development activity that are geared to providing decision support to stakeholders and allowing them to make sound resource-allocation decisions.

For example, in the case of the Chesapeake Bay TMDL, simulation modeling in support of TMDL development utilized a large-scale model that was needed to address the hydrological complexity of the Basin. However, because implementation is, by necessity, conducted at a finer scale watershed level, it requires a more detailed model that is capable of modeling load reductions from planned BMPs, paying more attention to local factors that were key to success.

In addition, some TMDLs may have been formulated based on load-monitoring data from multiple permittees that are discharged to the receiving water. This may complicate the implementation of the TMDL because loads from multiple permittes are combined into a single reduction factor. In these cases, a model that reliably assigns and partitions accountability would be needed for successful implementation.

12.2.1 Range of Pollutants and Pollutant Sources

Some models such as the storm water management model (SWMM) by USEPA (Rossman 2015) (Chapter 2) are flexible and can simulate the fate and transport of a large suite of common pollutants and pollutant sources. Other models may be more restricted in the types of pollutants they can track. For example, the GWLF model by Haith et al. (1992) can simulate only nutrients, sediment, sediment-borne pollutants (such as toxic stressors), and bacteria.

For TMDL implementation and post-TMDL assessment, it is preferable to have access to a model that can simulate the full suite of pollutants and pollutant sources listed in the TMDL. These sources may include wastewater discharges, septic systems, streambank erosion, agricultural runoff, concentrated animal feeding operation, livestock, atmospheric deposition, and/or groundwater. Models used to simulate the impacts of control actions need to simulate how a control action or management practice will impact loading sometimes at multiple scales.

12.2.2 Stormwater Best Management Practice Pollutant Control

The model used to simulate the effects of management measures and to track progress during implementation should include a method to select BMPs with removal rates for inclusion in a plan. These models should rely on methods and algorithms that are already accepted by the regulatory authority responsible for the TMDL to the extent possible. The suite of potential BMPs should include structural BMPs, nonstructural stormwater management solutions such as nutrient management plans and incentives to reduce fertilizer and chemical application, stream and shoreline restoration, and changes in land use such as reforestation, riparian buffers, street sweeping, or impervious cover removal.

Pollutant removal should be simulated accurately in any model development for TMDL implementation. Pollutant-removal mechanisms can be complex combinations of physical, chemical, and biological processes and it is not always possible to simulate them reliably because of insufficient data or other constraints impacting model performance. Many simple models used for implementation tend to equate stormwater treatment to a percent removal rate assigned to each type of BMP unless better information is available (CWP 2007, Schueler and Lane 2012, Clary et al. 2020). In the best case, TMDL regulatory agencies provide guidance for all implementers on how pollutant removal should be credited, along with the input factors needed to make the calculations (MDE 2014a, b; VADEQ 2017).

The modeler should identify situations where using a single percent removal for annual pollutant reductions to achieve the TMDL may be an oversimplification that might not apply to all pollutants, every locality, or critical condition. In some cases, the treatment options for an individual BMP are based on the local climate or rainfall associated with the impaired waterbody. For example, a BMP that uses a process relying on infiltration and vegetation will likely not function effectively during dissimilar conditions such as in freezing temperatures (Géhéniau et al. 2015, Roseen et al. 2009). Whenever possible, local research on the conditions under which a specific BMP is implemented should be used for a more accurate accounting of BMP pollutant removal.

Stormwater treatment methods are continuously evolving. Since the mid-1990s, the International Stormwater BMP Database has evolved into the largest publicly accessible repository for BMP performance monitoring study, design, and cost information in the water sector (Clary et al. 2020). For BMPs that employ innovative or new technology, additional research may be needed to determine the most likely long-term effects of BMP on pollutant loading. For example, research suggests that BMPs that recommend compost as a bioretention mulch layer could exacerbate phosphate loading because of enhanced leaching of phosphate from the mulch (Hurley et al. 2017).

The Maryland Phase I Watershed Implementation Plan for the Chesapeake Bay TMDL compiled an extensive database on implementable BMPs that can be applied for point source, urban stormwater, and agricultural load management (MDE 2010). Other nontraditional actions such as the rehabilitation of aging infrastructure can lower pollution loads by reducing the exfiltration of sanitary lines and/or infiltration of storm sewers. Ultimately, there is no substitute for monitoring, inspection, and enforcement after construction to ensure that remedial actions, whether they be classified as BMPs or not, achieve the desired reduction and removal of environmental pollutants.

12.2.3 Data Resources for Modeling

A major factor that encourages flexibility in model selection under the likelihood that a model different from the one used in TMDL development model could be used to support TMDL implementation is access to greater data resources and to data of better quality. TMDL implementing agencies may have access to better data at the time of implementation because considerable time would have elapsed since the beginning of TMDL development efforts. This would allow the consideration of more detailed and comprehensive simulation models better suited for TMDL implementation. Large-scale watershed models that were used for the initial analysis may have used input data based on statewide mapping that would have had insufficient resolution for TMDL implementation activities. The higher resolution needed to facilitate the placement and analysis of spatially distributed BMPs and other reduction measures may utilize other data sources made available through county-level and local agencies. In each case, the "value" of the higher-resolution model input data should be assessed with respect to decision support. More detail can sometimes add complexity to the simulation and selection of spatially distributed management practices without substantially improving the outcome of the TMDL implementation enterprise.

When specific pollutant-treatment processes are simulated, they should consider the sequence of unit processes that are needed to provide effective and reliable pollutant removal. A model's ability to accurately simulate these sequential treatment processes can impact model performance, and, hence, this aspect should be considered in the selection of an appropriate model to guide TMDL implementation.

12.2.4 Expertise and Access

In some instances, TMDLs developed with a loading model for a particular pollutant may not be useful tool for guiding TMDL implementation. Implementation agencies may not have access to the model and input files used to develop the TMDL, or it may be more complex and require more specialized experience than implementation agencies have available.

Just as TMDL development requires different models, no single model will be applicable for every implementation plan. Different pollutants may require different modeling approaches to achieve compliance. Different pollutant sources may require different levels of complexity in the model. It is important to note, however, that increased complexity in models may not provide sufficient benefit to drive informed actions and implementation success.

Despite the evolving nature of implementation modeling, an ideal model may not be available to simulate the effectiveness of watershed improvements for a particular TMDL. In these cases, the use of analytical approaches, coupled with monitoring to gather additional data, could be the best route to developing an implementation plan. This performance-based plan uses continuous assessment to determine progress toward meeting water quality goals.

Availability of local expertise is an important consideration for model selection. If there are staff who either currently run or have experience with a particular model, then there will be a much shorter learning curve for the implementers. Decision makers and stakeholders are more likely to accept the model results if they are familiar with the output and have confidence in the model. In the case of proprietary models, if they are already in use by the implementers, the costs of new software acquisition can be avoided.

12.2.5 Availability and Support

There are well over one hundred models dealing with all facets of water quality available in the public domain. Many of these, developed by US government agencies, including USEPA, USGS, USDA, and US Army Corps of Engineers (USACE) have been in use for decades. In general, models with a long history and a large and active support group will be easier to implement and maintain.

12.3 POTENTIAL MODELS FOR IMPLEMENTATION

If there is no detailed, watershed-wide pollutant source characterization in the TMDL, those tasked with preparing and executing an implementation plan will have to develop this information with a more detailed loading analysis for the TMDL with their best local data to show that their implementation plans will meet TMDL goals. As previously discussed, the effects on receiving waters do not need to be modeled, so in general, implementation planning will require less sophisticated models than that are necessary to develop the TMDL.

Some state TMDL regulatory agencies either provide or recommend models to be used for implementation decision support. The following sections describe several off-the-shelf models and one custom approach that could meet the need for TMDL implementation. Tables 12-1 and 12-2 present comparative information for the various models identified in the discussion.

12.3.1 State or Watershed-Specific Models

In certain states, the regulatory bodies overseeing TMDL implementation may have endorsed the use of several acceptable models. These regulatory

Table 12-1. Structure and Capabilities of Selected Implementation Models.

	CAST	MapShed/GWLF-E	WinSLAMM	P-8	WTM (custom)	STEPL
Model structure						
Watershed representation	Chesapeake Bay counties, HUC-12 watersheds, or predefined planning areas	Single lumped watershed	Subwatershed or site-level	Urban catchments	Single lumped watershed	Subwatersheds
Land use	Developed agricultural, natural including wetlands and streams	Urban, agricultural, forest	Urban	Urban	Urban, agricultural, forest	Urban, agricultural, forest
Time scale	Annual loading rates and loads	Continuous simulation, daily time step, daily, monthly, or annual results	Continuous or event rainfall, annual or seasonal loads	Continuous or event rainfall, daily or hourly time step	Annual rainfall, loading rates, and loads	Annual rainfall, loading rates, and loads
Hydrology	10-year average hydrology	NRCS curve number, water balance	Small storm hydrology, empirical runoff coefficients	NRCS curve number, water balance, snowmelt	Simple method runoff volume	NRCS curve number

(Continued)

Table 12-1. (*Continued*).

	CAST	MapShed/GWLF-E	WinSLAMM	P-8	WTM (custom)	STEPL
Groundwater	Implicitly modeled	Yes	No	Yes (water balance only)	Yes	Yes
Pollutant loading	Annual loading rate by load source and delivery factors at the edge-of-stream and edge-of-tidal area of the Chesapeake Bay	Urban: buildup/washoff; rural: USLE and export coefficients	Particulate solids by source, sediment nutrient concentration	Buildup/washoff	Urban: EMC, rural: export coefficient	USLE, sediment nutrient concentration, EMC
Pollutants modeled	Nutrients, sediment	Nutrients, sediment, bacteria	Nutrients, sediment, bacteria, metals, chemical oxygen demand	Nutrients, sediment, metals, hydrocarbons	Nutrients, sediment, bacteria	Nutrients, sediment, BOD-5
Pollutant sources						
Runoff loads	Developed, agricultural, natural including wetlands and streams	Urban, agricultural, forest	Urban	Urban	Urban, agricultural, forest	Urban, agricultural, forest

Wastewater	CSO, WWTP, OSDS	WWTP, OSDS	No	No	CSO, SSO, WWTP, OSDS	WWTP, OSDS
Other	Stream erosion, livestock, manure application, agricultural production areas, Riparian pasture deposition	Stream erosion, livestock, animal feeding operation s, manure application	None	None	Stream erosion, illicit discharge (detection and elimination), livestock, Marinas	Stream erosion, livestock, animal feeding operation s, manure application
User requirements						
Data requirements	Low, input provided with program	Medium, defaults provided	High	High	Medium, defaults provided	Medium, defaults provided
Expertise	Medium	Medium	High	High	Medium	Medium
Availability	Online model, public access	From developer	From developer	From developer	From developer	Download from USEPA

Source: Frost et al. (2019).

Table 12-2. Treatment Practices for Selected Implementation Models.

	CAST	MapShed/ GWLF-E	WinSLAMM	P-8	WTM (Custom)	STEPL
Structural practices						
Urban BMPs	o	o	o	o	o	o
Erosion/sediment control	o	—	—	—	o	—
Riparian buffers	o	o	o	—	o	o
Impervious disconnection	o	o	o	—	o	—
Stream restoration	o	o	—	—	o	o
CSO/SSO repair	—	—	—	—	o	—
Septic system repair/upgrade	o	o	—	—	o	—
Septic system conversion	o	o	—	—	o	—
Nonstructural practices						
Land-use change	o	o	—	—	o	—
Agricultural BMPs	o	o	—	—	—	o
Turf management	o	—	—	—	o	—
Street sweeping	o	o	o	o	o	o
Inlet cleaning	o	—	—	—	o	—
Marina pumpouts	—	—	—	—	o	—
Illicit discharge detection and elimination	—	—	—	—	o	—
Point-source reductions	o	o	—	—	o	—

Source: Frost et al. (2019).

bodies do not restrict the use of alternate models, provided documentation of these alternate models are documented and permission is granted for their use for the intended purpose. The benefit of this approach is standardization of the approach taken that provides consistency of data collection and benchmarking that can be useful to both the user community and relevant regulatory agencies. This standard framework may also include support for nutrient trading calculators that are indirectly related to TMDL implementation. Some states provide support for TMDL implementation by preparing generic implementation plans that can be customized or borrowed by permittees, who then develop individual plans that reflect institutional knowledge within their jurisdictions.

12.3.1.1 Chesapeake Bay Program. The Chesapeake Bay Program, in conjunction with MDE and VA DEQ, developed the original version of the CAST, a model used by local jurisdictions to further BMP implementation planning (version 2019). The CAST encouraged planners to simulate the impact of BMP scenario implementation to meet the 2010 Chesapeake Bay TMDL (USEPA 2010) objectives for nitrogen, phosphorus, and sediment loads. Those BMPs that had the greatest load-reduction benefit were identified and the costs of these estimated using the CAST tool. Scenarios were saved for future comparisons and updated as more information became available for siting and sizing BMPs.

12.3.1.2 Pennsylvania. Beginning in 1999, the Pennsylvania Department of Environmental Protection (PADEP), along with the Pennsylvania State University, developed a geographical information system (GIS)-based tool using the Environmental Systems Research Institute ArcView software as the platform to enhance the capability of GWLF (Haith et al. 1992). The new tool was named AVGWLF. AVGWLF has used data provided by PADEP for implementation planning jurisdictions statewide. This has included compilation of data that characterize the hydrology, land cover, soils, and topography, along with weather data, and environmental data, to simulate sediment and nutrient loading within a watershed (Evans et al. 2001). (Chapter 2, "Watershed Models").

To reduce the need for proprietary software, AVGWLF was subsequently upgraded as a plug-in for MapWindows, a public domain mapping package, and reissued as the MapShed tool for use in TMDL implementation planning in Pennsylvania. MapShed incorporates an enhanced version of the GWLF model (GWLF-E). GWLF-E includes routines for streambank erosion, point sources, urban and agricultural BMPs, and pathogen loads. Input data for Pennsylvania watersheds are downloadable to be used in setting up TMDL implementation models using the data provided by the PADEP previously described.

12.3.1.3 Wisconsin. The Wisconsin Department of Natural Resources (WI DNR) has issued guidance to Municipal Separate Storm Sewer System (MS4) permittees to assist them in the process of implementation planning and facilitating load-reduction activities consistent with satisfying TMDL objectives (WI DNR 2014, 2016). The WI DNR endorsed two models, the Source Loading and Management Model for Windows (WinSLAMM) (version 10.4.1) and the P-8 Urban Catchment Model (Walker and Walker 2015).

WinSLAMM estimates pollutant loadings from urban areas by calculating runoff from rainfall events. Stormwater controls can be simulated as well as infiltration/biofiltration, wet detention ponds, grass swales, porous pavement, and catch basins. WinSLAMM can calculate pollutant removal from nonstructural measures, including street sweeping and catch basin cleaning.

The Urban Catchment Model P-8 was originally developed for estimating runoff from new urban development under various pollutant-treatment scenarios for a wide range of pollutants, including total phosphorus, total Kjeldahl nitrogen, five sizes of suspended solids, copper, lead, zinc, and total hydrocarbons. Several structural BMPs can be simulated, including wet, dry, and extended detention ponds, infiltration basins, swales, and buffer strips.

12.3.2 Spreadsheet Analysis

Spreadsheets can be used for assessing the success of TMDL implementation. These are most often used for watersheds where there are a limited number of sources and types of pollutant-treatment options. If a TMDL is largely focused on measured or estimated watershed drainage and associated pollutant loading, a spreadsheet may be sufficient for calculating pollutant loads and estimating the impact of direct pollutant load reductions without the need for a more complex and detailed simulation model. For this type of tool to be useful for decision support, realistic parameter values for pollutant loading and removal rates are needed. Land use is typically derived from remotely sensed imagery and GIS-based interpretation of the spectral signals associated with specified activities within the TMDL boundary. TMDL loading rates are either estimated by simulation modeling or determined by local outfall monitoring, measured application rates (e.g., road salts), or available monitoring data such as from the National Stormwater Quality Database, which is under the platform of the International Stormwater BMP Database (Pitt et al. 2004, Clary et al. 2020). A regulatory authority may be able to provide achievable pollutant-reduction rates for BMPs based on local experience. These may be based on statewide stormwater design criteria, regional TMDL modeling, or other sources. Load-reduction information may also be derived from published sources such as the International Stormwater BMP Database (Clary et al. 2020).

12.3.2.1 Watershed Treatment Model.   WTM, developed by the Center for Watershed Protection (Caraco 2013), enables the analyst or entity responsible for TMDL implementation to predict the impact on pollutant loads over a wide range of land uses under wet weather and dry weather conditions for both urban watersheds and some agricultural source areas. The model focuses on nitrogen, phosphorus, total suspended solids, and bacterial load reduction in the watershed. Several types of pollutant treatment can be simulated, including stormwater BMPs, stream restoration, stormwater retrofits, septic system improvements, point-source reductions, and non-structural measures. The WTM has the same limitations as any spreadsheet analysis, in that all stormwater runoff loads are lumped. Loads and treatment for other secondary sources are calculated separately. The model has worksheets to allow pollutant load and load reductions to be assessed for three scenarios: existing conditions, as of the date of the watershed assessment; new development conditions which are forecast from zoning, build out, or other land planning data; and proposed conditions, summarizing proposed changes resulting from improvements to meet TMDL requirements. Also refer to Chapter 5, "Simple Models and Methods."

Pollutant loading is calculated by using the model in several linked worksheets, as follows:

- Primary Sources worksheet summarizes loads from runoff sources that can be determined solely by land cover or land use. This requires basic watershed data, such as land use by type, annual rainfall, stream length, and soil distribution. Loading rates and loads are calculated using a variation of the simple method (Schueler 1987) considering hydrologic soil groups. The loads calculated in this worksheet utilize data from the "turf management" section of the "Existing Management Practices" tab and rely on model default values that reflect typical lawn care practices.
- Secondary Sources worksheet estimates pollutant loads from sources that cannot be calculated based on land-use information alone. Many of these pollutant sources, from combined sewer overflows (CSOs), septic systems, and sanitary sewer overflows (SSOs), contain wastewater.
- Existing Management Practices worksheet allows information on the degree of adoption and effectiveness of TMDL implementation programs and practices to reduce pollutants from urban lands. The data contained in this worksheet provide information required to develop a baseline BMP and treatment scenario, to guide TMDL implementation activities.

- WTM includes two additional worksheets where data on stormwater BMPs that were implemented after existing practices can be entered. The Retrofit worksheet allows the user to document individual stormwater retrofit practices. The Future Management Practices worksheet allows the modeler to enter other treatment practices. Documentation of current and prior BMPs followed in the watershed can be valuable in analyzing the effectiveness of these practices and guiding the adoption of additional and innovative BMPs to manage pollution of receiving waters.

12.3.2.2 Spreadsheet Tool for Estimating Pollutant Load. The spreadsheet tool for estimating pollutant load (STEPL) model was developed for the Office of Water of USEPA, with the latest version being 4.4b (USEPA 2020a). It has been used throughout the United States to simulate control programs to address nonpoint-source pollution and for quantifying potential pollutant load-reduction activities. Also refer to Chapter 5, "Simple Models and Methods."

The STEPL model is an Excel spreadsheet that employs simple algorithms to calculate surface runoff and pollutant loading. These include nutrient loads, such as nitrogen and phosphorus and sediment loads from various land uses. Nutrient loads are calculated based on land use, soils, and various stormwater management practices. Sediment loads are calculated based on the universal soil loss equation (USLE) and the sediment delivery ratio. The STEPL model also calculates load reductions that would result from the implementation of various BMPs. They are computed using BMP efficiencies that are provided as input by the user.

The STEPL model can be used to simulate pollutant loads to both surface water and groundwater. The model estimates stormwater pollutant loads using a variety of standard methods, depending on how land use is defined according to six basic categories: urban, cropland, pastureland, forest, feedlot, and user defined.

Calculations for pollution from urban land are based on estimates of runoff derived from the USDA curve number method. These are derived specifically for each drainage area from soil and land-cover data, using pollutant concentrations obtained from wet weather sampling data. These relationships can be adjusted by the modeler based on additional available information.

Sediment loads from nonurban, agricultural, and forest land are calculated with USLE using a sediment delivery ratio to derive pollutant loading from rainfall-runoff estimates. Nutrient loading for these land uses is calculated in a manner similar to urban land using assumed steady-state concentrations of pollutants and estimated annual runoff volumes.

For TMDL implementation, the STEPL model can provide estimates of pollutant loads and pollutant load reductions expected from the application of individual BMPs, without having to lump all control and management options for each watershed. This feature provides some flexibility in that it recognizes the effect of each BMP individually. This recognizes nontraditional BMP applications that for certain areas might perform better than standard approaches. Output from the STEPL model can be presented as an annual summary table for providing stakeholders with data on pollutant reduction by BMPs, treated and untreated pollutant loads, and the percent reduction that was achieved for each pollutant. The model also provides output showing pollutant load reductions by individual land use.

12.3.3 Custom Modeling Using a Geographic Information System Geodatabase

An alternate approach to implementation modeling may be to use a customized model developed from an existing geodatabase of land use, treatment types, and drainage areas. This approach assumes that the implementing agency already has a geodatabase that stores information on existing and planned BMPs in addition to BMP performance data. Queries made to this geodatabase would rely on lookup tables for accessing information on current pollutant loading rates and the effectiveness of pollutant management practices under a suite of implemented and implementable BMPs. This approach may work better for basins that comprise many subwatersheds subject to a range of TMDLs or statewide MS4 permits. Applications that require multiple counties, baselines, and watersheds to be simulated using a GIS-based model benefit from the processing power and query capabilities of GIS software. Being able to annotate the model and include images associated with a given application, BMP or TMDL can significantly improve stakeholder access and stakeholder involvement in the TMDL implementation process.

As GIS tools and associated geodatabases have improved in capability and have become more widespread in their use by environmental agencies, regulators, and stakeholders, they have moved into the realm of standard practice for TMDL implementation activities and BMP development and application associated with planning, design, construction, inspection, maintenance, and even credit verification. A geodatabase can provide locations for treatment that might serve the implementation of multiple TMDLs in a single watershed. In addition, depending on the level of progress toward full BMP implementation, the geodatabase can be set up to meet various monitoring and reporting goals at different stages of implementation. A GIS can provide an accessible archive for BMP treatment data obtained from multiple sources and assist in the application of statistical techniques to quantify the effectiveness of these and other pollutant-reduction methods. Credible and reliable load-reduction performance algorithms can be formulated that can be used in other models.

For example, the District of Columbia developed an integrated modeling tool for scenario development (Schmitt and Champion 2014, LimnoTech 2015) in a basin where multiple TMDLs were being implemented. The GIS-based tool that was developed to support these activities incorporated BMP implementation data from multiple programs within the District of Columbia that led to success in the program. Also refer to Chapter 4, "Integrated Modeling Systems and Linked Models."

12.4 SUMMARY

Modeling can be an excellent tool to support the successful and informed implementation of a TMDL. Models can play an important role in TMDL implementation by providing a consistent and reproducible analytical framework, especially in large, multijurisdiction TMDL implementation programs. If the regulatory agency responsible for developing the TMDL recognizes the limitations and can provide implementers with a model to be used or guidance on assessing compliance, then implementation planning can be better coordinated across the watershed. As previously discussed, this has been successfully accomplished in several states and for the entire Chesapeake Bay Watershed.

Provision of a model is particularly important for unusual or difficult TMDLs, such as temperature, toxins, or bacteria, where there may be a lack of data for conventional or spreadsheet modeling.

The implementing regulatory agency's goal is to assess the potential improvements that can be made and then analyze them to gauge their potential effectiveness. The model that is selected for the purpose should have the following attributes.

First, it is necessary for the model to be able to identify all the potential sources within the implementing jurisdiction. These could be stormwater sources from urban or rural areas, point sources, septic systems, and animals such as wildlife, domestic pets, or livestock. The TMDL may cover a large watershed, and a smaller jurisdiction within it may not have all sources identified and described in sufficient detail. The selected model should be able to estimate and quantify pollutant loads from all the identified sources. This allows the modeler to include source controls, typically the least expensive and most cost-effective pollutant control option.

Based on experience, guidance, or the already implemented TMDLs, implementers should be familiar with the type of pollutant-treatment technologies that could be successful if introduced and applied in their jurisdictions. The selected model will need to be able to simulate the expected performance of these potential treatment options.

Next, the implementing agency modelers will have to identify and access all available datasets that are useful as model input for calculating loads. For example, for stormwater modeling, land-use applications (residential, commercial, transportation) may have the most accessible and high-quality pollutant loading rate data. In other applications, land-cover (buildings, pavement, forest, and turf) data may be better suited and more readily accessed for model input data and for simulating pollutant loads. If local data are not available or provided by stakeholders engaged with TMDL implementation, loading rate data may need to be acquired independently. The simulation model being used will ultimately rely on the type of data readily available and analysts need to make an informed assessment of its quality. For example, if stream restoration is an option for reducing sediment loads, the model should incorporate calculations that can estimate the sediment load and sediment load reduction achievable from the implementation of BMPs and available pollutant-treatment interventions. The model adopted for this purpose will need to be able to compare multiple BMP and treatment implementation scenarios for pollutant-reduction planning. The model selected should be simple enough to operate so that it can be used within the limits of the agency's resources, but not so simple that the results will lead to inefficient or flawed implementation plans or not be accepted by the stakeholder community.

Finally, depending on the complexity of the TMDL, the type of pollutant, sources of loads, or treatment data, it will likely be cost-effective to develop and maintain a geodatabase to manage associated data that provide decision support for choosing between BMP and pollutant-treatment implementation scenarios.

From an overall implementation perspective, there are several ways that TMDL implementation can be carried out with a better probability of success. These include the following:

- Set realistic implementation goals. If the timeline is flexible, gauge the effort needed to meet TMDLs throughout the jurisdiction and adjust end dates accordingly, with approval from the regulatory authority.
- Apply an adaptive management approach for complex TMDLs. There may not be enough data or modeling to assess results in the early stages and monitoring data may not show any change. Be flexible and revise the plan to abandon approaches that are not working and refocus on more successful ones.
- Allow regulatory authorities flexibility to permittees (particularly, localities responsible for MS4 implementation) to demonstrate alternate pragmatic BMP implementation approaches when available to ensure compliance with their permit.
- Apply the most cost-effective BMPs and tackle the most feasible areas first. This should lead to better results and provide momentum for subsequent efforts.

- Seek effective community involvement and support for the implementation plan. As with any large, long-term project, support of the public is an important factor for success.

12.5 STATE-OF-THE-ART AND STATE-OF-THE-PRACTICE

It should be clear from the content of this chapter that TMDL implementation requires an analytical and data management framework that is best served using an appropriate modeling tool. There are several off-the-shelf modeling tools available, and it is a good use of time to research these tools thoroughly and effectively to make sure that the most appropriate tool is selected for the task at hand. This TMDL Manual of Practice has been designed and developed to serve this need.

The NRC (2001) report emphasizes the importance of using an adaptive implementation approach to help achieve TMDL goals and attain water quality standards. For example, when Chesapeake Bay sediment and nutrient TMDLs were approved by the USEPA in 2010, there was a specific section in the approved TMDL document for "Implementation and Adaptive Management" (USEPA 2010). Several important elements were in place during the TMDL implementation phase to ensure that all pollution control measures needed to be tracked for restoring the Chesapeake Bay and its tidal rivers. These elements included watershed implementation plans, establishment of milestones and midpoint assessment, wastewater pollution reductions, air pollution reduction, and trading and offsets.

Ideally, the same modeling tool that is selected to develop the TMDL, organize the input data required to run simulations, and develop watershed management scenarios should be the same tool that will help guide TMDL implementation. However, in reality, this is not always the case. Some TMDLs are developed with a broad application in mind following USEPA guidance and using models that rely on regional data sets. Current applications make heavy use of GIS to synthesize and parse these geospatial datasets for use in these models. The more sophisticated models are integrated, making it easy to use remote sensing, LiDAR, and other widely available data to develop input datasets that allow these models to be initialized and run without relying on agency and locally derived monitoring data (Chapter 7). However, very often, TMDL implementation needs to be accomplished at a much-reduced scale in a more distributed manner. In these instances, different models may be more appropriate that are able to recognize the characteristics of the watershed that cannot be captured by more generalized basin-scale models.

This chapter has introduced the reader to some of these tools that are, in general, more readily adapted and customized to watersheds with unique characteristics. These models have also been designed as repositories of performance data that help match TMDL pollutant load-reduction goals with the suite of technologies and techniques available to stakeholders and the entity responsible for TMDL implementation. The way the information on BMPs and various treatment technologies is stored and made accessible is changing.

As more TMDL studies result in implementation, the use of models for management planning and alternate analysis is increasing. Evaluating management alternatives and considering financial investments will need more sophisticated BMP modeling systems (USEPA 2005). Explicit incorporation of BMPs and low-impact development (LID) in the watershed and water quality models has advanced in recent years. For example, the latest version of SWMM (Chapter 2) can explicitly model eight different generic green infrastructure practices (USEPA 2019), which allows engineers and planners to represent combinations of these LID practices to determine their effectiveness in managing stormwater runoff for TMDL implementation. Furthermore, the latest version of the National Stormwater Calculator (USEPA 2020b), based on SWMM as its computational engine, has incorporated an LID cost-estimation module within the application. This enhanced model capability allows engineers and managers to evaluate seven different types of LID controls based on a comparison of regional and national project planning level cost estimates to support TMDL implementation.

The advent of machine learning techniques and other statistical data science technologies can assist the TMDL implementation manager in developing much more robust and effective tools for achieving TMDL pollutant load-reduction goals in a sustainable and cost-efficient and effective manner. The speed with which these techniques and technologies has penetrated almost every aspect of environmental science has been truly impressive. This Manual of Practice may become a "living document" and need to be updated to account for these potential advances in the practice of TMDL development and implementation.

ACKNOWLEDGMENTS

Reviews, edits, and comments provided by Nigel W. T. Quinn, Harry X. Zhang, and G. Padmanabhan in this chapter are greatly appreciated.

REFERENCES

Caraco, D. 2013. *Watershed treatment model 2013 documentation*. Ellicott City, MD: Center for Watershed Protection. Accessed March 21, 2016. http://owl.cwp.org/mdocs-posts/watershed-treatment-model-documentation-final/

Clary, J., J. Jones, M. Leisenring, P. Hobson, and E. Strecker. 2020. *International stormwater BMP database: 2020 summary statistics.* Alexandria, VA: Water Research Foundation. Accessed November 16, 2020. https://www.waterrf.org/system/files/resource/2020-11/DRPT-4968_0.pdf

CWP (Center for Watershed Protection). 2007. *National pollutant removal performance database, version 3.* Ellicott City, MD: CWP.

Evans, B. M., S. A. Sheeder, K. J. Corradini, and W. S. Brown. 2001. *AVGWLF version 3.2. Users guide.* State College, PA: Environmental Resources Research Institute, Pennsylvania State University and Pennsylvania Dept. of Environmental Protection, Bureau of Watershed Conservation.

Frost, W., R. C. Lott, R. LaPlante, and F. Rose. 2019. "Modeling for TMDL implementation." *J. Hydrol. Eng.* 24 (6): 05019010.

Géhéniau, N., M. Fuamba, V. Mahaut, M. R. Gendron, and M. Dugué. 2015. "Monitoring of a rain garden in cold climate: case study of a parking lot near Montréal." *J. Irrig. Drain. Eng.* 141 (6): 040104073.

Haith, D. A., R. Mandel, and R. S. Wu. 1992. *GWLF: Generalized watershed loading functions.* Ithaca, NY: Cornell University, Dept. of Agriculture and Biology Engineering.

Hurley, S., P. Shrestha, and A. Cording. 2017. "Nutrient leaching from compost: Implications for bioretention and other green stormwater infrastructure." *J. Sustainable Water Built Environ.* 3 (3): 04017006.

LimnoTech. 2015. *Consolidated total maximum daily load (TMDL) implementation plan report (draft).* Washington, DC: District Department of the Environment.

MDE (Maryland Department of the Environment). 2010. *Maryland phase I watershed implementation plan for the Chesapeake Bay total maximum daily load.* Baltimore: MDE.

MDE. 2014a. *General guidance for developing a stormwater wasteload allocation (SW-WLA) implementation plan.* Baltimore: MDE. Accessed July 8, 2014. http://www.mde.state.md.us/programs/Water/TMDL/DataCenter/Documents/General_Implementation_Plan_Guidance_clean.pdf

MDE. 2014b. *Accounting for stormwater wasteload allocations and impervious acres treated: guidance for National Pollutant Discharge Elimination System stormwater permits.* Baltimore: MDE. Accessed September 21, 2014. http://mde.maryland.gov/programs/Water/Stormwater ManagementProgram/Documents/NPDES%20MS4%20Guidance%20 August%2018%202014.pdf

NRC (National Research Council). 2001. *Assessing the TMDL approach to water quality management.* Washington, DC: National Academy Press.

Pitt, R., A. Maestre, and R. Morquecho. 2004. "The National Stormwater Quality Database (NSQD, version 1.1)." Accessed November 13, 2021. http://rpitt.eng.ua.edu/Research/ms4/Paper/Mainms4paper.html

Roseen, R. M., T. P. Ballestero, J. J. Houle, P. Avellaneda, J. Briggs, G. Fowler et al. 2009. "Seasonal performance variations for storm-water management systems in cold climate conditions." *J. Environ. Eng.* 135 (3): 128–137.

Rossman, L. A. 2015. *Storm water management model user's manual, version 5.1.* Cincinnati: National Risk Management Research Library, Office of Research and Development, USEPA.

Schmitt, T. M., and J. Champion. 2014. "The District of Columbia's consolidated TMDL implementation plan—A methodology for addressing multiple MS4 WLAs." In *Proc., WEFTEC 2014, New Orleans. LA, 27 September - 1 October 2014. Water Environment Federation,* 2439–2450.

Schueler, T. R. 1987. *Cntrolling urban runoff: A practical manual for planning and designing urban BMPs.* Washington, DC: Metropolitan Washington Council of Governments.

Schueler, T., and C. Lane. 2012. *Recommendations of the expert panel to define removal rates for urban stormwater retrofit projects.* Ellicott City, MD: Chesapeake Stormwater Network.

USEPA (US Environmental Protection Agency). 2005. *TMDL model evaluation and research needs.* Rep. No. EPA/600/R-05/149. Prepared by L. Shoemaker, T. Dai, J. Koenig, and M. Hantush. Cincinnati: National Risk Management Research Laboratory, Office of Research and Development, USEPA.

USEPA. 2010. *Chesapeake Bay total maximum daily load for nitrogen, phosphorus and sediment.* Annapolis, MD: USEPA Chesapeake Bay Program Office. Accessed December 29, 2010. https://www.epa.gov/chesapeake-bay-tmdl/chesapeake-bay-tmdl-document

USEPA. 2019. *National stormwater calculator.* Desktop version 2.0.0.1 (08/01/2019) and mobile web-based application version 3.2.0. Washington, DC: USEPA. Accessed August 1, 2019. https://www.epa.gov/water-research/national-stormwater-calculator.

USEPA. 2020a. *Spreadsheet tool for estimating pollutant loads (STEPL) 4.4b.* Prepared by Tetra Tech Inc. Washington, DC: USEPA. Accessed October 27, 2020. https://www.epa.gov/nps/spreadsheet-tool-estimating-pollutant-loads-stepl

USEPA. 2020b. *Storm water management model (SWMM), version 5.1.015.* Washington, DC: USEPA. Accessed July 20, 2020. https://www.epa.gov/water-research/storm-water-management-model-swmm.

VADEQ (Virginia Department of Environmental Quality). 2017. *Guidance manual for total maximum daily load implementation plans.* Guidance Memo No. GM17-2004. Richmond, VA: VADEQ.

Walker, W. W., and J. D. Walker. 2015. "P-8 documentation, version 3.5." Accessed September 29, 2018. http://www.wwwalker.net/p8/v35/webhelp/p8HelpWebMain.html.

WI DNR (Wisconsin Department of Natural Resources). 2014. *TMDL guidance for MS4 permits: Planning, implementation, and modeling guidance.*" Guidance No. 3800-2014-4. Madison, WI: WI DNR. Accessed January 24, 2021. https://dnr.wi.gov/topic/stormwater/documents/ms4tmdlimpguidance.pdf.

WI DNR. 2016. *TMDL guidance for MS4 permits: Planning, implementation, and modeling guidance, Appendix A (percent reduction).* Guidance No. 3800-2015-13. Madison, WI: WI DNR. Accessed January 24, 2021. https://dnr.wi.gov/topic/stormwater/documents/WTMS4TMDLImpA.pdf.

APPENDIX A: CONVERSION OF UNITS

SI Units	Customary Units
m: meter	yd: yard
cm: centimeter	in.: inch
km: kilometer	mi: mile
ha: hectare	acre
L: liter	gal.: gallon
mL: milliliters	qt: quart
kg: kilogram	lb: pound
g: gram	oz: ounce
N: Newton ($m \cdot kg \cdot s^2$)	lbf: pound-force (lb/ft)
Pa: Pascals (N/m^2)	psi: pounds per square inch
kPa: kilopascals	atm: atmosphere
J: Joule	ft $\cdot$ lbf: feet per pound-force
W: watt	Btu: British thermal unit
kW: kilowatt	hp: horsepower
s: second	s: second

min: minute

h: hour

day

°C: degrees Celsius

ppm: parts per million

min: minute

h: hour

day

°F: degrees Fahrenheit

ppm: parts per million

Length	1 m: 3.2808 ft: 1.0936 yd	1 ft: 3 yd: 0.3048 m
	1 cm: 0.3937 in.	1 in.: 2.54 cm
	1 km: 0.6214 mi	1 mi: 0.869 nautical mi: 1.6093 km
Area	1 m^2: 10.7643 ft^2	1 ft^2: 0.0929 m^2
	1 km^2: 0.3861 mi^2	1 mi^2: 2.59 km^2
	1 ha: 2.4710 acre	1 acre: 43,560 ft^2: 0.4047 ha
Volume	1 L: 0.2642 gal	1 gal.: 4 qt: 3.7854 L
	1 ml: 1 cm^3	1 ft^3: 7.481 gal: 28.32 L
Mass	1 g: 0.0353 oz	1 oz: 28.3495 g
	1 kg: 2.2046 lb	1 lb: 0.4536 kg
Force	1 N: 0.2248 lb/ft	1 lbf: 4.4482 N
Density	1 kg/m^2: 0.2048 lb/ft^2	1 lb/ft^2: 4.882 kg/m^2
	1 kg/m^3: 6.2427 lb/ft^3	1 lb/ft^3: 16.018 kg/m^3
Pressure	1 kPa: 0.145 psi	1 psi: 6.8948 kPa
	1 atm: 14.7 psi: 101.35 kPa	
Energy and Power	1 J: 1.00 W·s: 0.7376 ft·lbf	1 ft·lbf: 1.3558 J
	1 kJ: 0.2778 W·h: 0.948 Btu	1 Btu: 1.0551 kJ
	1 W: 0.7376 ft·lbf/s: 3.4122 Btu/h	1 ft·lbf/s: 1.3558 W
	1 kW: 1.3410 hp	1 hp: 550 ft·lb/s: 0.7457 kW

Flow	1 L/s: 15.85 gal./min: 2.119 ft^3/min	1 gal./min: 0.1337 ft^3/min: 0.0631 L/s mg/L: ppmm (in dilute solutions)
Concentration		
Temperature	°C: (°F − 32) × 5/9	°F: (°C × 9/5) + 32
Fundamental Constants and Relationships	Acceleration of gravity	32.2 ft/s^2: 9.81 m/s^2
	Density of water (at 4 °C):	1,000 kg/m^3: 1 g/cm^3
	Specific weight of water (15 °C):	62.4 lb/ft^3: 9,810 N/m^3
	Weight of water 1 gal.:	8.345 lbs: 3.7854 kg

APPENDIX B: GLOSSARY

Assimilative Capacity: Ability of a body of water to cleanse itself; its capacity to receive waste waters or toxic substances without deleterious effects. It is the capacity of the ambient environment to accept and dissipate pollutant discharges without exceeding environmental limits.

Beneficial/Designated Uses: Using a waterbody for water supply, fishing, swimming, boating, navigation, aquaculture, and several others. Water quality standards are federal, state, and tribal requirements that define the water quality objective for a waterbody by designating the beneficial uses and setting criteria to protect these uses.

Best Management Practices (BMPs):   Methods, measures, or practices determined to be reasonable and cost-effective to control nonpoint-source pollution. Best management practices include structural and nonstructural controls and procedures for operations and maintenance.

Biochemical Oxygen Demand (BOD):   Also called biological oxygen demand. The BOD refers to the amount of oxygen required for the biotic degradation of organic matter in bodies of water. The BOD is a pollution parameter mainly to assess the quality of water and wastewater.

Breakpoint Rainfall: Point in time during a rainfall that rainfall intensity changes from one approximately constant rainfall rate to another approximately constant rate (http://onlinelibrary.wiley.com/doi/10.1017/S135048270100202X/pdf). These are points in time when rainfall measurements are made and recorded and rainfall intensities during the time intervals are calculated.

Calibration: Process of adjusting model parameters within scientifically defensible ranges until the resulting simulations fit observations as close as practicable.

Clean Water Act: Public Law 92-500, as amended by Public Law 96-483 and Public Law 97-117, 33 U.S.C. 1251 et seq. Also known as the Federal Water Pollution Control Act or Federal Water Pollution Control Act

Amendments of 1972. The Clean Water Act contains a number of provisions to restore and maintain the quality of the navigable water of the United States. Section 303(d) requires the calculation of TMDLs for all impaired waters.

Code of Federal Regulations (CFR):   Code of Federal Regulations (CFR) annual edition is the codification of the general and permanent rules published in the Federal Register by the departments and agencies of the Federal Government.

Confirmation or Corroborative Testing: Testing the accuracy of a calibrated water quality or watershed model with a set of information that is independent of the information used for calibration. It replaces the archaic misnomers verification and validation.

Critical Condition: Worst-case scenario of flow, temperature, and other environmental conditions in the waterbody for which the TMDL for the pollutant of concern will meet water quality standards.

Designated Uses: *See* Beneficial/designated uses.

Dissolved Oxygen (DO):   Amount of oxygen that is present in water. Waterbodies receive oxygen from the atmosphere and from aquatic plants.

Jurisdictional Agency: State agency that is tasked with implementing the TMDL program.

Impairment: Lake, river, or stream is considered "impaired" if it fails to meet specific water quality standards according to its classification and intended use.

Implementation Modeling: Differs from modeling for TMDL development mainly in that receiving water models are not needed. Instead, only models that can simulate the effects of management practices are required. Only pollutant loads corresponding to different scenarios need to be estimated.

Implementation Plan: Completion and agency approval of a TMDL is only one step in the water regulatory or restoration process. A comprehensive TMDL implementation plan outlines management goals, projects, partners, priorities, schedule, and finding along with tracking, monitoring, and re-evaluation processes.

Information/Results: Outputs generated by computer models that may occasionally be used in lieu of data. This may be processed using mathematical or statistical tools to convert the original data into usable form.

Integrated Modeling Systems: They provide a unified system with a single interface that launches and manages several models concurrently. They may also provide software that facilitates data exchange; uses common spatial and point data formats; and prepares input files. Some modeling systems are based on independent models with an open set of supporting tools.

Load Allocation (LA): First defined in 40 CFR 130.2(g). According to EPA, "Amount of pollutant from existing nonpoint sources and natural background (e.g., farm runoff and atmospheric mercury)." Also, the portion of the waste assimilative capacity of a waterbody allocated either to existing or future nonpoint sources of pollution or to natural background sources.

Low Flow (7Q10): Minimum 7-day average discharge with a 10 year recurrence interval (occurring once in 10 years on an average). This probability-based statistic is used in determining stream design flow conditions and for evaluating the water quality impact of effluent discharge limits.

Model: Mathematical representation of the impaired water system and the effect of pollutants on the water quality. These may be simple models that are easy to implement and only approximately represent many of the processes and complex models that are more difficult to implement but incorporate many of the key processes of the system.

Monitoring: Systematic collection of data over temporal and spatial scales to provide empirical evidence and define the current environmental status and trends.

Margin of Safety (MOS): Required component of the TMDL that accounts for the uncertainty in the relationship between the pollutant loads and the quality of the receiving waterbody. Source EPA CWA section 303(d)(1)(C) (2010). Margins of safety are approved by EPA either for each TMDL or in agreements between each state and EPA.

Monte Carlo Simulation: Stochastic modeling technique that randomly selects sets of specified parameters for repetitive simulations to generate probability distributions of receiving water quality concentrations.

Management Practices: These are practices that are currently in effect or that are being planned; they are aimed to improve water quality or reduce pollutant loads. These could be structural (related to physical installations such as water/wastewater treatment facilities, hydraulic flow controls, etc.) or nonstructural (institutional changes, ordinances, etc.).

National Pollution Discharge Elimination System (NPDES) Permit: Permit issued by EPA or a state regulatory agency that sets specific limits on the type and amount of pollutants that a municipality or industry can discharge to a receiving water. The permit includes a compliance schedule for achieving the specified limits. The permit process was established in the CWA.

Nonpoint-Source Pollution: Pollution that originates from nonpoint, diffuse, or any sources that does not meet the legal definition of a point source in Section 502(14) of the CWA.

Natural Resources Conservation Service (NRCS): Formerly known as the Soil Conservation Service (SCS), is an agency of USDA that provides technical assistance to farmers and other private landowners and managers to conserve soil, water, air, and other natural resources.

Pollutant: Any water quality parameter that has exceeded its standard to such an extent that the designated use of the water system can no longer be met.

Point-Source Solution: According to Section 502(14) of the Clean Water Act, the term "point source" means any discernible, confined, and discrete conveyance, including but not limited to any pipe, ditch, channel, tunnel, conduit, well, discrete fissure, container, rolling stock, concentrated animal feeding operation, or vessel or other floating craft, and from which pollutants are or may be discharged. This term does not include agricultural storm water discharges and return flows from irrigated agriculture. See http://www.epa.gov/polluted-runoff-nonpoint-source-pollution/what-nonpoint-source

Process/Mechanism: Physical/chemical/biological phenomena that occur within the system and act on the water quality parameters.

Receiving Waters/Receiving Waterbodies: Streams, rivers, lakes, estuaries, coastal zones, or other surface waters that receive pollutant loads.

State: Chapter 26 – Water Pollution Prevention and Control § 1362 Definitions (3) The term "State" means a State, the District of Columbia, the Commonwealth of Puerto Rico, the Virgin Islands, Guam, American Samoa, the Commonwealth of the Northern Mariana Islands, and the Trust Territory of the Pacific Islands.

Steady-State Model: Mathematical model of water and fate and transport of pollutants that uses constant specifications of controlling conditions over time to simulate constant receiving water quality concentrations

Synoptic Data: Site-specific data on ambient conditions (e.g., ambient physical, chemical, and biological data collected through a synoptic survey that can be used to support modeling analysis).

Total Maximum Daily Load (TMDL):   Calculation of the maximum amount of a pollutant that a waterbody can receive and still meet water quality standards, and an allocation of that load among the various sources of that pollutant.

USEPA (US Environmental Protection Agency):   Independent agency, specifically an independent executive agency of the United States federal government for environmental protection including water quality of waterbodies.

USGS (United States Geological Survey: Sole science agency of the US Department of the Interior that manages water time-series data nationally from 16,500 stream gaging, groundwater, water quality, and precipitation sites.

Waste Assimilative Capacity: Amount of contaminant load that a receiving waterbody will be able to absorb without exceeding water quality standards or criteria. It is also the amount of contaminant load that can be discharged to a specific waterbody without exceeding water quality standards or criteria.

Watershed: Drainage area of a receiving waterbody (e.g., river) within which all the precipitation that occurs should theoretically eventually be collected in the waterbody. All the nonpoint source loads within the watershed will eventually be collected within the receiving waterbody through the runoff from the watershed.

Watershed Models: Models used to simulate interpret, quantify, and assess flow and pollutant transport processes in a watershed. Simulated processes include rainfall-runoff transformation, erosion of upland soil and stream bed and banks, sedimentation, as well as fate and transport of chemicals and bacteria. They are also used to evaluate land-use changes and best management practices (BMPs) in watershed management.

Watershed Implementation Plan (WIP): Plan that documents how the watershed jurisdiction will partner with federal and local governments to achieve and maintain water quality standards outlining the impairments, the method of treatment, and the modeling method used.

Waste Load Allocation (WLA): Portions of a receiving water waste assimilative capacity that is allocated to each existing or future point sources of pollution. The waste load allocation for each impaired water constitutes a water quality–based effluent limitation [40 CFR 130.2(h)].

Waterbody or Water Body: Geographically defined portion of navigable waters, waters of the contiguous zone, and ocean waters under the jurisdiction of the United States, including segments of rivers, streams, lakes, wetlands, coastal waters, and ocean waters.

Water Quality Parameter: Any physical/chemical/biological constituent that is suspended or dissolved within the water column and affects the ability of the water to meet a designated use (DU), such as meeting a minimum standard for potable use or maintaining a healthy ecosystem.

Water Quality Standard: Law or regulation that consists of the beneficial designated use or uses of a waterbody, the numeric and narrative water quality criteria that are necessary to protect the use or uses of that particular waterbody, and an antidegradation statement.

APPENDIX C: ABBREVIATIONS

ADEM	Alabama Department of Environmental Management
AGNPS	Agricultural Nonpoint Source
AnnAGNPS	Annualized Agricultural Nonpoint Source
ANSWERS	Areal Nonpoint Source Watershed Environment Response Simulation
ARS	Agricultural Research Service
ASTER	Advanced Spaceborne Thermal Emission and Reflection Radiometer
ATTAINS	Assessment and Total Maximum Daily Load Tracking and Implementation System
AVGWLF	ArcView Generalized Watershed Loading Functions
AVIRIS	Airborne Visible Infrared Imaging Spectrometer
AVSWAT	ArcView combined with SWAT
BASINS	Better Assessment Science Integrating point and Non-point Sources
BMC	Bayesian Monte Carlo
BMP	Best Management Practice
BOD	Biological Oxygen Demand
CASC2D	Cascade of Planes in Two-Dimensions
CAST	Chesapeake Assessment Scenario Tool
CAT	Climate Assessment Tool
CBOD	Carbonaceous Biochemical Oxygen Demand
CCHE	Center for Computational Hydroscience and Engineering
CCHE1D/2D/3D	Center for Computational Hydroscience and Engineering-1D/2D/3D
CDWR	California Department of Water Resources

CEAM	Center for Exposure Assessment Modeling
CE-Qual-W2	Hydrodynamic and Water Quality Model (2D)
CEPA	California Environmental Protection Agency
CFS	Critical Flow Storm
Chl-*a*	Chlorophyll-*a*
CMAQ	Community Multi-scale Air Quality
CN	Curve Number
COD	Chemical Oxygen Demand
CVWB	Central Valley Water Board
CWA	Clean Water Act
DHSVM	Distributed Hydrology Soil Vegetation Model
DNR	Department of Natural Resources
DNREC	Delaware Department of Natural Resources and Environmental Control
DO	Dissolved Oxygen
DP	Dissolved Phosphorus
DRBC	Delaware River Basin Commission
DSS	Decision Support System
DST	Decision Support Tool
DU	Designated Use
DWSM	Dynamic Watershed Simulation Model
DYRESM	Dynamic Reservoir Simulation Model
DYRESM-WQ	Dynamic Reservoir Simulation Model-Water Quality
EFDC	Environmental Fluid Dynamics Code
EPA	Environmental Protection Agency (state level — preceded by the state name)
EPD	Environmental Protection Division
EPD-RIV1	Dynamic One-Dimensional River Model by Georgia Environmental Protection Division (EPD)
ESRI	Environmental Systems Research Institute
EWRI	Environmental and Water Resources Institute
FC	Fecal Coliform
FDC	Flow–Duration Curve
FOEA	First-Order Error Analysis
FOVA	First-Order Variance Analysis
F&W	Fish and Wildlife
GIS	Geographic Information System
GLUE	Generalized Likelihood Uncertainty Estimation
GSA	Growing Season Average
GSSHA	Gridded Surface and Subsurface Hydrologic Analysis
GUI	Graphical User Interface
GWLF	Generalized Watershed Loading Function

HEC	Hydrologic Engineering Center
HEC-DSS	HEC Center – Data Storage System
HEC-HMS	Hydrologic Engineering Center-Hydrologic Modeling System
HEC-RAS	Hydrologic Engineering Center-River Analysis System
HSPF	Hydrologic Simulation Program-FORTRAN
HSPEXP+	HSPF Enhanced Expert System
IDEQ	Idaho Department of Environmental Quality
IDNR	Iowa Department of Natural Resources
IHM	Integrated Hydrological Model
IR	Infrared
IS	Importance Sampling
KINEROS	Kinematic Runoff and Erosion
KTH	Royal Institute of Technology in Stockholm, Sweden
LA	Load Allocation
LARM	Laterally Averaged Reservoir Model
LC	Load Capacity
LDC	Load–Duration Curve
LHC	Little Hoover Commission
LHS	Latin Hypercube Sampling
LiDAR	Light Detection and Ranging
LSPC	Loading Simulation Program in C++
LULC	Land Use/Land Cover
MAE	Mean Absolute Error
MC	Monte Carlo
MCMC	Markov Chain Monte Carlo
MDEQ	Montana Department of Environmental Quality
METI	Ministry of Economy, Trade, and Industry
MGD	Million Gallons per Day
MIKE SHE	Mike Systém Hydrologique Européen
MOCAU	Management Objectives Constrained Analysis of Uncertainty
MOS	Margin of Safety
MPCA	Minnesota Pollution Control Agency
MRBC	Multiple-response Bayesian calibration
MS4	Municipality Separate Storm Sewer System
MW	Microwave
MWCOG	Metropolitan Washington Council of Governments
NASA	National Aeronautics and Space Administration
NASS	National Agricultural Statistics Service
NC	Natural Condition

NCCHE	National Center for Computational Hydroscience and Engineering
NCDC	National Climatic Data Center
NCEI	National Centers for Environmental Information
NED	National Elevation Dataset
NERRS	National Estuarine Research Reserves System
NH3-N	Nitrogen-Ammonia
NHD	National Hydrography Dataset
NLCD	National Land Cover Dataset
NMED	New Mexico Environment Department
NOAA	National Oceanic and Atmospheric Administration
NPDES	National Pollutant Discharge Elimination System
NPK-Z	Nitrogen Phosphorus Potassium and Zooplankton
NPS	Non-Point Source
NRC	National Research Council
NRCS	National Resource Conservation Council
NRMSE	Normalized Root Mean Squared Error
NSE	Nash–Sutcliff Efficiency
NURP	Nationwide Urban Runoff Program
NVDEP	Nevada Division of Environmental Protection
NWIS	National Water Information System
ODEQ	Oregon Department of Environmental Quality
OE	Organic Enrichment
OEPA	Ohio Environmental Protection Agency
OTEQ	One-Dimensional Transport with Equilibrium Chemistry
PBIAS	Percent Bias
PC	Permit Condition
PCB	Polychlorinated Biphenyl
PCS	Permit Compliance System
PCM	Probabilistic Collocation Method
PCT	Calculation of Percent
PE	Percent Error
PEC	Performance Evaluation Criteria
PEST	Parameter Estimation
PET	Potential Evapotranspiration
PM	Performance Measure
PNL	Pacific Northwest Laboratory
POWER	Prediction of Worldwide Energy Resources
PRISM	Parameter-elevation Regressions on Independent Slopes Model
PS	Point Source
PWS	Public Water Supply
QAPP	Quality Assurance Project Plan

RMSE	Root Mean Squared Error
RSA	Regionalized Sensitivity Analysis
RSR	Ratio of Root Mean Squared Error (RMSE) and standard deviation of observed data
RUSLE	Revised Universal Soil Loss Equation
RUSLE2	Revised Universal Soil Loss Equation 2
SAMR	Stochastic Analysis of Model Residuals
SCDHEC	South Carolina Department of Health and Environmental Control
SCE	Shuffled Complex Evolutionary
SCS	Soil Conservation Service
SNTEMP	Stream Network Temperature
SJRIO	San Joaquin River Input–Output
SPARROW	Spatially Referenced Regressions on Watershed Attributes
SRTM	Shuttle Radar Topography Mission
SSTEMP	Stream Segment Temperature
SSURGO	Soil Survey Geographic
STATSGO	State Soil Geographic
STEPL	Spreadsheet Tool for Estimating Pollutant Load
STORET-WQX	Storage and Retrieval and Water Quality Exchange
SWAT	Soil and Water Assessment Tool
SWAT-CUP	SWAT Calibration and Uncertainty Programs
SWMM	Storm Water Management Model
SWSTAT	Surface Water Statistics
TAUDEM	Terrain Analysis Using Digital Elevation Models
TDS	Total Dissolved Solids
TKN	Total Kjeldahl Nitrogen
TMDL	Total Maximum Daily Load
TMDL-DB	Total Maximum Daily Load Database
TMDL TC	Total Maximum Daily Load Analysis and Modeling Technical Committee
TN	Total Nitrogen
TOPAZ	Topographic Parametrization
TP	Total Phosphorus
TPMC	Two-Phase Monte Carlo
TRS	TMDL Report Selection
TSS	Total Suspended Solids
UDEQ	Utah Department of Environmental Quality
USACE	United States Army Corps of Engineers
USDA	United States Department of Agriculture
USEPA	United States Environmental Protection Agency
USGS	United States Geological Survey

USLE	Universal Soil Loss Equation
VADEQ	Virginia Department of Environmental Quality
VIS	Visible
WARMF	Watershed Analysis Risk Management Framework
WASP	Water Analysis Simulation Program
WBD	Watershed Boundary Dataset
WDMUtil	Watershed Data Management Utilities
WETMANSIM	Wetland Management Simulator WIP: Watershed Implementation Plan
WinSLAMM	Source Loading and Management Model for Windows
WISKI	Water Information System KISTERS
WLA	Waste Load Allocation
WMS	Watershed Modeling System
WMTC	Watershed Management Technical Committee
WQP	Water Quality Portal
WRDB	Water Resources Database
WTM	Watershed Treatment Model
WWTP	Wastewater Treatment Plant

APPENDIX D: SYMBOLS

The following symbols are used in this manual:

1D	One-dimensional
A1	Groundwater flow coefficient
ACQOP	Bacteria accumulation on land
AGWETP	Fraction of remaining evapotranspiration from active groundwater
AGWRC	Base groundwater recession
ALPHA_BF	Baseflow alpha factor
ANION_EXCL	Porosity fraction from which anions are excluded
AWC	Available water capacity
b	Detachment velocity coefficients
BACTKDQ	Bacteria soil partitioning coefficient
BACTMIX	Bacteria percolation coefficient
BASETP	Fraction of remaining evapotranspiration from baseflow
BC1	Constant rate for biological oxidation of ammonia
BC2	Constant rate for biological oxidation of nitrite to nitrate
BC3	Local constant rate for hydrolysis of organic nitrogen to ammonium
BC4	Local constant rate for organic phosphorus mineralization
BCNST	Direct-source concentration
C	Pollutant concentration (Chapter 2)
C	Cropping factor (Chapter 8)
CEPSC	Interception storage capacity

CF	Rainsplash parameter
CFRT_KG	Bacteria loading rate
CG	Hydraulic erosion transfer coefficient rate
CH_K2	Channel conductivity
CH_N	Channel Manning's coefficient
CN and $CN2$	Curve number
CNAF	Uniform Curve Number adjustment factor
COND	Effective lateral saturated hydraulic conductivity
C_P	Storage coefficient
CV	Coefficient of variation
d	Model skill (i.e., measures the degree to which the model predictions are error free)
DDRAIN	Depth of subsurface drains
D_E, E_M, and A_3	Density gradient diffusion coefficients
DEEPFR	Fraction of groundwater inflow to deep recharge
DF	Overland flow detachment rate
D_M, A, and A_2	Wind mixing diffusion coefficients
d_r	Specified root depth
DR	Rainfall detachment rate
DSC	Dimensionless sensitivity coefficient
Dstore	Depression storage
EC	Evaporation magnitude
e_{gw}	Porosity
$f(y_k|Y_{obs})$	Probability distribution of output y_k, given observations Y_{obs}
$f(y_k|\theta)$	Probability distribution of the output y_k, given parameter vector θ
EMC	Event mean concentration
ERORGN	Organic nitrogen enrichment ratio
ERORGP	Phosphorus enrichment ratio
FAFC	Uniform friction adjustment factor for channels
FAFO	Uniform friction adjustment factor for overland planes
FDCI	Flow detachment coefficient
FSTDEC	First-order decay rate
$F(X, \theta)$	Mathematical Model with input X and parameters θ
G_{Max}	Maximum growth rate
GW_DELAY	Groundwater delay
GWQMN	Threshold depth of water in a shallow aquifer required for the return flow to occur

GW_REVAP	Revap coefficient
I_a	Initial abstraction
Imperv	Imperviousness
INFILD	Ratio of maximum/mean infiltration capacities
INFILT	Index to mean infiltration rate
INTFW	Interflow inflow parameter
IOQC	Interflow bacteria concentration
IRC	Interflow recession parameter
JGER	Exponent in soil matrix scour equation
JSER	Exponent in sediment washoff equation
K	Convective heat factor
K	Detachment velocity coefficients
K	Hydraulic conductivity
K	Mineral weathering rates
K	Saturated hydraulic conductivity
K	Soil erodibility factor
K	Soil erosivity
k	Reaction rates
KADP	Phosphate adsorption factor
KDSAM	Ammonium desorption factor
KDSP	Phosphate desorption factor
K_{eff}	Soil erodibility factor
KGER	Coefficient in soil matrix scour equation
K_{gw}	Hydraulic conductivity of the media
K_h and K_V	Soil hydraulic conductivity
KIMNI	Nitrate immobilization factor
KIMP	Phosphate immobilization factor
K_N and K_P	Half-saturation constants
K_{rb}	Riverbed hydraulic conductivity
KRER	Coefficient in the soil detachment equation
K_S	Saturated hydraulic conductivity
KSER	Coefficient in the sediment washoff equation
K_{SOD}	Sediment oxygen demand
KU	Cover coefficient for calculation of the evapotranspiration
L_c	Compliance load corresponding to the reference simulation
L_β	β-compliance mean load considering random parameters and analysis uncertainty
LA	Nonpoint sources load including background sources
LAI	Leaf area index
LC	Loading capacity

LZETP	Index to lower zone evapotranspiration
LZSN	Lower zone nominal soil moisture storage
$L(\theta) = P\left(Y_{obs}\vert\theta\right)$	Likelihood function
M0 and Mf	Snow melting rates
MAE	Mean absolute error
MBE	Mass Balance Error
MG	Infiltration suction
MK_S	Saturated hydraulic conductivity
Mn	Manning's coefficient
MOS	Margin of safety
MSE	Mean squared error
n	Manning's coefficient (Chapter 8)
n	Number of data points (Chapter 8)
N	Number of time steps (Chapter 11)
N, n_O, NSUR, and OV_N	Surface Manning's coefficient
n_C and n_M	Channel Manning's coefficient
NPERCO	Nitrate percolation coefficient
NRMSE	Normalized Root Mean Squared Error
NSE	Nash–Sutcliffe efficiency coefficient
$\bar{O}$	Average of the observed values
O_i	Observed value at time i
5%	Percent Bias
PCT	Percent
PCT_Above	Percent of observed data that fall above the 5 day window minimum–maximum range of simulations
PCT_Below	Percent of observed data that fall below the 5 day window minimum–maximum range of simulations
PCT_Within	Percent of observed data that fall within the 5 day window minimum–maximum range of simulations
$\bar{P}$	Average of the predicted values/model results
PB	Percent bias
P_i	Predicted value/model result at time i
PE	Percent Error
PHOSKD	Phosphorus soil partitioning coefficient
PPERCO	Phosphorus percolation coefficient
PRF	Peak rate adjustment factor
PSP	Phosphorus availability index
$P(X)$	Prior probability distribution of input X
$P(\theta)$	Prior probability distribution of parameter set θ

$P\left(\theta\vert Y_{obs}\right)$	Probability distribution of θ given observation Y_{obs}
$P\left(Y_{obs}\vert\theta\right)$	Probability distribution of observation Y_{obs} given θ
Q	Flowrate
q_m	Transport capacity
r	Pearson product moment correlation coefficient
R	Groundwater recession coefficient
R^2	Coefficient of determination
RE	Relative error
REVAPMN	Threshold depth of water in a shallow aquifer required for revap
RCHRG_DP	Deep aquifer percolation factor
RCN	Nitrogen concentration in the rain
RDC	Rainfall detachment coefficient
RMSE	Root mean square error
RSR	Root mean square error standard deviation ratio
RS4	Local settling rate for organic nitrogen
RS5	Local settling rate for organic phosphorus
RSR	Ratio of RMSE and standard deviation of observed data
RUSLE	Revised universal soil loss equation
$RUSLE_C$	RUSLE cover management factor
$RUSLE_P$	RUSLE support practice factor
S	Deep seepage coefficient
S_f	Wetting front suction
SFTMP	Mean air temperature at which precipitation is equally likely to be rain as snow/freezing rain
SKPLP	Factor to adjust plant phosphorus uptake from surface layer
SLMPF	Percolation factor to adjust solutes from surface to upper layer storage
SLSOIL	Slope length for lateral subsurface flow
SMTMP	Snowmelt base temperature
SNO50COV	Fraction of SNOCOVMX that provides 50% cover
SNOCOVMX	Minimum snow water content that corresponds to full snow cover
SNOWCF	Snow gage catch correction factor
SOL_K	Saturated hydraulic conductivity

SQOLIM	Maximum bacteria accumulation on land
SPCON	Coefficient in sediment transport equation
SPEXP	Exponent in sediment transport equation
S_S	Specific storage coefficient
$Stdev_O$	Standard deviation of observed data
SURLAG	Surface runoff lag coefficient
S_y	Specific yield
t_C	Time of concentration
T_{dry}	Drying time
TIMP	Snow temperature lag factor
TMDL	Total Maximum Daily Loading
t_L	Lag time
T_L, T_O, and T_U	Temperature tolerant ranges
T_S	Snow formation temperature
TSNOW	Temperature at which precipitation becomes snow
UKPLP	Factor to adjust plant phosphorus uptake from surface layer
ULPF	Percolation factor to adjust solutes from upper to lower layer storage
USLE	Universal soil loss equation
USLE_C	Minimum value for the cover and management factor for the land cover
USLE_K	USLE soil erodibility factor
USLE_P	USLE support practice factor
$USLE_C$	USLE cover management factor
$USLE_K$	USLE soil erodibility factor
$USLE_p$	USLE support practice factor
UZSN	Nominal upper zone soil moisture storage
W	pollutant load
WDPQ	Bacteria die-off coefficient in soil
WDPRCH	Bacteria die-off coefficient in stream
Width	Width of overland flow path
WLA	Waste load allocation
WSQOP	Rate of surface runoff that removes 90% of stored bacteria from a pervious land surface
X	Matrix of p input or forcing variables
$\bar{X}$	Expected input forcing
X^*	Conservative input forcing values
Y	Model output
Y_{obs}	Observation
Y_{sim}	Model simulation (output) Type equation here.
Z	Soil layer thickness

α	Adsorption coefficient
α	Dispersivity
β	Probability of exceeding the water quality standard
$\hat{\beta}_o$	Intercept in standard regression
$\hat{\beta}_1$	Slope in standard regression
ε	Model residual errors
λ	Soil thermal conductivity
λ_S	Snow thermal conductivity
Λ	Pore distribution index
θ	Porosity
θ	Soil initial moisture
θ	vector of q model parameters
θ_{fc}	Soil field capacity
θ_S	Saturated water content
θ_S	Soil porosity
$\bar{\theta}$	Expected parameter values
θ^*	Conservative parameter values
$\Phi - \theta_i$	Volume moisture deficit
ρ_b	Soil bulk density
σ_e^2	Variance of the residuals (ε)
σ_i^2	Variance of residual errors
σ_O^2	Variance of observations
σ_X^2	Variance of X
σ_Y^2	Variance of Y
σ_θ^2	Variance of model parameters (θ)
μ	Degradation rate
ψ_b	Bubbling pressure

INDEX

Note: Page numbers followed by *f* and *t* indicate figures and tables.